W9-AYO-070

Two favorite ongoing series—
Rebecca York's "43 Light Street" and
Caroline Burnes's "Fear Familiar"—
come together in one extraspecial book!

AFTER DARK
Two couples must hide from the day...
and anything can happen after dark....

Counterfeit Wife by Rebecca York
When a madman comes after her, Marianne
pretends to be Tony's wife—and can no longer
deny the desire burning between them....

Familiar Stranger by Caroline Burnes
When Molly's son is kidnapped, she has no
choice but to find her mystery love—and
tell him of their son's existence....

RUTH GLICK writing as Rebecca York

Award-winning, bestselling novelist Ruth Glick, who writes as Rebecca York, is the author of close to eighty books, including her popular 43 LIGHT STREET series for Harlequin Intrigue. Ruth says she has the best job in the world. Not only does she get paid for telling stories; she's also the author of twelve cookbooks. Ruth and her husband, Norman, travel frequently, researching locales for her novels and searching out new dishes for her cookbooks.

CAROLINE BURNES

Caroline Burnes has published thirty-five Harlequin Intrigue novels, many of them featuring horses, cowboys, or the black cat detective, Familiar. From the age of four, Caroline wanted to be a cowgirl and write mystery books. Though she is far from a cowgirl, she lives on a farm in south Alabama with six horses, six cats and six dogs. One of the cats, E. A. Poe, is a prototype for Familiar. Although she spent most of her riding career jumping, she recently took up team penning, a sport that demonstrates that cows are far smarter than humans.

REBECCA YORK & CAROLINE BURNES

AFTER DARK: FAMILIAR STRANGER

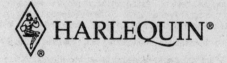

HARLEQUIN®

TORONTO • NEW YORK • LONDON
AMSTERDAM • PARIS • SYDNEY • HAMBURG
STOCKHOLM • ATHENS • TOKYO • MILAN • MADRID
PRAGUE • WARSAW • BUDAPEST • AUCKLAND

If you purchased this book without a cover you should be aware
that this book is stolen property. It was reported as "unsold and
destroyed" to the publisher, and neither the author nor the
publisher has received any payment for this "stripped book."

ISBN 0-373-80960-3

AFTER DARK: FAMILIAR STRANGER
Copyright © 2005 by Harlequin Books S.A.

The publisher acknowledges the copyright holders of the
individual works as follows:

COUNTERFEIT WIFE
Copyright © 1999 by Ruth Glick

FAMILIAR STRANGER
Copyright © 1999 by Carolyn Haines

Originally published as AFTER DARK
by Harlequin Books S.A. © 1999

All rights reserved. Except for use in any review, the reproduction or
utilization of this work in whole or in part in any form by any electronic,
mechanical or other means, now known or hereafter invented, including
xerography, photocopying and recording, or in any information storage
or retrieval system, is forbidden without the written permission of the
publisher, Harlequin Enterprises Limited, 225 Duncan Mill Road,
Don Mills, Ontario M3B 3K9, Canada.

All characters in this book have no existence outside the imaginations of
the authors and have no relation whatsoever to anyone bearing the same
name or names. They are not even distantly inspired by any individual
known or unknown to the authors, and all incidents are pure invention.

This edition published by arrangement with Harlequin Books S.A.

® and TM are trademarks of the publisher. Trademarks indicated with
® are registered in the United States Patent and Trademark Office, the
Canadian Trade Marks Office and in other countries.

www.eHarlequin.com

Printed in U.S.A.

REBECCA YORK

Ruth Glick writing as Rebecca York

Counterfeit Wife

Prologue

The moon was a bloodred disk hanging in the dark sky. It was big. Scary. Like so many things in the child's young life.

She pulled away from the window and stuck the outside of her index finger into her mouth, sucking to comfort herself as she cringed from the terror waiting to swallow her up.

Big girls weren't supposed to suck their fingers. Mommy would be mad if she saw her doing it. But Mommy wasn't here. She had taken the car and gone…somewhere. With Nick.

She shivered as angry voices drifted to her from downstairs. It was Daddy, Uncle Vance, and the man named Doo Valve with the creepy voice and the mean eyes.

They had all come here to this broken-up house in one of the cars and the van with no windows, driving fast through the black night because Daddy was sick. He had wanted to call someone named Doc Wayne. Uncle Vance had said that was a bad idea.

Suddenly it was quiet. Maybe Doo Valve had taken the station wagon and gone away. The little girl ran down the steps, then tiptoed along the hall to the room where Daddy was lying down.

Uncle Vance was talking, and Daddy was stretched out

on a sleeping bag near the window. In the light from the lantern, she could see blood soaking the bandage on his shoulder.

"Daddy!"

His head jerked toward her. "Lil' Bit," he said, his voice so low she could hardly hear.

Uncle Vance gave her a smile, but she knew he was worried.

"Is everything going to be okay?" she asked, trying to keep her teeth from chattering.

"Yes. Do you want to talk to your daddy?" Uncle Vance asked.

She nodded eagerly.

"Then I'll go find us something to eat."

Slipping into the room, she saw that Daddy's skin looked like paste with beads of water on it.

"Are you gonna die?" she blurted.

"I'm going to be fine."

"Mommy put ant septic on you. It smells bad."

He nodded.

"I'm scared."

"I know, Lil' Bit." His hand reached for her. "Come here so we can talk."

She crept closer till her ear was near Daddy's mouth, so he didn't have to talk loud. Then she heard footsteps behind her. It wasn't Uncle Vance; it was Doo Valve. The bad man.

"What did you tell her?" he growled.

"None of your damn business."

"You're dead wrong." Doo Valve grabbed her daddy by the front of his shirt and shook him, making him groan.

"No!" Rushing at the bad man, she pounded on him with her fists. He whirled, cursed and flung her away. Then everything happened so fast. One minute the lantern was sitting on the floor, the next it was broken on the pile of bandages.

They caught fire, the flames leaping up like bright, hot snakes. Hissing snakes. Doo Valve started beating at them with a blanket. But the blanket caught fire. He threw it down, and the floor began to smoke. Daddy rolled away. With a curse, Doo Valve dived though the window.

Lil' Bit ran toward her father.

"No, get back! Go out the door!" he shouted as the fire licked toward him across the wood floor, making a flaming wall between them.

The room was filling with thick, stinging smoke, and she couldn't see the door, couldn't even see her daddy. Confused, terrified, she spun around, unsure which way to run. The flames roared in her ears. Then she started to cough, her chest burning as she tried to fill her lungs. Flames danced toward her; heat seared her skin. She screamed.

Dimly she heard someone call her name. Then she felt arms grab her, pull her back from the licking orange tongues. There was something wet and cold over her head, and she couldn't see. She could only cling to the strong shoulders of her rescuer as he dragged her from hell.

Chapter One

Heat. Skin-searing heat.

Marianne Leonard hated days like this when the blistering July sun danced on her skin like flames. Slipping into her car, she winced as the seat cover scorched her thighs. Too bad she hadn't found a parking spot in the shade.

Maybe she should move to Alaska, she mused as she gingerly touched the steering wheel. It was worse than the seat, the hard plastic too hot for her fingers to get a good grip.

Lifting her damp golden hair, she leaned toward the vent as the first feeble wisps from the air conditioner stirred the sweltering air. There were a couple of problems with fleeing to the far north: She'd have to give up a great job. And she'd cut herself off from all contact with the Marco family.

Well, not the family, anymore. Mr. Marco had died six months ago. And, to be truthful, she hadn't seen Tony since the reception after the funeral.

She'd spotted him in the corner, isolated from the small crowd of people who had come to pay their respects, his broad shoulders slightly slumped and his chiseled features more daunting than usual. He'd never liked formality, never been comfortable with chitchat. Now he'd taken off his suit jacket and tie—making him stand out in sharp relief to the other men in the room who were still all buttoned up.

The mourners were friends and acquaintances. Not relatives. Like her, Tony was on his own now. Softly, she called his name, and he turned to her with a swiftness that had made her heart leap in her chest. He was tall and solid, yet dark smudges marred the skin under his eyes, and his cheeks had a hollow look that spoke of grief and sleepless nights.

As she crossed the room to stand in front of him, his expression changed, and she saw something flicker in the depths of his dark eyes—something that she'd seen only a few times: Need—basic and primitive—that set off a response deep within her.

"Tony, what can I do?"

At the sound of her voice, his tight expression eased, and he searched her face. "I saw you at the cemetery. You didn't have to drive all the way out there."

"Of course I did. Your dad was like…" She fluttered her hands fumbling for the right words. "He was like a…a kind of stepfather to me."

A warm smile bloomed as memories flooded through her. "He got me through Algebra II. He even taught me to drive. Remember when I stepped on the gas instead of the brake and almost went through the garage door?"

Tony laughed. "He had quite a bit to say about that afterwards."

"The key point is that he didn't bite my head off." She made a small sound of protest. "I'm going to miss him."

Tony nodded solemnly, his total concentration focused on her.

"Let me help," she whispered. "What do you need?"

He didn't answer. But his hand reached toward her in slow motion, and his knuckle stroked across her cheek, then her lips, in a light caress that she felt in all the hidden places of her body.

For several heartbeats, she couldn't move. Then she parted her lips a fraction, giving him the shadow of the kiss that she wanted to press against his mouth, although how she could be having such carnal thoughts at his father's funeral reception was beyond her.

She forgot where they were and why, as his gaze locked with hers, dark and potent. His hand moved to her cheek and then the sensitive line where her jaw met her neck—stroking lightly, sending hot currents through her.

He murmured her name, the barest of whispers. And for a few breath-stopping moments she was sure that his thoughts were running as hot and wild as hers—that he wanted to go someplace where they could be alone and do all the things she had imagined doing with him.

Then his hand fell to his side, and the too-familiar impenetrable mask was once again back in place.

"Tony?"

His shoulders lifted in the barest shrug; then, after a few seconds of stiff conversation, he excused himself and drifted off into the crowd.

The way he'd distanced himself had cut her to the bone. Remembering it still hurt her now—months later.

Unconsciously Marianne tightened her fists around the steering wheel, then loosened her grip as the hot plastic seared her palms.

One by one, she'd lost the people who mattered to her. She supposed her father didn't even count; he'd been out of the picture so long. But her mother had died last year. Then Silvio Marco.

Even before that, for all intents and purposes, she'd lost Tony. Once he'd been like her protective older brother—her defender, her confidant. Then she'd started to mature, and he'd rebuffed her first, shy efforts at changing the relationship. She'd told herself he thought he was too old for her. Maybe that was true when she'd still been a teenager and he was in his early twenties. But the gap had lessened now that they were both adults—for all the good it had done her.

Unconsciously, her lips pressed into a thin line. Really, she should stop obsessing about Tony Marco and try her luck with one of the other guys who wanted to get close to her.

Mom would like that, if she were still alive. Mom had warned her to stay away from him. But Mom hadn't been right about everything.

A flash of movement at the corner of her vision brought her back to the present. With a surge of fear, she swung her head to the side—and saw only a sheet of paper swirling in a sudden updraft.

On a sigh, she ordered her pulse to stop pounding as she pulled out of the parking lot and headed home. For the past few weeks she'd been on edge—seeing things, hearing things, afraid that someone was dogging her steps. Yet each time she whirled to catch sight of her stalker, no one was there.

The irrational anxiety was starting to interfere with her concentration at work—which was darn inconvenient, because as the newest social worker with the Light Street Foundation, she was still trying to prove herself.

Fifteen minutes later, she pulled up beside the kitchen door of the modest bungalow-style house she'd inherited from her mother. It needed fresh paint and a few minor repairs, but basically it was a comfortable place to live—a good place to raise kids, if she ever got married and had any.

Entering through the side door, she set her briefcase on the counter and stood in the middle of the kitchen, thinking that the house smelled wrong. Like stale sweat, she decided. Before she started dinner, she'd better wash the shorts and T-shirt from last night's workout.

She headed for the front door to check the mail, her pocketbook still slung over her shoulder. Halfway across the living room, she stopped. The light in the upstairs hall was on—and she remembered switching it off before coming down.

All the nagging doubts of the past few weeks coalesced into sudden, choking certainty. Someone had been stalking her, all right. Now he was in the house.

"Little girl, do you remember me?" A soft voice wafted toward her, and she froze. She knew the voice. But it couldn't be. He was dead.

Goose bumps rose on her arms. "Mr. Marco?" she gasped.

The only answer was a laugh—a rich, ghostly laugh that rooted her to the spot where she stood.

"Gotcha!" The voice changed. It was rougher, deeper, mocking.

It wasn't Mr. Marco. Reflexively, she took a quiet step toward the door, then turned and fled. Before she made it across the rug, a hand shot out and grabbed her by the throat, cutting off the scream of terror that rose toward her lips.

Gasping for air, she struggled to wrench herself away, clawing at the hard-as-steel hands that choked off her breath. But the unseen attacker held her fast.

No oxygen reached her lungs, and she felt her vision dim as burly arms dragged her away from the windows. The man was strong, his body rank with sweat.

Black dots danced before her eyes, and she knew she was going to die. Then, just before she passed out, he eased up on the pressure enough for her to gulp in a blessed draft of air.

Keeping his hand clamped on her throat, he lowered himself to the sofa and brought her with him.

Horror was like a wire tightening inside her chest as he held her against his body, her face turned away from him.

"I'm going to take my hand off your windpipe," he growled, his foul breath puffing against her cheek. "If you scream, I'm going to kill you. Nod if you understand."

She managed a small nod, and the hand shifted from her neck to her upper arm. Gasping, she waited to find out what he was going to do, even as she calculated her chances of escape. Next to zero.

She could see his feet encased in black running shoes and his black sweatpants. The sleeve of his T-shirt was also black. It seemed he was dressed for breaking and entering.

Her heart was pounding like a jackhammer inside her chest, but she struggled for calm, trying to take in details.

"I've been waiting a long time for this," he growled.

"For what?" she managed.

"You know damn well."

The words and his confident tone brought a wave of total confusion. "I—I don't know what you're talking about," she croaked, then tried to steady her voice. "And you'd better get out of here because my fiancé is on his way over for dinner."

He laughed again, this time it was a nasty sound that scraped the raw edges of her nerve endings. "Don't play games with me, Miss Marianne Leonard. I've been watching you. I know you don't have any fiancé. You're all alone now that your mom is dead."

"I—"

He cut her off with a snarl, then began to talk in a low, rapid voice that she could hardly follow. He was babbling about her father, saying he had told her a secret. As he spoke, he gave her a shake that rattled her teeth.

Her father? Another ghost from the past. Total mystification fogged her brain. Her father had left their family stranded when she was just a baby—so long ago that she couldn't even remember his face.

"You were there. You know. He told you." The voice in her ear brought her back to the present.

She cringed. "Are—are you sure you have the right woman?"

"No mistake. Even if you did change your name."

"What? My name?"

Meaty fingers dug painfully into her arm. "Don't play games with me. Where is it? Where are you hiding it?"

Marianne tried to keep her brain from going numb, knowing her life might depend on figuring out what this guy was talking about. The only thing she knew for sure was that whatever he wanted she didn't have.

Her mind scrambled, came up with a desperate plan. "You don't think it's here in the house, do you?" she asked in a voice that shook only a little.

"Keep talking!" he growled, and she wondered how she'd ever mistaken his voice for kindly Silvio Marco.

"I…have a letter he left me," she lied, then improvised quickly. "He said not to open it unless I needed his help. It's…it's upstairs. In my room."

He hauled her to her feet, held her as she stood swaying on legs that felt like cooked spaghetti. "One wrong move and I'll shoot you," he warned.

When he gave her a push toward the stairs, she grabbed the lamp table to keep from falling on her face. Did he really have a gun? She hadn't seen it. Maybe he was lying.

She wanted to ask him how he'd get what he wanted if he killed her. She didn't dare confuse him with logic as she stumbled toward the steps, then climbed them slowly, breathing deeply, knowing that she'd better get this right.

A kind of deadly calm descended on her as she reached the upper hall, then took a steadying breath, waiting for him to catch up before she turned right and headed for the spare room.

When she reached the door, she pretended to stumble, her

hand going down on the floor as she grabbed for one of the barbells she'd left lying on the exercise mat. Half whirling, she slung the twenty-pound weight at the madman.

It hit him in the stomach, and he gasped, crumpling in surprise as she slammed the door and spared precious seconds to lock it behind her.

Shots sounded, and bullets splintered the wood as she wrenched open the window and flung herself onto the porch roof.

Too bad he hadn't been lying about the gun.

Using the downspout, she slid to the ground, rounded the house and jumped into the car, her hand fumbling for the keys in the pocketbook that amazingly still dangled from her shoulder.

Angry shouts pursued her to the car. Then the intruder was leaping to the ground like a movie stuntman. In a minute, he'd be on her again.

Her breath coming in ragged gasps, Marianne started the engine, backed out of the driveway, and cannonballed down the block, turning the corner with tires squealing. At the cross street, she turned again, weaving through the familiar neighborhood like a mad dog.

Sparing a quick glance in the rearview mirror, she saw no signs of pursuit—for the moment. Slowing only slightly, she felt between the seats, found her sun hat, and jammed it down over her head. A poor disguise—but it would have to do.

Her first thought was to drive straight to a police station and make a report of the attack. Yet when she actually pictured herself sitting down face-to-face with a detective, she felt a sudden painful tightening inside her chest.

Not the police. She couldn't go to them—because she'd known for as long as she could remember that something about the law had struck a deep, abiding terror in her mom.

A shuddering sigh wracked her chest. Mom was dead. It shouldn't matter. But it did.

There had been so many things she and her mother had never discussed, buried truths simmering below the surface of their seemingly normal existence. And the law was one of those off-limits subjects.

But she'd sensed things, seen things, like the way Mom went rigid when a patrol car pulled up beside them at a red light. And the way her face lost its color when they passed a patrolman at the shopping center.

The police were supposed to be your friends. But Marianne had always known on some deep, subconscious level that they were the enemy. And she'd better stay as far away from them as she could get if she valued her life.

The knowledge brought a kind of terrible despair. She was alone, with no hope of rescue. Then an image of Tony Marco stole into her mind and some of the tightness eased in her chest. Although they had grown apart in the past few years, she still believed he would protect her—the way he had when she'd needed him most. Like when he'd beaten up a gang of boys who were teasing her on the way home from school, saying she didn't have a father. Or when he'd chased off a big black dog that was snapping at her heels.

He would know what to do now, she told herself with a surge of relief. Making a quick right turn at the next intersection, she sped toward the impressive redbrick house he'd bought several years ago. When she pulled up at the curb, however, she saw all the lights were off. And when she rang the bell and pounded on the front door with her fists, there was no answer.

A MILE FROM Marianne Leonard's house, Arlan Duvalle pulled to the curb, his angry curses reverberating in the confines of the stolen car.

He'd thought he could pick up the bitch's trail—until

she'd vanished into the maze of streets surrounding her house. Half of them were one-way, and that had made him lose even more time as he tried to figure out which way she'd gone.

Savagely he pounded his fists against the steering wheel, stopping only when pain shot up his arms. He'd been so close, close enough to wrap his hands around her slender white throat. Then she'd pulled that stupid trick with the barbell. He reached down to rub his gut where she'd slammed the weight into him.

He'd had plenty of time in prison to think about what her family had done to him. Today there was more damage to add to the score, and before he finished with her, he'd make sure she understood what she owed him.

He glanced back over his shoulder. No use flapping around in circles now like a chicken with its head cut off. Better to toss her house, find that letter. If she wasn't lying about that, he thought, his fists making another violent assault on the steering wheel.

Struggling to contain his fury, he took a deep breath. There was no percentage in getting riled. Anger was dangerous. So was overconfidence.

He ordered himself to relax as he thought about the good parts of their encounter. Like that trick with the voice— making her think he was her good old friend Silvio Marco. He'd always been a great mimic, and he'd had years to perfect the skill. Maybe he should have played *her* father instead of Marco. Wouldn't that have been a hoot!

He smiled as he thought about the fun he could have with her when he caught her again. But first he'd have a nice dinner and a couple of beers while he made some plans. Then he'd drive by the house and check things out. If Ms. Leonard was stupid enough to have come back, so much the better. But it didn't really matter. Either way, he'd catch up with her soon enough.

TEARS OF FRUSTRATION stung Marianne's eyes as she leaned her head against the door. Tony wasn't home. The idea flashed through her mind of driving around back and waiting for him. But she reconsidered almost immediately. He had built up a very successful import business, which meant he went on buying trips several times a year. He could be in Europe or Asia for all she knew. He could be gone for weeks.

With leaden steps she made her way back to the car and started the engine again, this time with no idea where she was going or what she was planning to do. The only thing she knew was that she had to put as much distance as she could between herself and the madman.

Dimly it registered that the sun was setting. As the sky turned navy and then black, she kept driving in a kind of trance until she saw a highway sign—and realized with a jolt of recognition that she was on Route 50, heading for the shore. For Paradise Beach, to be exact. It seemed that if she couldn't get help from Tony, her subconscious had served up this substitute—the summer place he'd inherited from his father, where she'd spent at least a month every year. It was set back from the road. Isolated. The perfect place to hide while she figured out what to do.

After filling her almost-empty gas tank at a station on the edge of town, she turned onto the two-lane country road along the Severn River and scanned the mailboxes.

When she found the one that said "Marco" she let out a little sigh, turned in at the drive that wound through the woods, and pulled around to the back of the comfortable white and green Victorian house. After cutting the lights, she got out and stretched her cramped muscles.

She was starting for the front walk when the powerful beam of a flashlight suddenly hit her full in the face. Blinded, she threw up her hands.

Lord, he had found her again. The madman who had been

waiting for her at home. Through some evil magic, he'd figured out where she was going and had gotten here first.

Heart pounding, she was backing toward the car when a voice with a marked country twang halted her. "This is private property, missy. What are you doing here?"

Not him. It wasn't him. That much registered in her terror-numbed mind.

"Who are you?" the speaker demanded gruffly, the flashlight beam pinning her.

Her hand tugged convulsively at the brim of her hat. "Tony Marco's wife," she heard herself say, shocked and dismayed at the bald-faced lie that had tumbled from her mouth, yet knowing it had come from deep within her subconscious.

"Oh yeah?"

Instantly, she wished she could take it back. But she had already trapped herself, and the only thing she could do was plunge ahead and pray for the best. "Tony's meeting me here," she said, straightening her shoulders.

"You're Tony's missus? When did you get married?"

Her mind went blank, until another fib rose to her lips like a cork bobbing to the surface of a pond. "Last week."

"I've been workin' down here all month. Tony didn't mention nothing to me about getting married."

"Well, you know how he is about keeping his personal life to himself," she tossed off. At least that was true. Moving toward the front steps as if she had every right to be there, she reached for the fake rock sitting under an azalea bush. It was back farther than she expected, and she had a few bad moments as she scrabbled in the dirt. Then her fingers latched on to the rounded surface. As she extracted the key, she raised her eyes, and the man lowered the flashlight beam.

A sigh of relief trickled out of her when the key fit the

lock. Without glancing over her shoulder, she marched inside, aware that he had followed.

"I'm Horace Haliday," he said as he blocked her exit from the kitchen. "Did Tony change his mind about sellin' the place?"

Horace Haliday. She remembered him now. He'd done odd jobs for Tony's father, but she hadn't seen him in years.

"We're thinking about staying," she answered, trying to decide whether to remind him who she was. Probably it was better not to get into a long discussion.

"Yeah. Well, you could get a good piece of change for prime waterfront property. Not that you need the money with Tony doin' so well in his business and all." He cleared his throat. "Sorry about flashing that light in your eyes, Miz Marco. I wasn't expecting you."

The form of address made her cringe. Lord, how was she going to worm her way out of this? Clearing her throat, she pasted a smile on her face. "I'm pretty tired. It was a long ride down from Baltimore, so I'd like to get some rest."

He stood uncertainly in the doorway, then backed away. A few moments later, she heard a vehicle start. In the moonlight, she could see a pickup truck lumbering toward the main road.

When it was finally out of sight, she slumped against the kitchen counter and locked her knees to keep them from trembling as an instant replay of her cock-and-bull story flashed through her mind.

Tony's wife! For years that had been her secret dream. Too bad she hadn't kept it to herself.

If he ever found out, she could never look him in the eye again. For long moments she stood there with her head in her hands. But she was too wrung out to stay on her feet for long.

With a grimace, she pushed away from the counter, flipped on the light switch, and discovered that the electricity had been cut off. *Par for the course,* she thought as she rummaged in the pantry and found a flashlight. There were candles, too, but she hated open flames.

In the living room, she shined the light on the familiar surroundings, profoundly glad that nothing had changed. The place was furnished for comfort, with wicker chairs and tables and an overstuffed chintz couch set in the middle of the room, angled to provide a view of the river.

Although it was stifling inside, she was afraid to open the windows more than a crack. But her sweat-soaked dress and stockings were intolerable.

Climbing the creaking staircase to the second floor, she hesitated in the hall, then opened the door to Tony's room. She hadn't come in here much, but she assumed he kept clothing in the dresser. When she opened the second drawer and shined the flashlight inside, she found more than clothing. A box of condoms was wedged beside a pile of underwear.

Instant heat flared in her cheeks. Snatching out a T-shirt, she shoved the drawer closed, sorry that she had invaded his privacy—and sorry that her heart had started pounding again.

Squeezing her eyes closed, she ordered herself to stop reacting like an idiot. So he'd brought girlfriends down here. Well, what of it? He was a grown man. She knew he must have had relationships with women. Yet the hard evidence wasn't something she wanted to face.

Whirling, she trotted out of the room. Too tired to search for something else to wear, she undressed in the bathroom and pulled the T-shirt over her head. It was miles too big, but the fact that it was Tony's gave her a sense of security.

Wearily she tottered down the hall and eyed the bed in the guest room, but the thought of sleeping so far from an escape route made her nervous.

Somewhere in her shell-shocked mind she knew that she

shouldn't stay here. Not after that encounter with Mr. Haliday. But she was too mentally and physically exhausted to flee again. About all she could do was stagger back downstairs and huddle on the sofa with her arms wrapped around her knees, her mind blessedly numb. Soon sleep stole over her.

Sometime later, her eyes snapped open again. The heat was like an asbestos blanket lying heavily on her body, and her skin was covered with a fine sheen of perspiration. Was it the temperature that had awakened her? Or something more sinister?

Every muscle in her body rigid, she strained her ears, slitted her eyes. The flashlight she'd left on shone feebly now, but along with the moonlight filtering through the windows, the orange glow was enough to give her the outlines of the room.

Her anxious gaze probed the shadows, but nothing stirred. And no sound reached her. It must have been something outside—probably a fox or a raccoon—that had wakened her. That was all, she assured herself, trying to force her tight muscles to relax again. Feigning sleep, she shifted uneasily, all her attention focused on the darkened doorway leading to the hall.

When a floorboard creaked, she bit down on her lip to keep from crying out.

Oh, Lord. No.

The quality of the darkness changed, and she realized there was a figure blocking the entrance—a large male figure, she judged from the height of his head and the width of his shoulders. He was turned toward her, his face hidden by the shadows, but she could feel the force of his gaze pressing against her body.

The breath solidified in her lungs. Without moving, she flicked her eyes to the right and left, looking for something to use as a weapon. She found nothing.

Sheer blinding panic threatened to swallow her whole as she remembered the feel of those steely fingers squeezing her neck. A whimper rose in her throat, but she clamped it off by digging her nails into the palm of her hand. The pain cut through the fog swamping her brain.

Summoning all her resolve, she leaped up and vaulted over the sofa back—making for the rear of the house.

Behind her she heard a surprised exclamation. Then the invader was scrambling after her. Within seconds, he was on her, catching her from behind the way he had before and stopping her forward motion. His hands were on her shoulders, his supple body pressed to her back.

The position fueled her panic. Again, she couldn't see his face. All she knew was that he was strong and deadly—and he should have been able to hold her. But her strength came from desperation as she began to fight him, kicking at his legs, stamping down on his feet with all her strength.

"No," she whimpered. "No! Let me go."

As she spoke, he made a strangled sound, and his grip loosened. She hadn't really believed he would let her go. But she took advantage of the opportunity to wiggle out of his grasp. Stumbling forward, she found her footing, sprinted toward the back door, and flung it open before fleeing mindlessly into the night.

She could hardly see in the waning moonlight. But she kept running, her only goal to escape his clutches again.

"Wait! Stop." The wind caught his voice, distorting it and carrying it away.

Not in this lifetime, her mind screamed. Weeds whipped at her legs, stinging her flesh as she dashed headlong into the darkness, heedless of everything but the sound of his footsteps pounding closer.

Rough boards slapped against the bottoms of her feet. Gasping for breath, she put on a desperate burst of speed.

"No! Stop! Marianne!" He called her name, and this time

the sound of his voice pulled at her, almost checking her steps. But her whole being was tuned to flight and only physical force could have stopped her.

She reached the end of the boards and went sailing into space. A scream of denial tore from her lips as she plummeted down, down—her fall broken only by bone-freezing water.

Chapter Two

Her arms flailed as dark water sucked her downward into oblivion. Then she reached the murky river bottom and reflexively pushed upward with all her might. Lungs bursting, she struggled toward the surface, hardly sure if she was moving in the right direction. Finally, finally her head broke into the cool night air, and she dragged in a gasping breath.

Swim, she ordered herself. *You can swim if you don't panic.* But the dark and the fear made her limbs stiff, and she felt herself going under again.

Beside her, the water splashed and churned, then strong hands grabbed her shoulders, and she screamed, flailing out as she tried to free herself.

She went under again, sputtering as she came up.

"Marianne, don't. It's Tony. Don't fight me, baby."

The words hardly registered as her fists pounded against his chest, pushing him down, clawing at him with the last of her strength. If she was going to drown, she would do her best to take him with her.

"I won't hurt you. Please." He was breathing hard as he pulled her roughly to her back and locked his arm across her breasts. Far stronger than she, he brought her body under control, and she sobbed in fear.

His hand tightened on her shoulder. "Don't fight me, Marianne. It's Tony," he said, over and over, his familiar voice finally cutting through the temporary insanity of her panic.

Tony. It couldn't be. Yet the reality was finally sinking in. It was Tony whose rock-hard arms held her head above the water.

The mind-numbing terror evaporated, and she went slack, except for the coughs racking her body.

"Good, that's good," he crooned, his hand touching her shoulder. "I'm going to tow you to shore. Okay?"

"Yes," she managed as he began to pull her through the water, his muscular legs kicking and his free arm stroking. Then he was stumbling onto the beach, his breath harsh in her ears as he lowered her to the sand.

She lay with her eyes closed, unable to stop coughing.

Crouching low, Tony pulled her up, draping her across his forearm and pounded on her back as she rid her lungs of river water.

"Marianne. Marianne." He said her name over and over, his tone low and urgent. "Are you okay?"

"Yes," she managed.

As her mind began to function again, she became aware of her dripping hair and the way her breasts were plastered against him. The plunge into the river had made her nipples hard, and she felt them stabbing against the shirt. *His* shirt, she suddenly remembered, keeping her face turned away from him in chagrin.

Eyes closed, she tried to put a few inches of space between them.

"Rest. Just rest." He eased her back so that her head was cradled in his lap, then pushed the wet hair away from her eyes with a touch so gentle she barely felt the pressure.

She cleared her throat as she took in her surroundings. They were on the narrow beach where she'd played as a kid. And she'd plunged off the end of the boat dock.

"Why did you run away?" he rasped.

Raising her face, she tried to read the expression in his eyes. But she couldn't penetrate the darkness or his lowered lashes.

"I...I didn't know it was you," she stammered. "You...you came at me like a—a lion bringing down its prey," she wheezed.

He rubbed a hand across his eyes. "Yeah, well, when I saw you on the couch, lying there like you owned the place, I didn't know who you were. Then you leaped up and ran. I thought—"

"What?"

"That you'd lied your way into the house and you were trying to get away when the owner showed up."

When she sucked in a sharp breath, he cupped his hand around her shoulder, the fingers pressing painfully into her flesh. "What did you expect me to think? Horace called me. Asked me if I'd gotten married. When I accused him of being drunk, he said some woman was down here posing as my wife. I don't have a wife." The last part came out gravelly and strained.

Glad that the darkness hid the rising color in her cheeks, she tried to imagine the phone call. "I shouldn't have told him that," she murmured. "It was a stupid thing to say."

"Why did you?"

She heard the stiffness in his voice, and wondered what he must think of her. Looking up at him, she became aware for the first time that he was sopping, too.

Lord, he'd come charging down here to deal with a trespasser. And what he'd gotten for his trouble was a dunk in the river rescuing a crazy woman who'd done her best to drown him.

Thoroughly mortified, she pushed herself off the ground and tried to cover her naked thighs by tugging at the hem of the shirt. She stopped when she saw from the corner of her eye that he was watching her intently—and that she was probably making things worse, if modesty was her intention.

"Baby, take it easy. Tell me why you came down here."

At the moment, she didn't trust her voice, so she gave him a quick shake of the head and wheeled toward the house, wincing when the bottom of her foot slapped down on a sharp piece of gravel.

TONY RAN HIS HAND through his wet hair, then strode after her. God, he was so off balance he was asking her all the wrong questions. But as soon as he'd gotten off the phone with Horace, he'd leaped into his car and sped down here fully prepared to do battle with a sneak thief or worse. Instead he'd found Marianne Leonard—so frightened that she'd fought her way out of the house and dashed headlong into the river.

Either she had figuratively gone off the deep end, or... It was the "or" that made the hairs on the back of his neck prickle. Marianne Leonard was one of the most steady, reliable people he'd ever met. If she was scared out of her mind, then something pretty bad had happened—and he had to find out what it was.

He watched her marching toward the house, her wet T-shirt and panties revealing every breathtaking line of her lithe body. The sight made him respond the way he'd been responding to her since her shape had changed from child to woman—with a quick, predictable zing of sexual awareness that he always fought to repress.

Usually he coped by putting some distance between them. Tonight that wasn't going to be an option. Not when she was strung as tightly as a wire about to snap. Not when she so obviously needed his help.

In a few quick strides, he caught up with her. "Marianne. Wait."

"I didn't mean to make trouble for you," she whispered,

her head down, tears edging her voice as she marched toward the porch. "I'm sorry about telling Horace that stupid story. And I'm sorry you got wet. I'll clear out as soon as I change."

"No." The self-accusation in her voice was like a lash against his skin. Catching hold of her arm, he pulled her toward him, feeling the stiffness of her muscles as she resisted any attempt at comfort from him.

"Marianne, baby. Don't run away from me now," he muttered, folding her against his chest, cupping the back of her head and bringing her face against his shoulder.

For endless seconds she stood as unyielding as a department-store mannequin. Then her entire body began to shake.

"Ah, baby, don't," he crooned. "It's okay. Everything is going to be okay."

"No," she said again, the tiny syllable laced with tears that she was struggling to contain.

"Whatever it is, we'll deal with it," he murmured as he held her in the moonlight, stroking his fingers across her back, trying to comfort and calm her.

When she lost the struggle for control and began to sob in his arms, all the tender emotions he had tried to keep in check where she was concerned swept over him like a flood tide.

One hand caressed the damp strands of her hair. He couldn't see them in the darkness, but he knew they were like spun gold, heating his fingers even wet from the river. He couldn't see her face, either, but it didn't matter. He had already committed the details to memory—the small pouty mouth, the sea-green eyes with lashes and brows several shades darker than her hair, the ivory skin. The totality added up to an enticing picture that had captivated him long ago.

His other hand smoothed over her shoulders, then down her spine, setting off a little shiver in her body that transmitted itself to his. How long had it been since he'd let himself hold her like this, he wondered, his senses dazed by the feel of her, the scent, the warmth of her skin.

Never. Never precisely like this.

Unable to check himself, he turned his head, his lips skimming the tender edge of her cheek. It was soft and dewy like a flower petal.

She had stopped crying, her feminine body pliant in his embrace, her hand moving restlessly across his back. Somewhere along the line he forgot why he was cradling her in his arms—his only conscious thought was that she was finally where she belonged.

Even through their wet clothes, the heat of her body seared him, the imprint of her breasts against his chest and the pressure of her hips against his promising untold delights. He wanted more, needed more.

His own body hardened in helpless arousal, and when his hand slid downward to cup her sweetly rounded bottom and pull her against his swollen flesh, she made a small sound and moved against him as though they'd practiced these moves a thousand times.

Only in his dreams.

But this was no dream, and the reality of her eager response brought him back to his senses. What the hell was he doing? He'd sworn never to touch her like this, but when he'd taken her into his arms, he'd thrown every good intention out the window.

While he could still command his mind to work, he eased her body away from his, sucking in a strangled gasp of cold night air as he tried to gather his scattered wits.

She tipped her face upward, her parted lips inches from his. For a moment he couldn't move, couldn't do more than stare at her quivering mouth, imagining the taste of her, the warmth, the wet stroking of his tongue against her inner lips.

Then he shook himself, knowing he could never have the very thing he longed for most in the world.

"Marianne," he managed. "Come inside. You have to change before you catch your death of cold."

"Cold?" she answered, the puzzlement in her voice rich and vibrant. "I'm not cold."

"I am," he lied, turning and making for the steps, giving her a gentle tug. "You'll feel better when you've washed off the river water. Then you can tell me why you came down here."

He guided her into the house, then let go of her hand before striding to the breaker box in the utility room and switching on the electricity. When he returned to the living room, she was blinking in the sudden brightness. Tempted past good manners, he allowed his eyes one hot sweep over the curves of her body, barely hidden by the wet, clinging T-shirt. His T-shirt, he assumed from the size.

His hot gaze traveled upward and focused on a patch of red spread across her right cheek. From his beard. His brand. *Damn.*

She looked away, as if her thoughts were following the same track. He watched her eyes darting around the room, searching for a point of focus—and knew to the heartbeat when she discovered the gun he'd set on the coffee table before charging after her.

She made a little wheezing sound, her gaze shooting back to his face. "Were you planning to shoot somebody?"

"No. But I was prepared for trouble." Crossing the room, he picked up the weapon and casually slipped it into the end-table drawer, out of sight.

"Are you always prepared for trouble?"

"Yeah," he answered, wondering if she had caught the wealth of meaning in his answer. He'd been waiting for trouble since he was a kid. And he had the sudden, almost preternatural conviction that it had finally found him—found both of them.

Or was he letting his runaway imagination overcome his judgment? If he tried hard, he could come up with a couple of scenarios for why she'd fled down here. But until she told him the reason for her panic, there was no point in making assumptions.

When her eyes went back to the drawer, he cleared his throat. "I'll get you something dry to wear. You can change in the bathroom. Then we'll talk."

She pulled her gaze away from the end table, but kept her face averted. "Okay," she finally answered. "I guess I owe you that much."

He wanted to tell her she didn't owe him a damn thing. Instead he stood there staring at her pale face and huge eyes, aching to fold her back into his arms and feel her body pressed to the length of his again.

Shaking himself out of the trance, he turned and made for the stairs, taking them two at a time. In his room, he found more of his clothes for her—a green T-shirt and shorts. He even remembered to add a towel, which he laid on the sink, along with the clothing.

For himself he grabbed a blue button-down shirt and cut-off jeans. When he heard her close the bathroom door, he went downstairs and through the kitchen, to the outdoor shower enclosure they used to wash the sand off when they came back from the river. It was cold. But cold was what he needed.

After stripping off his sodden slacks and shirt, he turned the tap and stepped under the icy spray, tipping his face up to wash away the heat from his cheeks.

LIKE HE'D PLANNED, Arlan Duvalle had come back to the Leonard house. Now he waited in the shadows, his attention trained on the darkened windows.

Leonard. You'd think the widow could have come up with a name that was a little more imaginative. But that was typical of her mentality. She'd been a stubborn cow of a woman, always whining and complaining and bitching at her poor husband.

Really, the bastard was better off in his grave.

"Leonard. And Marco." This time he said it in an angry parody of Bobby St. Paul's voice, another voice from the past. The kids might have new names, but he had found them anyway. Too bad the senior Marco was dead, along with his pal, St. Paul. One less score to settle. But the two kids would do. All these years they thought they'd gotten away free and clear. Now it was time to settle up.

Finding them had taken money, a good part of the stash he'd hidden before the law had caught up with him. But he wasn't worried about that at the moment.

Satisfied that little Miss Leonard hadn't called the cops, he slipped through the shadows to the back door where he'd gotten in the first time. He was amused that she hadn't invested in a decent dead bolt—although it wouldn't have stopped him for long.

It had been easy to get in. It was easier now, because nobody had come back to lock the door. Slipping inside, he stood in the kitchen listening, watching. But everything was still and quiet.

Clicking on his flashlight, he aimed it at the floor. He'd learned the layout of the house on one of his previous visits, so he headed straight for the little room down the hall that she used as an office. Maybe the letter from her father was there. Or maybe it was in her room. If it was here, he'd find it.

MARIANNE HAD HEARD guys joke about cold showers. She hadn't figured she'd need one—until tonight.

One moment she'd been crying in Tony's arms like a

bedraggled little kid. Then she'd stopped crying and begun to pay attention to the touch of his hands on her back, the pressure of his hips against hers, the heat leaping between them.

All this time, she'd thought he wasn't attracted to her, but tonight had changed her perspective. The flow of electricity between them hadn't all been one-sided. The hot current had come from him as well as herself. Or was she so unhinged that she was reading things into his comforting touch that weren't intended?

Stepping out of the shower, she gave an unconscious little shrug. She might not be sure of herself when it came to man-woman responses. But she was darn sure about the wild tale she'd told to Mr. Haliday. She'd claimed to be Tony's wife. Now she was going to have to explain that to the man who was supposed to be her husband.

Lifting her head, she stared at her face in the mirror, at her wide eyes and the color staining her cheeks. It was partly from embarrassment—and partly from where Tony's beard had burned her flesh when he'd moved his cheek against hers.

Delicately, she ran her fingers over the tingling skin. After everything that had happened, the thought of confronting him again was simply too much. Maybe she could get out of here, make it to her car before he realized she was gone.

But then what? The madman was out there. Although facing Tony might be humiliating, it was better than getting strangled. However, her nerves were too raw to expose herself quite yet, so she snatched up the towel and began to dry her hair, rubbing it until her arms ached.

When he called her name from the bottom of the stairs, she jumped.

"Marianne? Are you all right up there?"

She cleared her throat to steady her voice. "Yes."

"Then come down."

"In a minute," she answered, wondering how she was going to get through the next half hour.

Silently she descended the steps, grateful that he'd turned off most of the overhead lights. In the glow from a couple of lamps, she could see him pacing back and forth between the sofa and the window.

"I'm a mess," she whispered when he stopped and gave her a long look, his expression tight.

"You're fine," he said in a clipped tone, and she was instantly sure that she had imagined his response to her after the river. This was the old Tony. The man who deliberately kept her at arm's length—unless she needed his help. Which was definitely the case tonight.

He'd changed into cutoffs that hugged his narrow hips and an old blue shirt that defined the broad expanse of his shoulders. But his lean cheeks were dark with the day's growth of beard that had stung her skin.

Stiffly, she perched on the edge of the couch, her fingers twisting the hem of her second borrowed T-shirt of the day. Although he'd opened the windows wide, and the room was a little cooler, she felt a trickle of sweat rolling down her neck.

Desperately, she tried to distance herself from him, but couldn't prevent a treacherous thought from stealing into her mind. If she were his wife, then this would be their honeymoon. But if he were her new husband, he would have shaved so that his beard wouldn't do any more damage to her skin when he—

Appalled by that dangerous line of thinking, she compressed her lips.

Unfortunately, he picked that moment to glance up, his gaze drawn to her mouth as he took several slow steps toward the couch. Before reaching her, he stopped and shook his head as if to clear it.

"Marianne, whatever it is, we'll deal with it," he said in a thick voice.

She sighed inwardly. At least he hadn't caught the drift of her thoughts. Had he? Determined not to make an even bigger fool of herself than she already had, she tried to focus on something besides the way his tall male body dominated her vision. But it was impossible to stop herself from taking in the details. Apparently he hadn't found a replacement for his waterlogged shoes because his feet were bare. So were hers, and somehow that made the encounter more intimate. Pulling up her legs, she tucked her feet under her body and searched for a safe place to center her gaze.

It landed on a can of soda on the glass-topped wicker coffee table. Her favorite brand, she noted, as she picked it up and wiped the beads of moisture forming on the outside. When she realized that Tony was watching her intently, she took a quick sip to moisten her dry mouth.

"Start from the beginning," he ordered, then began pacing the room again. "Tell me why you're hiding out down here."

She rolled the can between her hands. "It's cold," she whispered. "I thought the electricity was off."

"I got it from Horace's ice chest. Now quit stalling and tell me what happened to you." His eyes turned fierce. "Was it some guy?"

When she blinked at him, he continued with repressed anger. "Did some guy you were dating hurt you? If he did, I'll kill him!"

The violent reaction brought her head up sharply. "It's nothing like that." She gulped a swallow of soda and almost choked. "At least, not what you're thinking."

"Then what? Marianne, you can trust me."

"I know," she answered, then forced herself to start speaking. "When—when I got home tonight, there was a man in my house. Some of the time he sounded plain crazy.

And some of the time he acted like he knew me—like I should know *him*."

Stopping in midstride, Tony whirled toward her, his eyes burning into hers. "What man? What did he look like?"

"He didn't want me to see him. He held my back to his front." Clutching the soda can, she went on. "He said I knew some secret. That my father had told me something." She spread her hands, mystified. "I never knew my father. But this guy thought I did. He said if I didn't tell him what he wanted to know, he—he was going to kill me."

She almost jumped off the couch as Tony's fist came smashing down against the sideboard. "Tell me everything you remember!" he demanded. "Everything he said."

"I—I thought he'd escaped from a lunatic asylum. Are you saying I'm supposed to know him?"

"Yes! Dammit."

She'd wanted to believe she was a random victim. Somehow that had given her a measure of safety. Tony's savage reaction extinguished that dim hope. When she lost the battle to keep from shaking, he came and sat down beside her on the couch, turning her so that he could cradle her close.

"Who is he?" she whispered. "I don't even know what he wants."

"He won't touch you again," he vowed, and she clung to the assurance in his voice.

His hand kneaded the tight muscles of her back. "Tell me the rest," he said more gently. "All of it. I need to know exactly what happened."

Hesitantly she began to give him the details. When she got to the part about the attacker sounding like his father, Tony cursed. "The bastard!"

Next she told him about the barbell, and his hand squeezed her shoulder. "Good. Good for you!"

Finally, she ran out of words and slumped against him,

exhausted. Yet she felt the tension radiating from his arms, from his whole body.

"Duvalle," he ground out.

"Who?"

"It has to be Duvalle," he repeated the unfamiliar name. "That's the only thing that makes sense. Imitating my dad's voice sounds like his sick sense of humor."

"None of it makes sense!" she almost shouted, pushing herself away from him. "I don't have a clue about what he wanted!"

He angled his upper body so he could meet her eyes. "That name doesn't mean anything to you?"

She shook her head, yet somewhere in the back of her mind, memories prickled like ants creeping along her skin.

His eyes drilled into her, and she wanted to hide from him—from herself. But she could see he wasn't going to let her duck away from this, whatever it was.

"How long have we known each other?" he asked.

She made a rapid calculation. "Eighteen years."

"It's longer than that," he growled, leaving her no room for argument.

When she shook her head helplessly, he watched her like a hawk watching a rabbit.

"Look, we never talked about it, but you were five when you moved to Baltimore. You must have *some* specific memories from before that," he prodded. "What about your fifth birthday party? Most kids remember birthdays. Christmas? Don't you remember the dollhouse you wanted so badly?"

She could only stare at him.

"You were real sick with the chicken pox. Then when you felt better, you sneaked downstairs and ate a box of chocolates. Or what about that stuffed bear you used to drag around everywhere you went? Don't you remember that your dad gave it to you?"

An image of her beloved Mr. Edgar flashed into her mind. She'd clung to the bear like a security blanket until it had literally fallen apart. But she didn't remember who'd given it to her—not on a conscious level, anyway. Raising her shoulders, she shrugged, although this time she felt the teeth of nightmares nipping her cold flesh.

"Okay," he said, in a weary voice, then dug his hands into the pockets of his cutoffs. Through the worn fabric, she could see that his hands were clenched into tight fists. She felt the waves of tension radiating from him and wanted to shout at him to get on with it—whatever *it* was. But she knew that making demands would get her nowhere. Tony Marco had never let himself be pushed.

Finally, he sighed. "There's no way to make this pretty—so I'll say it straight out. My father and yours robbed liquor stores. Then banks."

She tried for a laugh, but it came out high and false. "Tony, you're kidding me."

"No joke," he bit out. "The really hellish part came when they took on another partner—a bastard named Arlan Duvalle. I know they were sorry about getting hooked up with him—especially after he went crazy and shot a bank teller."

Stunned, she could only stare at him. "What are you saying?"

"The truth," he spat out. "Your dad and mine were best buddies—and damn criminals. That's how they supported their families—until it all blew up in their faces."

Chapter Three

"No!" Marianne cried out again, twisting away from him. Springing off the couch, she stood in the center of the room trembling, her skin suddenly icy. "My mother said..."

Tony climbed to his feet, his jaw tight, his hands balled at his sides. "Forget everything your mother told you about your dad. Did you ever ask her why she despised *my* father so much? Did you ever ask her why she'd warned you to stay away from me?"

"You knew that?"

"Of course."

She looked down, unable to meet the fierce challenge in his gaze. Her mother had been so closed, so angry about certain subjects that asking questions had been impossible. So she had never tried to find out why nice Mr. Marco was on Mom's blacklist. Still, the questions lingered in her mind: If Mom hated Mr. Marco so much, why did they see him all the time? Why did she let him do things for them and help out with expenses? Why did Mom let her come down here every summer for a vacation? Why did Mom act like Tony would protect her—while at the same time warning her not to get involved with him?

It hadn't made sense. Yet there was a lot about Mom's own private rules for living that hadn't stood up to close scrutiny. Marianne had learned that it was sometimes prudent to keep her thoughts to herself, and life with Mom hadn't really been bad—just a tad strange.

Tony was speaking again, his voice flat and dead, in sharp contrast to the anger flashing in his eyes. "Your dad and mine were two grunts who came home from Vietnam and couldn't get jobs because half of society was down on vets. For months they sat around the living room drinking beer and complaining about how the country owed them a living. Then my dad got the brilliant idea that they should take what they deserved. From their point of view, it all worked out okay for a while." Tony stood there, his mouth twisted in disgust. "Now their partner Arlan Duvalle is out of prison and looking for—" He stopped, and opened his palms. "Revenge."

"Revenge for what?"

"He was the only one of the three the police caught."

"But why did he come after me?"

"You and me," he corrected sharply. "Because we're the only ones left." He raked a hand through his dark hair. "I knew *something* was going on these past couple of weeks. I just didn't know what." His head jerked toward her. "Did you get the feeling someone was checking up on you, poking into your business?"

She made a small sound. "I felt like someone was following me. Then I'd look up, and nobody would be there." Helplessly, she gestured with her hands. "I was scared. But I couldn't figure out what was going on."

"You should have come to me."

She felt her jaw muscles tighten. "Come on, Tony. You haven't exactly invited me over in the past few years."

His eyes took on a haunted look. "If I'd thought you were in trouble, I would have been there. All you had to do was ask."

She crossed to the window and stared out into the darkness, unable to tell him she'd been too proud to come begging—until the attack had changed everything.

Everything—because she understood now, deep in her bones, that the framework of her life had been shattered like a crystal bowl struck by a hammer. As she raised her eyes again and stared at Tony's bleak face she knew something else as well.

"You've been expecting this," she breathed. "All these years, you've been waiting for him to come back."

"No," he said, then sighed. "Okay. Yes. In the back of my mind I knew he held a grudge. From his twisted perspective, he had valid reasons. But I thought my dad might have done a good enough job of hiding our identities."

"And you didn't want me to know about any of it," she added, watching his eyes, searching for new truths.

"I didn't figure he was going to come after *you!* I assumed I'd be the target, and I thought I could handle him. Apparently I underestimated his devious mind."

For long moments she stood listening to the blood pounding in her veins. Her father and Tony's had been criminals. And Tony and everyone else had hidden the truth from her.

"You've had eighteen years of peace," he said, his voice very quiet. "Now you have to remember what your life was like before you came to Baltimore."

"Why?"

His tone turned fierce. "Because something happened the night it all went to hell. Something between you and your father. Or your father and Duvalle. And you've got to figure out what it was."

"I don't know *anything!*" she flung at him. "*You* have to tell *me!*"

He shook his head. "I wish I could, but I wasn't there. I was out with your mother at a drugstore getting bandages and painkillers for your father."

She jerked around to face him. "My father," she

wheezed as another detail shifted in her mind. "Wait a minute. What are you saying? I thought my father left us when I was a baby. That's what Mom always told me. Now you're saying that isn't true?"

Tony shook his weary head. "No. But maybe it would have been better if he had."

Reaching behind her, she gripped the window ledge to steady herself. "It's hard to believe all this," she whispered.

Tony took a step toward her. In a deceptively quiet voice, he asked, "Did you ever wonder why you're afraid of fire?"

The mere question brought a choking sensation to her chest, even as an automatic denial sprang to her lips. "No."

"Don't lie to me! At least, don't lie."

"Why not? You lied to me. For years you lied to me. From what you're telling me, everybody lied."

"We did it for your own good! When we first got to Baltimore, we were all living in the same rented house, and you used to wake up screaming in your bed. When the nightmares stopped, we all breathed a sigh of relief. Lots of times I wanted to ask if you remembered anything, but I never did."

Turning away, she held on to the window ledge for dear life. The nightmares hadn't stopped. They had never stopped—not entirely.

"It all ended in a fire," Tony said, his voice low and urgent as he stood in back of her, blocking her escape. "You were in the middle of it. Maybe you've shut it out of your conscious mind, but it's there—somewhere!"

Against her will, visions of an inferno flickered at the edge of her awareness. When she shuddered, he stroked her arms, and she knew he could feel the goose bumps. "It's all right. I'll keep you safe."

Memories beckoned—but they were just beyond her grasp. Were they real, or had he planted them in her mind

with his wild stories about outlaw parents and a confla-
gration?

His father and hers. Bank robbers. And their careers had
ended in a blaze of fire.... No, he couldn't have made that
up.

For years, it had been a secret locked behind a steel door
in her mind. Tony's words had opened the door a crack and
beyond it was a vision of hell.

Against her will, the door flew open—revealing the dancing flames in all their terror. She tried to slam the door
closed, but it was too late. She was swept back in time—
suddenly immersed in the awful heat. "Fire," she gasped.
"There was fire all around me."

Tony's hands tightened on her shoulders, and she
moaned, trying to twist out of his grasp.

He held her fast, his body like a shield in the inferno.
"It's okay. It was a long time ago. It can't hurt you now."

He was wrong. It could hurt her. She had always known
it could hurt her. She had awakened from dreams choking,
gasping for breath, her lungs on fire and her eyes stinging.
But as she'd lain shaking in her bed, she had never cried
out for her mother—lest she find out where the nightmare
came from.

Today a man named Duvalle had snatched away her security blanket. Still caught in the flickering memories, her
mind spun back to the heat, the fear as fire raged around
her. Then someone was picking her up, cradling her in his
arms, pulling her to safety. Someone bigger than she—but
not a man. A boy, she suddenly realized.

Pivoting, she faced Tony, her expression gravely serious
as she focused on his broad chest. "Why did you always
wear a T-shirt when we went swimming?" she asked.

He didn't answer.

Slowly she raised her hands to his shirt front and slipped

her fingers under the placket so that she could feel warm skin and crisp hair.

"Don't," he warned, taking a quick step back.

But this time she wasn't taking orders from him or anyone else. With deliberate care, she closed the distance he'd put between them, then began to slide open the buttons of his shirt, her fingers not quite steady as she bared his chest.

Under her hand she could feel his heart racing. It matched the frantic pounding of hers. She kept her eyes down, unable to meet his beseeching gaze as she pushed back the edges of the shirt, exposing his well-muscled chest. Dark hair spread across it, swirled around his nipples, arrowed downward toward his abdomen.

Yet near his right shoulder was a patch of rough, red skin where the hair didn't grow. She touched the broad scar, feeling his flesh quiver beneath her fingertips.

As her hands made a foray over his warm skin, she was caught in a web of emotions—frightening memories at war with sensual awareness. Astonished at her own boldness, yet unable to change her course of action, she pushed the shirt off his wide shoulders, revealing more scars. Reaching higher, she traced the line of his collarbone, then slid her hands to his back—where her questing fingers found another place with the same roughened flesh.

He didn't move, didn't pull away.

"You were burned," she said, her voice barely above a whisper.

His lips moved, but he didn't answer.

"You were burned rescuing me," she gasped out. "That's what happened all those years ago, didn't it?"

"Yes!" He flung that one syllable at her, then wrenched himself away. But she only reached for him, pulled him back into the charged space that seemed to enclose them.

Her eyes squeezed shut, she pressed her face against his

skin, feeling the rapid rise and fall of his chest. "You could have gotten killed."

"I had to get you out of there," he rasped, every muscle in his body rigid with the tension that arced between them.

"Tell me what happened."

"We were on the run, and we were spending the night in an abandoned house. When your mom and I got back from the store, we could see the flames shooting into the air. I jumped out of the car and ran to the house and saw you in there, crying, choking, trying to get out."

Her face moved against his broad chest, letting the deep thumping of his heart sink into her flesh. Into her soul. Turning her head, she trailed her lips against him. "You should have told me."

"I couldn't."

To protect her—or himself?

She let go of the question as his hand stroked her hair, gently, the barest whisper of a touch, yet the contact was strong enough to send a vibration through her.

Breathing in his familiar scent, she dared to touch her tongue to his crinkly hair and heated skin. She should move away, stop touching him like this. Yet now that she had dared so much, her legs wouldn't cooperate.

A strange sense of power and weakness fought for dominance within her—aided and abetted by the knowledge that the intimacy was affecting him as powerfully as he was affecting her. This time, she was sure. This wasn't just *her* fantasy come to life. *His* body had tightened, hardened, in response to her touch.

Slowly she raised her face to his. His hands clasped her shoulder, drawing her toward him, pressing the length of her body to his. She melted into his embrace, closing her eyes as she simply absorbed this new level of awareness between them while his arms drew her closer, then closer still.

When he had her where he wanted her, his hold shifted, his hands splaying across her ribs, exploring their delicate ridges, sending ripples of sensation coursing through her. The hands stole inward, the sides of his thumbs finding the lower curve of her breasts. A sound of wanting welled in her throat as she waited for him to cup her, mold her.

When he did, it was like a thousand tiny shocks electrifying her nerve endings.

"Tony," she breathed.

"Ah, baby. You feel so good."

"Yes. Oh, yes."

He seemed to read her mind, seemed to know that she wanted his fingers to circle her nipples, to stroke them, squeeze them so that heat shot downward through her body.

Earlier she had boldly said she was his wife. If they were husband and wife, there would be nothing wrong with touching each other like this—this and a lot more.

Before she could wrap her mind around the thought, his hands dropped away from her breasts, leaving them hot and aching with need. When she tried to reach for him again, he took a step back and shook his head. "We can't."

"Why not?" she asked, trying and failing to come up with one valid reason. They both wanted this—and more. Much more.

Yet the look in his eyes wasn't what she expected. They brimmed with an anguish that stole the breath from her lungs. "Tony?"

He made a low sound in his throat. "We have to talk. About Duvalle. We have to figure out what he wants and how he's planning to get it."

True enough, she agreed silently, fighting to take hold of reality. Somewhere along the line, she had forgotten why they were standing there with his shirt unbuttoned and their bodies hot and aching. But she also knew from the set of his mouth that he was reaching for excuses to distance himself from her again. So much for her fantasies.

When he began to button his shirt, she turned her head away. Keeping her gaze down, she walked stiffly to the couch again and sat. He stayed behind her, out of her line of vision. Maybe he didn't even know that he was hiding from her, but she understood. Too much was happening between them. Not just the sudden flare of sexual need. In the space of half an hour, their whole relationship had changed—and neither of them knew how to cope with it. But there was one thing she knew for sure. It was time for the truth, the whole truth. "What happened to my father?" she demanded.

"He...he died in the fire."

"Why? Why couldn't he get away?" she pushed.

When he didn't answer immediately, she pounded her hand on the coffee table, making the soda can jump. "You started this! You have to finish it."

"Okay, I guess you need to know how it went down," he agreed, sounding weary. "I already told you Duvalle started a shoot-out at the bank where they'd gone to make an unscheduled withdrawal."

When she nodded tightly, he went on. "Your father took a bullet in the shoulder."

Though she winced, he kept talking.

"My dad grabbed him and dragged him to the car. The two of them drove back to the house where your mother was waiting with us. Duvalle came roaring up just as they were ready to leave. Maybe he'd decided to split, then changed his mind."

Marianne tried to imagine the horror and confusion of the scene as Tony continued. "We left most of our stuff and piled into the car and the station wagon. That night we had to stop because your father wasn't fit to travel. Something happened while I was gone. By the time I got back, the house was on fire. I got you out. Duvalle escaped, but he was captured later. Your father never got out of the house.''

She sat staring into space, trying to absorb the terse explanation. All her life she'd believed a different story. Mom had told her that Dad had abandoned them.

Maybe from her point of view, it was true.

IN A STRANGE WAY it was a relief to have finally come clean with Marianne. Now Tony didn't have to watch his step with her, guard every word lest he give away the dirty little secret that he'd shared with her mother and his father. Still, seeing the pain and uncertainty in her eyes tore at him.

"I'm sorry you had to find out like this," he said, coming around to the front of the couch.

"My father," she said, experimenting with the words. "I have no memories of him. Now all I've got is the story of a terrible death." She swallowed convulsively, then pleaded, "Tell me something good about him."

"He cared about you and your mother. He was a good father—kind, loving. He used to tell you stories and take you places like the zoo and the park. You loved him. But you made yourself forget, and your mother helped the process along."

"She hated him."

"Take it from me, living with two guys hiding out from the law wasn't much fun. We had to be careful what we said. We couldn't make friends. We couldn't even go to the grocery story without checking our cover story. If anybody asked me questions, I'd be drilled on the correct answers."

"Oh, Tony, that must have been..." she fumbled for words. "Hard."

"Yeah."

Another basic question struck her. "Why were they dragging us around with them? Why didn't they have us live somewhere safe?"

"There was no one Dad could leave me with. And your mother wanted to stay with your father. God knows why, since she was always—" He stopped, wondering how much to say.

"Complaining?" Marianne asked.

"Right."

"Are you tactfully trying to say that she treated my father the way she treated yours?"

"Yes. She was needy and dependent—and afraid to try to make it on her own. And when things weren't going her way, she got depressed."

Marianne's vision turned inward as she remembered those characteristics. Tony was right, but it wasn't the whole story, and she desperately wanted him to understand better. "Life with Mom was never easy, but at least I knew the bottom line was that she loved me and she was doing her best to cope. I knew she wanted me to be happy. I knew she was in my corner when it counted."

"I could see that," he acknowledged.

She gave him a little nod. "I could tell it was different for you. I knew your father was hard on you, but I didn't understand why. Were you angry—like my mother?"

His eyes narrowed. "I wasn't obsessed with the past, if that's what you mean. I was too busy trying to deal with my old man on a day-to-day basis. I know my father liked to play Mr. Nice Guy with you, maybe because he wanted to make up for your not having a dad. With me, it was different. He beat the crap out of me if I got in trouble, even cursed—anything that made him think I was going to turn to a life of crime. He had impossible standards for me." He laughed sharply, bitterly. "But he bought this place with stolen money. How's that for family values?"

When she couldn't dredge up an answer, he plowed ahead. "He didn't need to hold me to a standard! I have my own values. And they're a lot higher than his ever were." He struggled to bring his roiling emotions under control. "At first I understood why he kept some of the money. He paid a lot to establish new identities for all of us. Your mother, you, me, himself."

"What do you mean—new identities?"

"New names. New backgrounds. Documents to back them up. His name used to be Vance Rossi. I suppose you don't remember calling him Uncle Vance?"

When she shook her head, he went on. "Your parents were Robert and Jeanette St. Paul. You were Margaret. Now you're Marianne Leonard—with a birth certificate and social-security number to prove it. I've even got fake school records in the name of Tony Marco."

He found that watching her try to take it in was too painful, so he moved to the bookcase, his gaze fixed on the darkened windows across the room.

She lifted her head toward him. "Who were you?" she murmured.

"Nick."

She said the name aloud. Then the others. After several seconds of silence, her shoulders rose in a little shrug. "They don't mean anything."

"Margaret doesn't sound vaguely familiar?" he pressed. "The little girl I carried out of the fire was Margaret."

"I'm sorry. I don't remember the name." Her voice quavered, and he cursed himself for not playing fair. God, she'd been to the depths of hell today, and she was trying to climb back onto solid ground. Instead of helping her, he was blocking her escape. Yet he needed information if he was going to save her from Arlan Duvalle—because her buried memories were the key to her own salvation.

Levering himself away from the bookcase, he crouched down in front of her, so that his face was level with hers. Her skin was pale and pinched, her hands clasped together so tightly that the knuckles were white, and he realized that he'd pushed her to the end of her endurance—maybe even to the end of his. He longed to offer her some comfort. There was none he could give. Except maybe the chance to escape from the pressure he was exerting on her—at least for a while.

"You need some sleep."

She gave him a tight, grateful nod. When she didn't move, he wondered if she was planning to flop back down on the sofa where he'd found her when he first came in.

"You can take your old bedroom," he said.

With a sigh she heaved herself up, and when she swayed on her feet, he moved swiftly and caught her. Effortlessly he supported her weight and for a moment she leaned into him. Then she pushed away and wove toward the steps without looking back—and he knew that she was hurting more than she wanted to admit.

ARLAN STOOD in the center of the ruined bedroom, breathing hard, his hands clenching and unclenching. He'd torn the house apart—starting with the obvious places. Then he'd gone on to the rest, growing more frustrated as he finished with each room. There was no escaping the truth. Little Miss Leonard had lied to him through her perfect white teeth. There hadn't been any letter from her father. She'd told him that so she could get away.

With a vile curse he kicked at a drawer that he'd dumped onto the floor, caving in the side. The splintering sound gave him a moment's satisfaction. Picking up a little china dog, he hurled it at the wall and watched it shatter into jagged pieces.

If he had her here he would do the same to her. Marianne Leonard, who used to be Margaret St. Paul. The daughter of the dearly departed, Bobby St. Paul.

He snorted, then said the names aloud, using first one voice and then another. Bobby and his partner Vance Rossi had been family men, afraid to take chances until they'd hooked up with him, and he'd taught them to think big. It had worked out real good. Real good. Until that lamebrain bank guard had lost his cool and gone for his gun.

Arlan squeezed his eyes shut, trying to blot out the scene in that suburban Pennsylvania bank. But it was fixed in his memory, burned into his brain. The flash of movement to his right, the guard's hand on the gun. His own hand quicker with his automatic pistol.

He'd fired first. Like in an Old West gunfight. The guard had gone down, but he'd brought down St. Paul with him. Rossi had grabbed his friend and run.

And of all the dumb bad luck, Arlan had been the one who ended up getting caught and put away. But now he was out, and he was going to get even. Anger flashed through him again. When he was calm enough to think straight, he pulled out the little spiral notebook where he'd been keeping notes. Sitting down comfortably in one of her kitchen chairs, he flipped the book open. Chapter One: "The Life of Marianne Leonard."

She worked at a nonprofit organization called the Light Street Foundation. And he'd done some research on them. Some of her co-workers had money. Some were tied into a protection service called Randolph Security. If she'd gone to them, he was in trouble. But he didn't think so. His guess was that she'd run straight into the arms of her friend Tony Marco. And if she had, he had a decent chance of finding them both—and killing two birds with one stone.

He'd also dug into Marco's import-export business, looking for a weakness he could exploit. The kid was doing pretty well for himself—and keeping his nose clean. Strange that Vance Rossi's son would be so scrupulous about morality—especially in a business where you could make big bucks by slipping stuff past customs. Either he was afraid to get on the wrong side of the law, or he was a nut. Either way, he was a chump who deserved whatever he got.

Arlan pushed himself out of the chair and walked to the door, his shoes crunching on broken crockery and the scattered contents of cereal boxes. His next step was Marco's house. If Leonard and Marco weren't there, he'd enjoy a little more constructive demolition.

MARIANNE MADE IT to the bedroom and pushed open the window, letting blessedly cool night air into the stifling room. Weaving her way to the bed, she pulled down the covers, profoundly grateful that she didn't have to go hunting for sheets and pillowcases. Pausing to strip off her borrowed shorts, she eased onto the mattress.

Since childhood, she'd never been able to sleep without something over her—even on the hottest nights. Instinctively, she burrowed under the sheet, the covering a small protection from the terrors of the night. Now at least she knew where her nightmares came from.

As she lay in the darkness, she strained her ears, hearing Tony come up the stairs and move down the hall. Apparently, her traitorous mind wasn't willing to let go of the husband-and-wife theme, maybe because it was a lot more appealing than the night's revelations of murder and fire. Mentally, she pictured Tony walking into her bedroom—and followed his arrival with an image so sexually explicit that she kicked the sheet away from her suddenly overheated body.

She pressed her palms over her face, then dug the heels of her hands into her eyes, trying to wipe out the picture of her body twined with his.

His wife. Fat chance.

Irony made her mouth twist. She had always felt a kind of secret bond with him. Tonight he'd finally told her what it was, and she'd learned she was forever tied to a life he had despised. Every moment with her was a reminder of it. No wonder he had kept his distance from her these past few years.

But it wasn't her fault, she silently railed. She hadn't done anything wrong. Neither had he. They had both been kids, dragged into a murky whirlpool of events by the adults who should have been protecting them. Until tonight, the horror had been in the past. Now it had come back to haunt them both.

She might have wept then, if she had been sure Tony wouldn't hear her. What she needed was to get away from him, where she could think, where proximity wouldn't torture them both. Yet Duvalle was out there in the night, searching for her. He had attacked her, and he might come after Tony if he couldn't get to her. So her only option was to stay and try and figure out the puzzle of her life.

But not until tomorrow. Tonight she was too wrung out to think.

Sleep claimed her once again that evening, and sometime later, a dream grabbed her by the throat.

She was a little girl, frightened and alone, wandering through the empty rooms of a dilapidated house, her terror growing as she realized everyone had gone away and left her.

Then she found a flight of stairs leading down. She knew they represented safety, and she breathed in a little sigh as she reached the bottom and stood looking around for the door.

She had taken a few quick steps when a bulky figure loomed at the end of a long hall—a man with shaggy hair and small, angry eyes.

Quickly she ducked into a room off the hall. Another man was lying on a sleeping bag on the floor, and she knew it was her father, although his face was hidden by shadows.

"Daddy, help me."

"I can't."

He slipped his hand under the sleeping bag, pushed at something beneath his shoulders. Then he reached toward her, called out a message she knew was important. But it was hard to make out the words.

All at once, the bad man was in the doorway. His arms lengthened, grabbed her, and she felt a choking pain as strong fingers squeezed at her windpipe, cutting off her supply of oxygen, filling her brain with swirling smoke.

Chapter Four

Swamped by terror, Marianne tried to call out for help. But no sound could get past the awful pressure of those fingers wrapped around her neck.

"The money. Give me the money," he said, over and over. "You know where it is."

A lantern loomed in the darkness. Then flames blazed up. They formed a circle around her and the man, a circle that grew smaller and smaller as orange and gold tongues licked painfully at her skin—and at his.

He shrieked—a high, frightened sound—and the choking hands slipped away from her neck. Gasping in a shuddering breath, she began to run, sobbing as she leaped through the wall of fire. But the man was right behind her, his footsteps pounding on the wooden floor, his hot breath coming in long puffs that seared her flesh as she dodged through endless dark rooms, where fire sprang from the walls.

Somewhere at the edge of her vision she saw a dark-haired boy. A boy named Nick, who had come to save her. He lunged toward her through the flames and snatched her away. It was all right. She was safe—until she realized there was a crushing weight pressing down on her chest. Panicked, she flailed out with her arms, her fists pounding against the hard wall of a man's chest.

"Marianne!" A voice penetrated the nightmare. "Marianne. Wake up. It's Tony. I won't hurt you. It's Tony."

Her eyes blinked open—and for several heartbeats she couldn't take in what was happening. All she knew was that a hard male body was pressing her into the mattress and viselike fingers had manacled her wrists.

"Baby, don't. It's all right. It's all right!"

She focused on his face, inches from hers, even as her frantic struggles subsided. He lay on top of her, his body fused to hers as his hands kept hers from beating at his head and shoulders.

When she raised her eyes to his, she found herself lost in their dark depths.

"Marianne?"

"Tony," she breathed, taking in the startling intimacy of their positions with a rush of sensation. In the next moment, she realized she'd been trying her best to pummel him. "Oh, Lord, did I hurt you?" she gasped.

"It's okay," he answered, his grip loosening on her wrists. Shifting his position, he rolled to his side.

"What…are you doing here?" she breathed.

"I heard you screaming in your sleep."

"Yes." Vivid nightmare scenes flashed in her mind. The man with his hands around her throat, choking her… The flames searing her… Suddenly she clutched at Tony's shoulders, pulling him closer, using his physical presence as a shield. "Don't leave. Don't leave me."

"I won't." Gently he cradled her body against his as she lay shaking, clinging to the one person she had always known would keep her safe.

His hands moved up and down her arms, across her back and shoulders. She closed her eyes, letting herself enjoy the sensations he aroused, feeling the fear seep out of her—but not the tension.

Her face was pressed to his naked chest. Casting her eyes down, she saw white briefs and long, hair-roughened legs.

He was practically naked in her bed. With guilty curiosity, she took a longer look and was treated to a very revealing view of white cotton knit stretched over an impressive male anatomy.

Restlessly, she shifted her legs. As they touched his, he sucked in a sharp breath, his stomach muscles tightening.

Moving quickly, he reached down, found the sheet where she had kicked it away and pulled it up so that it covered his hips and hers. Probably his intent had been modesty, but the sight of the sheet draped across the two of them, lying there like a man and a woman who had just made love was the most erotic thing she had ever seen.

"Are you okay?" he asked, his voice thick as he put a little space between their bodies.

"Sort of."

"Did you dream about the night of the fire?"

She shuddered. "Yes. But Duvalle was there. I mean the Duvalle who tried to choke me." Her hand fluttered. "It was the past and the present, all mixed up."

When she didn't volunteer any more information, he stroked her arm with his knuckles. "I need to hear about it. There might be a clue to what he wanted."

Her breath caught. She wanted to shove the evil images back into the recesses of her mind.

"How did it start?" he asked.

Hearing the urgency in his voice, she forced herself to remember. "I was in the old house. I think I was alone on the second floor."

"Yes. Your mother took you upstairs," he confirmed. "She didn't want you to see how badly your dad was wounded."

"But it's just a dream," she insisted, her temples pounding. "I mean, it's not what really happened."

"Tell me about it, anyway. Were you a little girl?"

She nodded, fighting the pain in her head as she spoke. "Yes. I saw the stairs. I went down and found my father. Then Duvalle grabbed me." She swallowed. "I mean, I guess it was him. He wouldn't let me see him yesterday."

"What did he look like in the dream?"

The image floated in her mind like the face of a spirit wavering in a crystal ball. For years she had tried to block it out. Now she deliberately opened to it. "Dark, stringy hair. Little eyes. A—a bad complexion."

Tony nodded. "That sounds like the guy I remember. Probably there's gray in his hair by now. Was he medium height and stocky?"

"Maybe, I guess. In the dream, he seemed...big."

His fingers tightened painfully on her arms. "What did he want?"

"Money," she answered as his words came back. "He said I knew where to find the money."

Tony's eyes narrowed. "What else did he say?" he demanded.

Paralysis numbed her brain. There had been more to the dream, she knew, but the images hovered at the edge of her awareness. If she concentrated, maybe she could bring them closer, into sharper focus. Yet the threat was simply too great for her to take the risk. Pain beat against the inside of her skull as her body began to shake.

She pushed at Tony. "Don't make me. Let me go!"

His hold on her gentled. "I'm sorry."

She managed a little nod. "I just can't."

He held her close, and the warmth of his body took some of the chill from her skin.

"I'd give a couple of years of my life if I could tell you what happened that night," he said grimly. "But I wasn't there."

She nodded against his chest, hearing the depths of his

anguish and knowing he didn't like this any better than she did.

She touched his cheek, and he closed his eyes. "You were in the dream," she murmured, clinging to the only part she wanted to remember. "At the end. You were trying to save me."

"Did I get to you in time?" he asked, his voice low and urgent.

"Yes." She didn't want to talk anymore, feel anymore. Like a coward, she let exhaustion overwhelm everything else. Gradually she slipped toward sleep, because this time it would be safe. This time Tony was holding her.

TONY CLOSED HIS EYES and tried to put some distance between his aching body and Marianne's. But it was impossible to hold her and ease the physical discomfort he was experiencing.

Her nightmare had brought him to her bed. But now she was asleep in his arms, and he was wrestling with his most erotic fantasy come true: Marianne snuggled up to him in bed. All he had to do was cover her mouth with his, and he could make them both forget about fires and robbers and a vengeful killer somewhere out there in the dark. But he was too damned honorable to take advantage of her—not when he'd seen the trust in her eyes and then the agony when he'd tried to force her back into the nightmare.

So he gritted his teeth and accepted the punishment for his sins. But his senses were filled with the woman next to him in bed. He could feel every inch of her long legs, her hips, the curve of her breasts. If he moved, his erection would be pressed against the juncture of her thighs. He wanted it there—wanted to bury himself in her warmth. Instead, he stayed where he was, concentrating on not waking her.

Yet he couldn't stop himself from raising his hand and

cupping his palm a fraction of an inch over her right breast where it strained against the fabric of her T-shirt. He could see the shadow of her nipple through the knit, and his fingers tingled with remembered sensations that sent the blood pounding through his body. God, she had felt so good.

And she had told Horace she was his wife.

His wife!

As he'd driven toward Paradise Beach, he'd fluctuated between anger, indignation and bemusement—and back again. He'd been prepared for anything.

And what he'd found was Marianne Leonard—playing house. Now here he was in her bed as if he had a right to make love to her. He angled his head, aching to lower his mouth to hers, to drink in her sweetness. The erotic images in his brain set his body on fire, and he had to summon every molecule of willpower he possessed to keep from thrusting his hips against hers. If he had ever needed a woman more than he needed Marianne tonight, he couldn't remember it.

But then, he'd been under her spell from the moment they'd met—when Dad and her father had initiated their strange blended family of outlaws. He had been a different person back then. An eleven-year-old without a clue to the nasty surprises life had in store for him. The first one had come one rainy morning when he woke up to find his mom had bailed out.

Then it was just him and Dad—and the little girl called Margaret and her parents. She had been four—a golden-haired angel who had snuggled up to him in the back of Dad's station wagon as they'd driven through the night and who had sneaked some of her french fries to him when her mother wasn't looking.

Life with Dad and Uncle Bobby had started out as an exciting adventure. Then he'd heard the angry, tense voices of the men and Margaret's mom, and he'd come to realize that he was on a trip to hell—and that his job was to shield Margaret from the worst of it. So he'd taken the blame for soft drinks she'd spilled and crumbs she'd left in the car, and he'd made up stories about the life they were going to live when they finally settled down. He'd spun tales about the nice brick house where she could watch Saturday-morning cartoons and play with her dog in the fenced backyard. And he'd promised to build her a tree house and teach her to ride a skateboard.

The endless wandering had stopped abruptly. With her father dead and her mother a wreck, he'd felt even more protective of Margaret, especially when he had to watch the way she withdrew into herself. Worry had finally turned to relief when he realized that Marianne—as she was now called—didn't seem to remember the bad stuff.

Then she'd burst into adolescence, and the budding curves of her body had turned him on. He'd been ashamed of himself for getting aroused over a girl so much younger, a girl who had been like a sister, a girl who trusted him. When her mother had come over one Saturday morning to tell him to stay away from her daughter, he'd told her she had nothing to worry about. Not because she'd warned him away, but because he'd already figured out the bottom line. If he and Marianne got too close, he'd have to tell her about their fathers. And then she'd have to share the burden he'd been carrying around all these years.

She'd already made herself forget it once. Which meant that dredging up the truth would be cruel—and dangerous. What if she were too fragile to cope with the knowledge? What if it destroyed her inner peace?

For all those reasons, he'd kept Marianne Leonard at arm's length, except for small lapses like the time after his father's funeral when he'd wanted to lose himself in her.

Tonight had changed everything. When he'd heard Duvalle had come after her, had tried to strangle her, razor-sharp fear had slashed through him. He knew it was the fear of loss.

The worst part was that he'd been pushed into the role he'd always shunned. Now he was the one forcing Marianne to remember the Rossi Gang—because *her* memories could be the key to figuring out what Duvalle wanted.

TONY WOKE with a start. He hadn't expected to sleep, and his senses were immediately on alert for whatever had jerked him from slumber.

When he heard stealthy footsteps in the hall, he cursed himself for leaving the gun in the drawer beside his own bed. Damn! All he'd been thinking about when he'd come running in here was that Marianne was having a nightmare, and he had to wake her up. Things had progressed from there, and he'd forgotten all about the weapon.

As he reached for the heavy candlestick lamp on the bedside table, he heard a familiar throat-clearing sound. At the same time, Marianne gasped and snatched frantically at the sheet that had slipped below her hips.

Her movements were punctuated by a loud guffaw from the doorway. With his jaw clenched, Tony raised his head. It wasn't Duvalle blocking their exit. Instead he found himself gazing into the grinning, weathered face of Horace Haliday.

"Hi, folks," he said pleasantly, his thumbs hooked in the leather strap of his tool belt.

When he didn't get a positive response, he shuffled his booted feet. "Sorry. I knocked, but I guess you two were sleepin' too sound to hear me." He laughed.

Tony's features contorted. "What the hell are you doing sneaking in here?"

"I'm not sneaking. You left me the key. I'm supposed to be workin' on this place. Next up is the leak in the attic. *You* said you wanted it fixed before we get more rain. Your wife didn't tell me otherwise. And last night, I didn't even know if she was really your wife. Or if you'd be here in the mornin'.'' He ended with an elaborate shrug.

"Of course," Tony muttered. From the smug look on Horace's face, it appeared that he'd planned this scouting mission well. So much for good manners. But then, he'd always known Horace was a little odd.

"Get out of here," Tony ordered.

The intruder stayed where he was for a second, craning his neck for a better look at Marianne, who had scrunched down into the bedding. From the corner of his eye, Tony could see that her face and neck had turned beet red.

Satisfied, Horace took a step back. "Brought some groceries for you and the missus," he announced cheerfully. "A little wedding present."

Marianne gave a low moan.

"Yeah, well, my wife and I don't appreciate being accosted in our bedroom," Tony heard himself growl.

"Then you don't want me to take care of the roof this morning?" Horace asked, all innocence.

"I want you to stay away from the house until further notice. Otherwise, you're fired."

Horace looked mortally offended. "I was only doin' the job you paid me for."

Tony started to climb out of bed, reconsidered, and sat up straight, his eyes blazing. "Listen, Horace," he growled. "Mrs. Marco and I came down here to be alone. We don't want company. And we don't want a lot of people knowing we're here. So keep a lid on the gossip. You understand?"

"Sure thing." The handyman scurried off down the hall. Moments later, his heavy footsteps sounded on the stairs.

When Tony turned back to Marianne, he saw her sitting with her knees drawn up and her face cradled in her hands.

"I'm sorry," he said.

"It's my own fault," she answered, her hands still covering her face. "I should have come up with some other cover story. But I...I couldn't think."

Tony wanted to tell her how much he'd like to participate in her current cover story. He was pretty sure that was a bad idea at the moment, so he climbed out of bed and went to the window, where he could watch Horace climb back into his blue pickup truck.

Marianne shifted her legs. "We might as well get dressed."

"I'll get out of your way." He made himself scarce in his own room, but he knew to the minute when she stepped out of the shower and went downstairs. By the time he finished shaving, he could smell the aroma of sizzling country ham wafting toward him. Apparently big-hearted Horace had gone all out for the happy couple.

He hurried down the stairs, then slowed his steps as he caught sight of her rigid back.

When she said nothing, he cleared his throat. "How are you?"

She pushed the sizzling ham around in the pan and shrugged.

"I need to know."

"I'm all right."

"Good," he answered, wanting to press for more information. All right about Horace? All right about remembering the past? All right about him? The only thing he knew for sure was that she wanted him to keep his distance.

MARIANNE WANTED to turn around and shout at Tony to give her some space. But she was the one who had told Horace the story about being married, so she stayed where she was at the stove, poking needlessly at the eggs.

When he cleared his throat, she braced herself. All he said was, "I'm sorry."

About what? Duvalle's attack? Her lame excuse for com-

ing here? In her present state, she couldn't ask, so she only nodded tightly.

He remained behind her, and again the silence lengthened. "I'm sorry my prodding triggered a nightmare," he finally elaborated.

"It's happened before. I'll survive."

She heard him let out a little breath. "Will it upset you if we talk about it some more?"

"No," she made herself answer, but kept her back to him.

"You said Duvalle demanded money."

She nodded tightly. At least talking about the dream was better than talking about their screwed-up personal relationship.

"The day the Rossi Gang robbed that last bank, they got away with several hefty bags of bills from the cashiers' stations."

"The Rossi Gang. Is that what you call them?"

He gave a mirthless laugh. "Uh-huh. But I only made the mistake once of saying it to my father's face. I got a smack across the mouth."

Picturing the scene, she felt her chest tighten.

Before she could say anything, he hurried on. "What if the money is the key? What if Duvalle thinks you know where the stash is hidden?"

She whirled to face him. "I don't!"

"Maybe not on a conscious level. But you were downstairs in the room with your father. I know that much. You must have been talking to him. Or maybe you heard him and my dad making plans."

She shook her head helplessly.

"The dream could be a clue. Otherwise, I wouldn't be asking you about it."

"It was just a dream! And it was a mixture of stuff that happened a long time ago and stuff that happened yesterday. If you're planning to take it to the bank, you're crazy."

Turning back to the stove, she began furiously stirring the eggs.

She was hoping he'd disappear; instead he remained behind her, and she felt her skin prickling as she waited for him to say something else.

When she was sure she couldn't take one more mute moment, he broke the silence. "Okay. There's another possibility. My father stored a lot of papers and records here. And he was a meticulous guy. What if he wrote down something about the missing money? Maybe if I go through his stuff, I can find out something."

"You'd do that for me? Go through his stuff?" she managed to say, around the sudden lump in her throat.

"Yes."

Slowly, she turned to face him and saw a mix of warring emotions cross his features. She was certain that immersing himself in the past was the last thing he'd want to do. Yet she knew he'd made the offer for *her*.

"Thank you," she murmured.

He gave a tight nod, opened the silverware drawer, and began to clank spoons and forks onto the table.

Then, as she lifted the pan off the burner and put the ham and eggs on a platter, along with the toast she'd made, he poured coffee and opened a jar of plum preserves. They worked well together, as if they really were a couple, and she allowed herself the pleasure of focusing on the vision of cozy domesticity as she spread preserves on her toast.

Tony shattered the illusion with his next words. "What we have to do is figure out enough so we can set a trap for that scumbag Duvalle."

Chapter Five

"Set up a trap?" Marianne asked. "Why don't we just call the police?"

"Why didn't you call them when Duvalle first came after you?" Tony shot back.

She considered the question, settled for a shrug.

"Maybe you didn't remember your father's criminal career. But on a gut level, you knew that calling the cops was a bad idea," he said. "Now you understand that explaining your background could be a problem. What if the *police* think the same thing as Duvalle—that you know where to find the stolen money?"

She bit back a sharp answer and pushed her eggs around the plate. Tony was trying to come up with a solution to their problem. What's more, he was trying to act as if nothing embarrassing had happened this morning.

But she was having trouble coping with something as simple as sitting across from him.

"I can go into town and pick up some things I need while you're looking through your father's stuff," she ventured.

"No." The answer was instantaneous and decisive.

She raised her eyes in surprise. "Why not?"

"Too dangerous. The fewer people who know you're in town, the better."

Despite the morning heat, she felt a shiver sweep over

her skin. "You don't think Duvalle is going to show up at Paradise Beach, do you?"

"I hope not. But I'm not going to take any chances. If you need anything from the store, I'll get it."

She thought about the things she wanted to buy. Clean underwear. Deodorant. Other personal items. Sending Tony with that kind of shopping list was out of the question.

"I—I guess I'll just wash some stuff," she murmured as she rose and carried her plate to the counter. Setting it down, she began to run water in the pan.

Behind her, she heard his chair scrape back. "Then I'll start on the research project."

She nodded, waiting to hear his retreating footsteps before turning around. Like her, he'd hardly touched his breakfast—a pretty good sign that he wasn't quite so calm, cool and collected as he pretended.

SHE HAD INTENDED to stay out of his way for the rest of the morning. But her plans had changed on her way back from washing her underwear and sticking it in the dryer. When she spotted the telephone, she stopped short. She was supposed to be at work today, and her boss was bound to be worried if she didn't call in.

Hesitantly, she tapped on the closed study door.

"Yes?" Tony called out.

She pushed open the door but didn't move into the room. He was sitting on the leather couch, cardboard boxes spread around him on the free cushions and the floor.

"Is it safe to use the phone here?" she asked.

"For what?"

"I forgot about the Light Street Foundation. I should call them. They're probably wondering what happened to me."

His face turned thoughtful. "Tell them you had a sudden emergency—with a sick friend. If they ask for the number, say you don't know it, and you'll get back to them."

She hesitated. "I don't like lying to them."

"I know, but it's necessary. Suppose when Duvalle can't find you, he starts nosing around your building. If they know where you are, he might find out."

She shuddered, silently admitting he was right. "How long am I going to be away with this sick friend?" she asked, her voice tight.

He shrugged. "A few days."

"I can't just take an unscheduled leave of absence. They need me."

"When we're in a position to explain, we will," he said with forced patience.

She didn't like the solution. But she couldn't think of anything better. So she dialed Erin Stone, her boss, aware that Tony was watching and listening.

"Marianne, are you all right?" Erin asked as soon as she picked up the phone.

"Yes. But something…unexpected came up."

There was a pause on the other end of the line. "Can we help?"

"I don't think so."

"Marianne, we're equipped to deal with all kinds of emergencies."

"Yes. Thanks. I—I'll call you if I can't make it back to the office in a couple of days."

She hung up as soon as she could, and raised her eyes to Tony. "Was that okay?"

"Fine. I know that was hard for you."

"Yes." She was about to turn and stride down the hall. But the brief exchange had convinced her that ignoring the tension between them wasn't doing either of them any good.

"Tony, we have to talk," she said.

"About what?"

"Us."

"Not now." He picked up one of the boxes and began shuffling through the papers. "I want to get this over with."

"I know," she answered. "But I need to say some things before we both blow our tops."

"Care to explain that last remark?" He raised his head, his eyes narrowed.

Any other time, the pose and the look in his eye would have been enough to stop her. Not today. With false steadiness, she plunged ahead. "Being thrown together like this is hard for both of us. Because we're both worried about Duvalle showing up. But that's not all of it." She stopped, swallowed. "We've been forced into a…a kind of relationship that makes us both uncomfortable. It's partly my fault, for making up that stupid story about being your wife."

"Forget it. We'll survive."

Too wound up to quit, she plowed ahead. "I used to wonder why you stopped being my friend when I grew up."

"I never stopped being your friend!"

"Okay. Maybe I mean I never understood why you acted like I was the most unattractive girl you'd ever seen. Now I get it. I'm from a part of your life that you hate—a past you wish you could forget."

The way his body jerked back told her she was correct. "But the Rossi Gang is out in the open now. And maybe there was one good thing that came out of what our fathers did." Gulping in a breath, she held it until her lungs began to burn, then blurted, "Maybe that good thing is us. Our fathers brought us together. And we got close to each other. We were like a family, only the bond was even stronger because of what we went through. After we moved to Baltimore, you cared enough to protect me from the past. But you don't have to do that anymore. We're both grown up, and we don't have to pretend anything."

When he didn't speak, she surged on. "I mean it's crazy to keep pretending like we're not drawn to each other.

We're not kids. We're a man and a woman, and it's obvious we both want to…to explore a relationship.''

She was dizzy with amazement that she'd dared to say so much. For years she'd wanted to tell him what was in her heart. Now it was out in the open.

She felt as if she were poised on a balance beam and could fall off either side. But would Tony be there to catch her? He didn't move, and she was suddenly sure that she'd gone too far. Or maybe she was dead wrong. Maybe his feelings for her were nothing like her feelings for him. In that case, she'd just made an utter and complete fool of herself.

Her only consolation was that she hadn't given everything away. She hadn't told him that she loved him and that the idea of pretending to be his wife must have come from some deep subconscious wish.

Head bowed, she spun away and hurried upstairs to the room where she'd slept. The sight of the unmade bed brought a blush to her cheeks as she remembered the way they'd woken up.

Quickly she straightened the sheets, plumped the pillows and did her best to erase the memories of the night.

TONY CLOSED the office door and leaned back against the wooden barrier. He still couldn't believe the things Marianne had said a few minutes ago. It seemed she could read him like a book. Still, if she knew how much he wanted to pull her into his arms and devour her, she'd be shaking in her sandals.

God, he wanted her. But in his mind, he'd always known that making love with her would mean making a commitment, and he didn't know if either one of them was ready for that—given the pressure cooker they were in. Not only were they dealing with the Rossi Gang, but their awareness of each other was on overload.

Pushing himself away from the door, he rubbed his damp palms against his jeans, unable to keep from thinking about the feel of her flesh under his hands. He'd taken advantage of every excuse to touch her.

And he'd better start thinking about something else—like Arlan Duvalle, for instance. He sighed. The way things were shaping up, it looked like he couldn't keep Marianne safe here and also go after the sicko. Much as he hated to admit it, he needed help. And that meant laying out the whole situation to someone else.

He clenched his teeth, then forced his jaw to relax and reached for the phone. Ironically, he was planning to call to the same building Marianne had phoned a few minutes ago.

Instead of dialing the number of the Light Street Foundation, however, he called private detective Mike Lancer, who had done some work for him in the past when he'd needed background checks on potential business associates. He was a good guy. Discreet. And very efficient.

SLIPPING QUIETLY down the stairs again, Marianne was relieved not to bump into Tony. If she was lucky, maybe he'd stay out of her way for the rest of the day. She retrieved her laundry and put her underwear back on. Feeling a little less vulnerable, she eased out the front door and flopped onto the porch glider, hoping she could save Tony from his self-appointed task by remembering some more details from the night of the fire. But after half an hour, she silently admitted that she was wasting her time trying to dredge up memories buried so deep in her subconscious that they fought to the surface only in nightmares.

Maybe on some hidden level she'd always known what was going on. Maybe she'd been a participant in the conspiracy of silence. Her mother. Uncle Silvio. Tony. They'd all kept the truth from her, and she'd let them do it. She'd never questioned the blank place in her memory because she'd sensed it might destroy her.

Clasping her knees, she rocked back and forth, thinking of all the lies she'd gladly accepted from her mother. Finally, too miserable to sit still, she stood and began to pace along the porch. Soon, the small space was too confining, and the sun slanting under the roof was too hot. Tiptoeing down the hall, she made a pitcher of iced tea and gulped a glass while she scribbled Tony a note telling him she'd be down at the dock.

A stiff breeze was blowing off the water as she reached the dock, and she lifted her hair, letting the wind dry the perspiration on her neck. Grateful for the slight relief from the heat, she stepped onto the worn boards and scanned the horizon. Dark clouds were gathering in the sky to the west, heralding a thunderstorm. Good. Maybe it would drive away some of the stifling air—and clear her head so she could think.

But it was no easier to concentrate out here, she discovered after yet another session of trying to force her mind past the old barrier. Apparently, on some deep level of self-preservation, she didn't want to know what had happened that night. All she could do was bring up images of a dark-haired boy who looked a lot like Tony.

Her eyes focused on the choppy water. Just as a tern swooped below the surface, she heard a noise behind her. Going very still, she listened intently, and the sound resolved itself into footsteps crunching along the gravel path.

Trapped! She should never have come out here—not to such an isolated place. Heart thumping inside her chest, she eyed the water, estimating her chances of getting away, then spared a frantic glance over her shoulder.

It was Tony, not Duvalle, and she felt her tension ease down several notches. Still, she realized that until the stalker was in custody again, she would always feel as if she were being followed.

He halted about two feet away on the narrow pier, the muscles in his arms clenching and unclenching as he squeezed his hand into a fist and loosened it again.

The wind picked up, filling the silence with its moaning voice, and she felt her nerves begin to snap. What had he discovered? All she knew was that it must be something bad. Yet he'd come to her.

"Tony?"

Seconds ticked by and she blurted, "Did you find out the fire was my fault?" she blurted.

"What?"

"The fire. Was it my fault?"

"Not the fire," he muttered, scuffing his foot against the worn boards. Something about the sound tore at her, and she pivoted. One quick glance at the desolation she saw etched into his stark features was enough to wedge an instant lump in her throat.

"Tony, what's wrong?"

He swiped a hand through his hair. "My dad and I didn't exactly get along," he muttered.

"Yes," she answered softly. That was nothing new.

"You told Duvalle a story about your father writing you a letter. Well, mine actually did. It was right at the top of one of the boxes." He took a crumpled piece of paper from his pocket, started to unfold it, then changed his mind and shoved it back. The look on his face was as stormy as the clouds gathering around them.

Taking two small steps forward, she put her hands on his shoulders. "What he wrote—is it something bad?" she murmured. "Something about the old days that he couldn't admit to you?"

Tony's jaw was rigid. "He said that he knew how I felt about his criminal career. He said that if I'd come looking through his things and found the letter, I must have forgiven him for the mistakes he made.'' He stopped abruptly, looking like a small boy who had lost his way in a swamp. ''Too bad he didn't know why I ended up poking in his boxes of stuff.''

''Oh, Tony.''

The color had drained from his face. ''When he was alive, we never had a decent conversation about his former life. All this time I was making assumptions—and they were wrong.''

He pulled the letter from his pocket again and held it out to her.

When she stared at him helplessly, he folded it into her hand. ''Read it.''

She shouldn't invade his privacy. Yet he obviously wanted her to know what his father had said.

Slowly she unfolded the paper, smoothed out the wrinkles and began to read the bold, slanting handwriting.

''Dear Son,

I made a lot of mistakes in my life. The worst one was letting my friend Bobby St. Paul talk me into a career of robbery.''

She raised her eyes to Tony. ''It was my father's idea?''

He gave a tight nod, but said nothing. Shaken, she dropped her gaze to the letter again, blinking to clear her vision.

''I'm not making excuses for myself. For a while, our life of crime was pretty exciting. We felt like we were beating the system. But then I realized I was tearing my family apart. Your mother walked away, and that left you and me. I needed you to be strong and steady, and you were. For me. For Margaret and her mother. I know I loaded you up with more than any kid should have to carry on his shoulders—while we were on the road and after we moved to Baltimore.

"Hooking up with Arlan Duvalle was our biggest mistake. And you know how the whole thing ended. I will never get over Bobby's death and never be able to make that up to Marianne and her mother—although I've tried my best.

"I bought them new identities. I've helped support them. I've been there for Marianne, and I hope I've made up at least in part for the loss of her father.

"I did other things, too, to make amends—like giving away a lot of the money we stole to charity and to the church. I know you think I bought the summer house at Paradise Beach with stolen money. That's only partly true. I made some good investments—and used the windfall to buy the property. I kept it over the years in case we ever needed a place to disappear.

"I know I've been hard on you—harder than a father should be. Probably you've guessed that I didn't want you to turn out like me. I will always feel guilty for taking away your childhood. But if you are reading this letter now, that means you feel good enough about our relationship to go through my papers. And perhaps you have even forgiven me for my past sins.

"You know I was never good at saying what I should to you. But I'm proud of you, son. I'm proud of the life you've made for yourself. And I hope you can find peace and happiness.

Love,
Dad"

Her eyes were wet by the time she finished reading.

"Oh, Tony," she breathed.

"Why couldn't he *tell* me any of that?" he grated.

"Because he was a lot like you," she answered. "He had strong feelings about...about the people he loved. But he was afraid to let himself express them," she added softly, blinking back the moisture in her eyes.

"One thing I learned from him is that feelings are painful," he answered, the wind whipping at his raw voice.

"Not always, Tony." Gambling everything on one roll of the dice, she reached upward and took him in her arms, her eyes locking with his. They darkened to onyx pools as she wrapped him close, offering him whatever he was willing to take from her.

Chapter Six

For heartbeats he held himself rigid, and she thought she had lost the gamble. Then a dam seemed to burst inside him, and he moved with sudden speed, dragging her into the prison of his arms as his lips came down on hers.

"Marianne." Her name sighed out of him, like a plea—a culmination of the feelings building between them since he'd first hauled her out of the water.

Finally she felt all the heat, all the desperation he had been hiding with such determination. With a little cry, she gave herself up to both.

He answered with a muted growl that welled from deep in his chest as his mouth traveled over hers, tasting, devouring, demanding.

Sensations burst within her—all the sensations she'd been struggling to contain. Now she was helpless to stop the rush of feelings—physical and emotional—that claimed her.

He needed her! At least for this moment in time, and she gloried in the knowledge.

So many nights alone in bed, she had longed for his kiss. She hadn't imagined the potency of his mouth melding with hers. All she could do was cling to this man she had loved for so long, letting him teach her with his lips and tongue and teeth how erotic a simple thing like a kiss could be.

As she clung to him, she was dimly aware of the wind

whipping around them and the waves dashing against the pilings. But the gathering storm was far less powerful than the reality of Tony's mouth tasting and teasing her and his arms clasping her heated body against his.

The air had grown chilled, magnifying the warmth of his hands as they slid beneath the hem of her T-shirt, the imprint of his fingers burning into the flesh of her back.

When he shifted her so that he could cup her breasts and stroke his fingers across the aching tips, she felt herself moan her pleasure into his mouth.

His hands went around her hips then, dragging her against him—letting her feel the hard shaft of his arousal. Mindlessly, she moved against him. Just as he began to move with her, a bolt of lightning arced in a jagged line across the sky, followed by a hollow clap of thunder that boomed over the water and shook the pier.

His head jerked up and he looked around, taking in the sudden darkness.

"We can't stay here. Come on."

Disappointment jolted through her as the warmth of his body detached itself from hers. Taking her hand, he started toward the house, his pace increasing when another thunderclap reverberated around them and a few large drops of water began to spatter onto the pier.

She stumbled after him, disoriented and disappointed. Of all the damn bad luck.

ARLAN DUVALLE SAT at a booth in the Dirty Duck Bar and Lounge, his large hands wrapped around a mug of beer to keep them from shaking. He'd come into this local hangout by chance, just to get out of the rain. When the bartender had eyed him pointedly, he'd ordered a beer and a crab-cake dinner. He'd soon found that listening to the locals chatter was very instructive. The most interesting topic of conversation was between a couple of old goats named Horace and Frank. It seemed Horace had stumbled onto something pretty juicy—Tony Marco and his new bride. Apparently the new Mrs. Marco had shown up last night—by herself. Marianne was her name. Tony had come down later.

Arlan clenched his hands on the beer mug, thinking about blind luck and modern technology. After running into a dead end in Baltimore, he'd done a quick computer check of Marianne Leonard's credit-card purchases and found she'd purchased a tank of gas at a station on the outskirts of Paradise Beach.

He figured she'd taken off randomly for some beach town, and he'd sped down here hoping she was still in the area. Within minutes of walking into the Dirty Duck, he'd come to find she was holed up with Tony Marco at an estate his dad had undoubtedly purchased with his ill-gotten gains.

Arlan suppressed a chuckle. He'd been in the dark about the estate, but now he was in the driver's seat again. Taking a couple of sips of beer, he thought about making a phone call to the lovebirds, surprising them with another one of his faultless imitations.

But he resisted the temptation. If he tipped them off that something was up, they might fly the coop. Instead, he'd wait until the rain stopped. Then he'd see about arranging a nice surprise for them.

He rolled his mug between his palms, thinking of interesting possibilities. One idea took his fancy, and he tipped back his head, downing the rest of his brew.

He'd have to buy some stuff. But that was no big deal. With the money he'd stashed while he was in prison he could get what he wanted at that new shopping center down the road. After throwing a couple of bills on the table, he slipped out of the booth and ambled toward his car.

A BARRAGE of fat raindrops caught them just short of the porch. Grabbing Marianne's hand, Tony pulled her under the shelter, then opened the front door.

When he made no move to go in, she laid a hand on his arm.

"I'm sorry," he said.

"About what?"

"Taking liberties."

She raised her head, forced herself to meet his gaze. Along with apology, she saw something dark and dangerous smoldering in the depths of his eyes.

"You weren't taking liberties," she said.

"What do you call it?" he tossed back.

She pressed her hands to her sides to keep them from trembling, amazed that she was still standing here arguing. Swallowing his rejection and walking away had become a habit. But this time she would fight for what she wanted— what he wanted, too, if he'd simply admit it.

"I think I already told you. I call it giving the two of us a chance. Not backing away because you think it's the honorable thing to do. Or because you're in the habit of protecting me from the Rossi Gang." She took a step toward him, then another so that she was almost as close as she'd been on the pier.

He didn't move back.

"Before the storm interrupted us, was I pushing you into something you didn't want to do?" she asked.

"No."

"Good," she finished the word with her lips lightly resting against his and her heart slamming against the inside of her chest. If he pulled away from her now, something inside her would die.

But he didn't pull away. Instead, his arms came up to imprison her, and his head angled to take her mouth in a hot, savage kiss.

She made a small sound that was part triumph, part surrender as his lips moved against hers—rekindling the fierce heat that had leaped between them on the dock. When he finally broke the contact, they were both breathing hard, both swaying on their feet.

"Come up to the bedroom," she murmured, the invitation punctuated by another jolt of lightning. Talk about symbolism!

"Marianne. You're not thinking straight. We can't just make love. I don't have any way to protect you."

"Uh…I think you do."

His eyebrows lifted.

She felt her cheeks flame. But she plowed ahead. "When I, ah, went to look for a shirt in your drawer I found a box of condoms."

She heard him mutter a low oath. Before he could elaborate, she grabbed his hand and bolted for the stairs. He stayed right behind her, making her both exalted and nervous with her victory. She wanted this. She had wanted this for a long time. But now that the moment had come, she was feeling suddenly shy as she pulled open the dresser drawer, retrieved the box she'd seen and set it on the bedside table.

Still with her back to him, she pulled her T-shirt over her head with a jerky motion and tossed it onto the chair. Her shorts followed. Clad in her underwear, she was pulling back the covers when his hand on her arm stopped her.

"Marianne?"

"Come to bed with me," she answered, without turning, fighting to keep her voice steady and her heart from pounding its way through her chest wall.

"Not when you're wound as tight as a mainspring. Why are you doing this? Are you thinking that you owe me something for trying to help you out of the mess with Duvalle?"

"Of course not! Are you still looking for excuses to back out?"

"I'm trying to figure out what's going on here. You're acting like a sacrificial virgin."

"I am not!"

Gently he turned her to face him. "Marianne?"

Her lower lip trembled. Stepping forward, she pressed her face against his shoulder. "Okay, I'm afraid that when you find out I don't have a lot of experience, you'll...stop." That was the truth—or part of it. The rest had to do with her own uncertainties.

With a hand under her chin, he tipped her face up toward his. "How much experience are we talking about?" he asked quietly.

She swallowed hard. Better get it over with. "Tony, when I thought about making love for the first time, it was always with you. I haven't accepted any substitutes."

He swore under his breath.

"Some guys would be pleased," she whispered, daring to trail her fingers across the front of his T-shirt, feeling the muscles in his broad chest quiver under her touch.

"Some guys would be worried about doing it right."

"Are you?"

"Yeah."

She gave a nervous little laugh. "At least you know I'm not going to be making comparisons."

When he didn't speak, her hand stilled, but she forced herself to say, "If you don't want me, I guess you'd better leave."

"I want you, all right." His arms enveloped her, folded her possessively to him, and she let out the breath she'd been holding. This time his kiss was gentler, softer. But that wasn't what she wanted. She wanted to feel his hunger, to feel the power flow between them again. Wordlessly, she moved her mouth against his, telling him she would take as much of him—body and soul—as he was willing to give her.

TONY WATCHED her face as he unhooked her bra, and tossed it out of the way, letting her know that things were on the verge of getting very serious. The combination of trust and nervousness he saw warring in her eyes threatened to swamp him.

All the more reason he owed her one last chance to change her mind. So he stayed planted where he was, admiring the view. She was gorgeous, her breasts rounded and high, the nipples already tightly budded for him. The sight of her made his own body tighten painfully.

She gave him a cocky smile that told him she knew exactly why he was standing there, looking but not touching. Closing the distance between them, she reached for the hem of his shirt, tugged it up, and pulled it over his head, just as another jagged flash of lightning split the sky.

Of course, she spoiled the bold effect by taking her lower lip between her teeth.

He stopped thinking about effects when she trailed her fingers over the old burn scars, then clasped her arms around him, drawing his chest to hers, naked flesh to naked flesh. A tremor of primitive desire shuddered through his body as he felt the sweet pressure of her breasts.

"Marianne…" he gasped, forgetting all the reasons he'd sworn he'd never hold her like this.

"Umm," she answered, her voice dreamy, heavy with promise as his fingers trailed up and down her back, lingering on her silky skin.

Shifting her in his arms, he rubbed his chest against her breasts. The sensation was so exquisite that his knees went weak. Hers too, it seemed, as he felt her sway on unsteady legs.

He anchored her with one arm, the other hand drifting up and down her spine as he rained tiny kisses along her cheek, down to her ear, and along her jaw.

She tasted wonderful. Bending lower, he found one distended nipple and swirled his tongue around it.

"Oh!" she breathed, then "oh," again as he took it into his mouth and sucked.

She clung to him, a tiny sob welling in her throat as his lips drew on her sweetness while his free hand found her other breast.

The depth of her response made him dizzy. Almost frantic with the need to possess every inch of her, he slid his hands under the waistband of her panties, stroking over her sweetly rounded bottom before slipping the wisp of lace down her legs.

"Okay?" he asked as he felt her tense.

"Yes," she answered against his chest.

Once again, he tipped her face toward his. "Don't hide from me, baby."

He saw her swallow. "I've never been naked with a man. It makes me feel kind of...exposed."

"It should make you feel beautiful. I never knew how beautiful until now."

She flushed, the color spreading across her chest, down to the tops of her breasts.

"So let's try it from a different angle." Scooping her up, he laid her on the bed, then stripped off his slacks. He left his briefs on, hoping the barrier of knit fabric would remind him to take this slow and easy. Then he lay down beside her and gathered her to him.

Still sensing the combination of arousal and tension in her, he kissed her cheek, stroked her shoulders, then turned on his back, taking her with him so that the length of her body was draped over his and his arms circled her shoulders.

"What are we doing?" she asked, her voice hitching.

"Hugging."

She gave him a low laugh. "I've never been hugged quite like this."

"Good."

Outside, rain drummed on the roof, but the storm was only a dull background noise. All his senses were focused on the woman above him.

Reaching for her mouth with his, he kissed her hungrily as his hands molded to her, stroking over her shoulders, down her hips, pressing her against him.

"Tony," she moaned, her body moving on its own, sliding over his with an erotic rhythm as old as time. Desire shot through him, and he ached to reverse their positions and bury himself in her warmth. But he kept her where she was, touching her, kissing her, as they pushed each other toward a place where there was only hot sensation, burning need.

When she lifted her head and looked down at him, her breathing was ragged and her eyes were deep, limpid pools.

"I think if you hug me any more, I'm going to...to..."

"Detonate?" he inquired thickly, describing his own desperate state.

She nodded gravely.

He eased her to her back. "Beautiful," he murmured, as his hand drifted over her, down to her abdomen...and lower.

When he took a gliding stroke and then another through her most intimate flesh, she arched into the caress, instinctively seeking more.

"And so sexy."

She was slick and wet, utterly his—and yet so vulnerable that his chest tightened to the point of pain.

"Oh, Tony. This is so good. So good."

"Yes," he answered, hearing the thickness in his own voice.

"Show me the next part."

His hand was shaking as he stripped off his briefs and found the box of condoms on the bedside table. When he turned back to her, she held out her arms to him.

His virgin bride, he thought, dazed by the notion. "I don't want to hurt you," he said as he moved between her legs.

"It doesn't matter. Nothing matters but loving you. Now. Please, now."

Her hands went around him, urging him to her, and he made the decision that a swift possession would cause her the least pain. Still, her sharp gasp as he breached the barrier tore at his soul.

"Are you all right?" he questioned urgently.

She managed a tight nod. But when he started to pull back, she held him firmly to her.

"Marianne—"

"Love me."

All he could do was obey, moving slowly at first, then faster as he felt her body ease into the unfamiliar rhythm.

She climbed with him in a spiral of demand until she was digging her nails into his shoulders, her little cries and the frantic movement of her hips driving him toward the point of no return.

"I…Tony…I need…"

He slid his hand between them, stroked her as his body moved within her. Exaltation flooded through him when he felt her inner muscles clench. As she sobbed out his name, he followed her over the edge into ecstasy.

MARIANNE FLOATED back to earth—or rather to the bed where Tony held her in his arms. She stroked her lips against his neck, longing to say the words swelling her heart. She loved him, and ached to hear the same confession from him. But he didn't say it, and she told herself she'd known that making love wasn't going to mean a commitment, even if this was—kind of—their wedding night. So she simply held on to him, to the joy he'd given her.

"How are you?" he asked, his lips playing with her ear.

"Good," she answered, fighting fatigue, her words slurring a little. "Very...very good."

He smiled down at her, then tenderly smoothed back a lock of her damp hair. "You didn't get much sleep last night. Close your eyes."

She watched him pull the sheet up and settle it around their waists. Like last night. Only this was the real thing, she thought with a satisfied smile. She wanted to stay awake, to savor the aftermath of making love, but between her fatigue and the drumming of raindrops on the roof, she found it impossible to keep her lids open.

Chapter Seven

Marianne woke to darkness and the smell of smoke. It seemed to wrap around her, choke off her breath like the hands of Arlan Duvalle wrapped around her neck.

Smoke. Fire.

Jagged claws of primal fear tore at her. With a muffled cry, she rolled toward Tony, her fingers digging into his shoulders. He came awake, blinking at her in the darkness.

"What?"

"Fire!" she gasped, her voice high and urgent.

"Your dream," he murmured, as he reached for her hand.

"No." She fought against him, against the seductive comfort of his embrace. Fire had been her nightmare for years, and now it was all coming true again.

"Can't you smell it?" She struggled to keep her voice below the level of hysteria.

He drew in a breath, his body stiffening as he caught the acrid scent. Then the sound of a chair toppling to the wood floor made them both go still.

Seconds later, Tony's feet were on the floor and his hands were fumbling for the clothing he'd discarded. "The bastard's found us!" he growled as he pulled on his jeans.

Panic rising like a flood tide in her brain, she whirled toward the door, suppressing a cough as a wave of smoke hit her. If they didn't get out of here right now, it was going to be too late.

Tony pushed the door closed, blocking off the smoke, and held her tight as she struggled to get free. "Wait. Not that way." He was already sliding open the drawer of the bedside table and pulling out the gun she'd seen last night.

As her gaze darted from the door to the weapon, he moved his mouth close to her ear again. "Somehow he figured out we're here. He filled the place with smoke, and he's waiting for you to come stumbling down the stairs. So you go out the window like you did at your house. Meet me at the car."

"What are you going to do?" she hissed.

"Go down there and get the bastard," he said as he handed her the shorts and shirt she'd discarded on the floor.

Every nerve in her body vibrated as she held fast to his arm. "No!"

His voice turned fierce, giving her no choice. "I'm not taking any chances with you. Get moving. And if—"

"If what?"

"If I run into trouble, go for help."

She stood there, almost too numb to react. The smoke from below had seeped into her brain like poison, making it almost impossible to think. When Tony gave her a push toward the window, she let him make the decision for her.

For the second time in two days, she climbed onto a porch roof. But she didn't know *this* porch, didn't know the location of the downspout—if there was one.

After the rain, the old shingles were slippery, and she had to move cautiously to keep her balance as she picked her way on all fours toward a large tree with overhanging limbs.

Halfway there, her foot slipped and she went down on her elbows. A gasp welled in her throat as she slid toward the roof edge, scraping herself against the rough surface as she fought for purchase. Frantically, she reached over her head, scrabbled for one of the branches and managed to stop herself from tumbling to the ground.

Then, willing her heart to stop thumping, she eased her body cautiously onto the limb, inching outward until she was clear of the porch. About six feet from the ground, she jumped the rest of the way, flexing her legs to break her fall. Swaying, she steadied herself against the tree trunk, her gaze trained on the house. Inside she could hear someone coughing and flinched from the sound.

Tony had ordered her to run for the car—to go for help. And every cell in her brain screamed for her to get away— to escape from the smoke and the fire.

Then shots cracked in the darkness, and she went stock-still. She wanted to shout to Tony, to make sure he was all right. But that would only put him in worse danger—and tell Duvalle she was outside.

Crouching low, she started for the back door, expecting at any moment to see the window erupt in flames. An angry roar from Duvalle stopped her in midstride. The exclamation was followed by the sound of splintering wood. Pounding forward, she looked wildly around for a weapon and spotted the shovel that Horace Haliday must have left leaning against the house.

Snatching it up, she leaped for the door. When she flung it open, smoke billowed out in a choking wave. The thought that Tony was inside kept her from running headlong into the night. Instead she dragged in a gulping draft of air and stepped into the kitchen.

Immediately her eyes stung and her lungs burned. But she pushed forward, and the sound of thrashing and crashing led her to the living room. Through the thick smoke, she made out the coffee table lying in pieces and two figures rolling on the rug, locked in deadly combat. There was no problem telling the men apart, since Duvalle must have outweighed Tony by fifty pounds.

At the moment, the intruder was on top. Before they could trade positions, Marianne brought the blade of the shovel down on his meaty shoulder.

Duvalle screamed, and Tony lifted him in the choking air, sending him crashing to the floor in front of the ruined coffee table where he sprawled—inert.

But the effort had taken every bit of Tony's strength, and he staggered back, hit the wall and slid to the floor, coughing.

"Tony! Tony, are you all right?" she shouted, leaping toward him.

His eyes were closed, and his breath had turned shallow. As she bent over him, scrambling sounds came from the other side of the room. Whirling, she made out Duvalle, who had pushed himself up and stood swaying on his feet like a ghost in the mist. But he was no ghost. She could smell the stale odor of his sweat through the fumes that clogged the room.

Moving to the back of the sofa, he snatched a smoking bucket from the floor and hurled it at them. Marianne screamed and ducked. But the missile only made it to the area rug.

With a curse, Duvalle turned and staggered away as the bucket rolled back and forth, sending charred wood and paper spewing out. Her heart in her throat, Marianne watched as small fires flared up and began to eat away at the rug's fibers.

If she'd been alone, nothing would have kept her in the house. But Tony was still sprawled against the wall only a few yards away.

Teeth clenched to keep from screaming, she leaped forward and grabbed the corner of the rug. Fear took on a new meaning as heat seared her hand. But she didn't let go. Instead, with a moan, she folded the heavy fabric over itself to smother the flames.

Choking, she tugged the burning mass toward the window. She was sure the whole thing was about to go up in her face, but somehow she managed to hang on long enough to pitch it through the window where it landed in a heap and flared briefly before the soggy ground dampened the fire.

Panting, coughing, she turned back to Tony. He had pushed himself to a sitting position and was gazing at her in a kind of stunned wonder. All she could do was stand there swaying.

He tried to move and groaned. The sound snapped her out of her trance. "Are you all right?" she gasped, dropping to his side.

"Yeah." He stared up at her in amazement. "That was the bravest thing I ever saw."

She shook her head. It hadn't been a matter of bravery, but of necessity.

"You were unconscious," she whispered. "I had to."

"You should have gotten the hell out of here."

"I couldn't leave you."

She saw him swallow, felt his fingers fumble for hers and squeeze. "Thank you."

"Thank you for coming down here when you knew Duvalle was trying to smoke us out."

He gave a little nod, then raised his head. "Where is he?"

"He threw the burning bucket at us and disappeared. But we'd better get out of here in case he comes back."

Tony moved with painful slowness as he pushed himself to a standing position, using a chair for support.

When she reached for his arm, he made a strangled sound, and she realized suddenly that his flesh was wet and sticky, with a trail of blood dripping down to his hand.

"Tony?"

"It's nothing," he muttered, swaying on his feet.

She bent to take a better look at the arm. "He shot you!"

"It's not so bad." Gritting his teeth, he started toward the kitchen. When he listed to his right, she hurried to steady him.

He stopped by a counter, opened a drawer, and pulled out a clean dish towel. Turning on a light, he inspected his mangled arm. Then he handed her the towel. "Wrap it around the wound and tie it tight," he ordered.

"You need a doctor."

"It can wait. It's a flesh wound, as they say in the cowboy movies. Just patch me up, ma'am."

She wound the makeshift bandage round his arm, biting her lips when he couldn't hold back a swiftly indrawn breath.

Blood soaked immediately through the cloth.

"Tony—"

"I'm fine! I want you out of here. Before he changes his mind and comes back to finish what he started."

Turning away, he eyed the phone, then shrugged and stepped briskly onto the porch. When he missed the first stair, he cursed sharply as he grabbed the railing to keep from pitching forward.

She followed behind, ready to pick him up if he blacked out. However, she wasn't entirely surprised that he made it to the car on his own. If Tony Marco was anything, he was tough.

After easing onto the seat, he dug into his pocket and fished out his keys, handing them across the console.

As she stared down at them, a thought struck her. "My purse—"

"We'll get it later."

"What if a cop wants to see my license?"

"Drive carefully."

"Right," she answered, feeling strangely light-headed. Leaning over Tony, she touched his face. His skin was cold, and moisture beaded his skin, giving her the sudden memory of another wounded man. Her father. He'd been shot, too. When she made a strangled noise, Tony pressed his fingers over hers.

"I'll be okay. Just get us out of here."

Throwing the car into gear, she eased forward, her headlights cutting through the gloom as she swung around toward the access road. When she hit the highway, she hesitated. "Where are we going?"

"Baltimore," he replied, his voice barely audible, his eyes closed.

"We should stop at the nearest hospital."

"No!" he growled, so she simply kept driving through the darkness.

He sat with his eyes closed and his head thrown back, breathing shallowly as she drove toward the city, glancing at him every few minutes. He looked like he was asleep— or passed out.

Her eyes flicked to the gas gauge. The tank was half-full, thank goodness, so they wouldn't have to stop.

An image of herself pumping gas stole into her mind, and her foot bounced on the accelerator. She had stopped to get gas outside Paradise Beach—and she'd been dumb enough to pay with a credit card. Was that how Duvalle had found them?

She wanted to confess her mistake to Tony, but bothering him now was out of the question. So she kept driving into the darkness, her hands fused to the wheel, her thoughts swirling in her head. Duvalle had known she was afraid of fire, and he'd used that knowledge against her tonight. But maybe it wasn't just the flames and smoke that terrified her. On the pier, she'd blurted out a question: *Did he say the fire was my fault?*

She stared ahead, her gaze fixed on the taillights of the car in front of her. Had she started the fire? Was that why she'd blocked that night out of her memory?

At the I-95 on-ramp, Tony startled her by speaking. "Take me...to Miguel Valero. You...know where...he lives?"

"Yes."

Turning off the highway, she headed for a neighborhood at the fringes of Fells Point, where the Valeros had recently moved. Like Marianne, Jessie, Miguel's wife, was a social worker at the Light Street Foundation. She'd been doing some of her work at home since their son, Michael, had been born seven months ago, and Marianne had brought her files from time to time.

She found the house, pulled up at the curb, and looked at her watch, amazed to find that it was only around ten in the evening. Somehow, she'd thought it was the middle of the night. Apparently Duvalle had made his move just after dark.

Miguel, who had opened a medical clinic not far from the house, answered her knock at the door.

"Were you in a fire?" he asked as soon as he caught a whiff of their clothing.

"Yes. We're not burned, but Tony's been shot."

"Then drive the car around back and we'll get him inside," he answered without missing a beat.

Miguel helped Tony into a small medical office in the walkout basement. As he eased him onto the examination table, Jessie drew Marianne into the waiting room.

"Sit down," she said. "Do you want something to drink? Water? A soda? Something stronger?"

"I'm fine." Marianne answered, sinking onto an imitation-leather couch and glancing toward the exam room. Miguel was blocking her view of Tony.

"Well, you may not be thirsty, but you're not fine. What happened?" her friend asked. "I know you called this morning and said you wouldn't be at work."

Her mind spun back to the phone conversation. She'd

been evasive with Erin earlier, but this was different. She and Tony had come to these people's house and asked for help—which meant she owed them the truth.

Hands clenched tightly together, she started with Duvalle's attack.

"It wasn't a random act of violence, was it?" Jessie asked.

Marianne shook her head. "He's a loose cannon—from our past." With a gulp, she started on the background of the Rossi Gang and saw Jessie struggling to keep her expression impassive.

"You were just a kid!" her friend said. "Why is he after you now?"

"On their last bank job, he shot a guard, and my father was wounded. Apparently we all fled to an abandoned house—where my father died in a fire." She wheezed. "We think Duvalle is looking for money that went missing."

"You don't have to tell me any more," Jessie murmured, laying a sympathetic hand on her shoulder.

"No. I want to explain the whole thing." Well, most of it, she thought. Jessica didn't need to hear the bit about how she'd claimed to be Tony's wife. "Before my father died, I was downstairs listening to the men talk. Tony's convinced that Duvalle thinks I know where the money was hidden. But I don't remember anything. I've blocked out that whole part of my life." She raised her eyes to Jessie's. "Tony, my mother, his father, they all thought it was better that way. It wasn't until after Duvalle attacked me that Tony filled me in."

When she finished, she was shaking. Then she saw Miguel standing in the doorway and stopped worrying about her checkered past. "How is Tony?"

"Good. And lucky. The bullet went through muscle tissue and came out the other side. I've given him an antibiotic, so there shouldn't be any infection."

She inhaled the news like a draft of cool, clean air. "Thank you, Miguel. Thank you so much."

"It's the least I can do."

"Can I see him?"

"He won't be too coherent. I've given him something for the pain and something to help him sleep. He'll feel better in the morning."

Crossing quickly to the exam room, she looked around and was startled to find it empty.

Miguel turned and pointed toward a section of paneling that opened into a door. "I have a room in the back. People stay here from time to time when they need shelter."

The statement was simple and unemotional, but Marianne knew that it held a wealth of meaning. Miguel had been on the run himself, and he understood very well what it was like to need a safe place to stay.

"Thank you," Marianne whispered, knowing that if she tried to speak louder, her voice would crack. She had thought she and Tony were alone in this. But help had been closer than she'd suspected.

Miguel stepped aside, and she entered a cheerfully furnished bedroom. Tony's clothes were lying over the arm of a chair, and he was stretched out on a double bed, his arm properly bandaged and the covers pulled to his waist.

His skin was pale, and dark, half-moon circles stood out below his eyes. But he was breathing peacefully, and the bandage on his arm looked clean and white, with no signs of fresh blood.

His eyes flickered open when she came down beside him and clasped his good hand.

"How are you?"

"About to conk out. Sorry," he apologized, his words slurred. His hand tightened ever so slightly on hers, but it was obvious that simply clenching his fingers was a major effort.

"Just sleep. And mend." Leaning over, she brushed her lips against his forehead. "I'll be here if you need anything."

He settled back against the pillows, his face contorting for a moment.

"What?" she asked anxiously. "Are you in pain?"

"Yeah. But it will…go away…" The disjointed words trailed off. She sat beside him, watching him off to sleep, then gently untangled her fingers from his, tensing when he stirred. She didn't want to wake him. He needed rest.

She wanted to keep watch, but thought she should speak to Miguel and Jessie again. So she brushed one last kiss against his cheek and stood.

When she returned to the waiting room, her hosts were quietly talking.

She caught the phrase "bank robbers" and knew they had been discussing the Rossi Gang. "I was filling Miguel in—if that's okay," Jessie said quickly.

"Of course."

"I am honored that you trust us," Miguel said gravely. "You'll need to stay for a few more days while Tony rests and gets his strength back."

"I wouldn't count on his getting much rest," Marianne murmured. "He won't want to sit still, let alone lie down."

"I know what it's like convincing a proud man that he needs someone to look after him," Jessie said, glancing pointedly at her husband, before turning back to Marianne. "I can lend you some clothes," she added. "And we…keep stuff around for visitors. So there's bound to be something that will fit Tony."

"Thank you," Marianne answered, overwhelmed by their kindness and the care they were taking.

"Right now, you need to get off your feet," Miguel said, then hesitated for a moment. "Are you and Tony—" He stopped, then started again. "Do you want to sleep down here with him? Or somewhere else?"

She felt her cheeks go warm, but didn't care how much she gave away by her answer. "Here."

Miguel kept his tone professional. "If he needs any medical attention, there's an intercom beside the bed. And I've left more pain medication on the bedside table." He glanced at his watch. "In four hours, he can have some more if he asks for it."

Marianne nodded, afraid that if she tried to thank them again, she'd burst into tears. When the Valeros left, she tiptoed back to the bedroom. He was sleeping soundly. For several minutes she stood looking at him, seeing the lines of stress on his face—even in sleep. Or maybe they were from the pain.

She wanted to slide down on the bed and gather him to her. But that would serve her own needs, not his. Instead, she slipped into the bathroom for a quick shower before putting on her T-shirt again and easing onto the bed.

As soon as her mind was free from other thoughts, she felt a wave of guilt—and an overwhelming need to tell Tony how Duvalle had found them. Unfortunately, that was going to have to wait.

Chapter Eight

When Marianne awoke and her eyes focused on the painting of a tropical flower garden on the wall across the room, she blinked. Then she turned her head and saw Tony, the bedcovers pulled to his waist and a white bandage on his left arm.

His eyes were open, and she caught a tender and unguarded expression on his face that made her heart squeeze. Before she could assure herself that it wasn't her imagination, he rearranged his features.

"How are you?" she whispered, wanting to know about the gunshot—and more.

"Okay."

"Good." She touched the back of her hand lightly to the dark stubble on his cheek, stroking the rough surface with her fingers, the way she'd wanted to that first night when he'd come down to the beach house and found her. Then she'd had no right to touch him. Now—now they had made love. And that changed everything—or did it?

For several heartbeats, neither of them moved, except for the gentle motion of her fingers.

"Tony?" she murmured.

He turned his head, his mouth brushing her flesh, and she felt his warmth as well as the erotic nibbling of his lips. It brought back memories of the night before.

She felt her insides go hot and moist as she remembered how it had been with her body rocking against his. Now here they were in bed again.

His eyes locked with hers as his teeth played with the edge of her finger, sending little shock waves of sensation through her.

"Marianne." When he reached for her, he couldn't conceal a wince of pain.

"Your arm hurts." Lord, she was picturing herself making love with him—when he had gotten shot last night because of her.

"I'll live," he answered dismissively.

"You need more pain medication," she said, turning toward the night table where Miguel had left the tablets.

Tony shook his head. "No. I want to keep my head clear so we can have a little discussion."

She didn't like the sound of that last comment, or the expression on his face as he slowly pushed himself to a sitting position and fixed his steely gaze on her in a way that made her chest tighten painfully.

"I told you to climb out the window and meet me at the car," he growled.

She shrugged and scooted up, so that her face was nearly level with his. "I heard shots—and you were in there."

"All the more reason to run the other way!"

"I wasn't just going to leave you in a burning house! You got shot because of me."

His eyes darkened. "I should have known better than to stay at the beach house."

Instantly, a vice seemed to grip her middle. "No! It wasn't your fault."

"Oh?"

The questioning look in his eyes made her gulp. She wanted to turn away, instead, she spoke in a rush. "Tony, Duvalle couldn't have found us at your father's unless he knew to poke around Paradise Beach.'' She gulped then went on. ''I bought gas at a station on the edge of town. I—I wasn't thinking. And I used my credit card.'' She dipped her head. ''I'm sorry.''

He didn't answer for several seconds, then slid his palm up and down her arm. ''You're just guessing that's how he got to the area. He could have researched me and my father up the kazoo.''

''Maybe. But I still made a mistake. Are you're saying it's okay for me to make an error in judgment, but not for you?''

''Right.''

''Why?''

''Because I should know better.''

''You mean because you have to be perfect—the way your father wanted? And I get to be human?''

As she felt the tension zinging back and forth between them, she realized nothing fundamental had changed. He was still dealing with her the way he had since they were kids. He was protecting her, taking responsibility, making decisions. Because his dad had given him that job.

The only thing different was that she'd enticed him into her bed. Now he was probably feeling guilty that he'd let himself be seduced by a virgin.

She was the one who looked away first, because she didn't know what to say. It seemed he didn't either, because the silence stretched like a watch spring wound too tightly.

The impasse was broken by a knock at the door.

The look of relief that flashed across Tony's face made her throat tighten. ''Yes?'' he called out.

The door opened, and Miguel stepped into the room, his expression carefully neutral as he looked toward the bed. ''I was waiting for you to wake up.'' Setting down a small pile of clothing on the dresser, he turned to Marianne. ''Jessie thinks these will fit you.''

"Thank you."

"How are you?" he asked Tony.

"Tolerable. What time is it?"

"Close to noon."

Tony shook his head. "You must have given me enough knockout drops to bring a horse down."

"Not quite. Just enough to make sure you'd get a good night's sleep. Come out to the exam room so I can have a look at the arm."

He strode from the room, and Tony tossed aside the covers. When he looked around for his clothes, Marianne took his pants off the chair and handed them to him.

It was obvious that putting them on hurt his arm, but she was pretty sure he wouldn't want her help getting dressed. So she grabbed the clothing Jessie had sent down and shut herself in the bathroom.

Fifteen minutes later, when she emerged and went into the exam room, she found that Miguel had finished with the bandage on Tony's arm.

Putting down the roll of gauze, the physician cleared his throat as he looked at her. "Last night you told Jessie the man who attacked you, Duvalle, is looking for money from a bank robbery, and he thinks you know where it's hidden. But your problem is that you can't remember any details from that time in your life."

She nodded tightly.

"If the memories are buried in your subconscious, maybe there's a way to bring them to the surface."

"How?" she asked.

"Hypnosis."

Tony's eyes darkened. "Forget it! Messing with her mind could be dangerous."

"No. Wait. I want to hear about it," she objected.

"Abby Franklin, one of the psychologists at 43 Light Street, has used it on a number of my patients," Miguel continued. "Individuals who had traumatic experiences in Latin America and needed to remember pertinent details so that they could apply for political asylum."

"Can you guarantee it's not harmful?" Tony challenged.

"I can't give you an absolute guarantee," Miguel responded quietly. "But I can tell you that Abby will be very careful. Why don't you call her and talk about it?" He held out a business card with the phone number, and Marianne took it, her hand closing tightly around the white rectangle.

"I don't think it's a good idea," Tony muttered.

"Let's at least hear what she has to say," she answered, feeling a swell of hope—and fear. He had wrestled with demons from the past for years. She had locked those demons in a place where they couldn't tear at her. Yet as she'd driven to Baltimore last night, she'd realized she had to know the truth.

Before she lost her nerve, she went to find a phone. By the time she reached the front hall, the card was a mangled mess in her grasp, and she had to smooth it out to read the number.

When she returned to the bedroom, after giving Abby a frank account of her background, Tony wasn't there. She finally found him in the kitchen, wearing a long-sleeved shirt that covered his bandage and stonewashed jeans. He was sipping a cup of black coffee.

"You're through with the phone?" he asked.

"Uh-huh."

"Then I'll call Mike Lancer."

"Tony, you and I have to talk."

"Not now!" With a jerky motion he rose from the table and exited the room, leaving her staring down at the half-full cup of coffee. She could have followed him and forced a confrontation, though she wasn't sure it would do either one of them much good at the moment.

HE STEPPED into the den, being careful not to slam the door behind him—knowing that he was hiding from Marianne and from himself. For long moments he stood staring at the phone, but he couldn't force his mind to focus on calling Mike Lancer.

Marianne wanted to finish the conversation they'd started in bed. No way was he prepared for that.

He grimaced. All of his adult life, he'd understood his goals, worked toward them, and accomplished what he set out to do. Maybe at the beginning he'd been out to prove to his father that he was better than Vance Rossi would ever be. But showing up his dad had slipped way into the background as he'd become his own man.

In the space of two days, however, everything had changed. Arlan Duvalle had thrown his life into chaos. And nothing was under his control anymore.

The worst part was that he'd lost his center of gravity—and he was having trouble finding it again, because it had shifted. He'd thought that he'd made himself self-sufficient. Over the past few days, he'd discovered how much he needed Marianne Leonard in his life. He was still shaken by the revelation—and shaken by the knowledge that he'd almost lost her. When he'd come to and seen her with that burning rug in her arms, he'd almost gone insane.

She'd done it for him. She'd done every damn thing he'd asked her to do, and more—except keep her distance from him.

Now she was going to get herself hypnotized, for God's sake—because he'd forced her to try and remember the night of the fire. And he was scared spitless at the prospect, because there was no way of knowing what it would do to her.

But there could be a way to head her off, he suddenly realized. If Mike Lancer could get a line on Duvalle before the hypnotist arrived, maybe he could persuade her that she didn't need to go ahead with the session.

Feeling a surge of hope, he reached for the phone. Unfortunately, Mike was out of the office. All he could do was leave a message on the answering machine, asking him to call Miguel Valero's as soon as possible.

Putting down the receiver, he slumped in the desk chair. He might have paced the room, waiting for the phone to ring. But he was starting to feel light-headed, so he leaned back and closed his eyes. Minutes later, he was asleep.

MARIANNE DIDN'T SEE Tony again until Abby Franklin arrived and he followed them into the Valeros' comfortable sitting room. Instead of taking a seat, he remained standing, leaned against the door jamb, gazing down at them like a judge about to sentence a couple of criminals.

"This is a bad idea," he growled.

"Maybe it's the only way to find out about the money."

"Forget the money."

She stared at him incredulously. "For two days we've been trying to figure out where the money went. Now you're saying you just want to forget about it?"

"We already know Duvalle isn't going to give up. He'll come after us again. All we have to do is make sure we pick the time and place. So we don't need a damn psychologist poking into your mind."

She moistened her suddenly dry lips. "Is there some reason you're afraid to find out what really happened that night?"

His face turned white, and she could see the question had shaken him to the core. "That's not the point. The point is that *you* look like you're on the way to an execution."

"I'm nervous. I think that's natural."

After several moments' hesitation, he pushed away from the jamb. "Okay, have it your way."

Silence filled the room as he exited and quietly closed the door.

Marianne looked down at her hands, twisting them in her lap. "I apologize for that crack he made about you," she whispered.

"Well, he's very protective of you," Abby answered.

"He's been watching out for me since we were kids," she shot back. "It was an obligation his father put on him."

"I think it's a little more personal than that."

"Right. I'm like his little sister who doesn't have sense enough to come in out of the rain. He's even mad at me for going back into the house when he and Duvalle were fighting it out."

"From where I'm sitting, he's not acting like a big brother. I'd say he's acting more like a man who wants to make sure his woman is protected."

Marianne felt her heart lurch inside her chest. With her training, could Abby see something that wasn't obvious?

"How do you feel about him?" the psychologist asked.

Well, she knew how to answer *that* question. "I've loved him for a long time," she said, astonished that she had blurted out the confession after five minutes with this woman whom she'd only met a few times. She squeezed her eyes shut, then opened them again. "There are a lot of issues between us. Stuff about our fathers—about the way we grew up. I got it in my head that if…if we made love, everything would change. But it hasn't."

"The experience didn't live up to your expectations?" Abby asked quietly.

"It was wonderful," she whispered, feeling her whole body turn warm. "But my guess is that he feels guilty about letting me tempt him. And he sure as heck can't stop playing the role of bodyguard. That's not what I want. I want him to act like we're in this together."

The therapist gave her a reassuring smile. "Well, the two

of you are in a pressure cooker right now. That makes working out your relationship difficult. Don't give up on him until things settle down."

Marianne sat very still, her thoughts turned inward.

"What are you thinking about?" Abby asked.

"I thought he wanted me to remember where the money was hidden, so we could set a trap for Duvalle. Now I'm sort of confused."

"If you want a quick analysis, I'd say he thinks the money is less important than your emotional well-being. And he's afraid that revisiting the day of the fire will be too traumatic for you to handle."

"You think *that's* why he's afraid to let me have this session with you?" she breathed.

"Well, I don't ordinarily make snap judgments. But that's what I think—off the top of my head."

Marianne nodded, trying to wrap her mind around that.

"The question is, what do you want to do?" the therapist asked.

"I want to find out what I've been hiding from myself all these years."

"Good. Because it's important to want this for yourself."

"I do. So maybe we'd better get started," she pressed, praying that she wouldn't lose her nerve.

"Okay. If we had more time, I'd spend several sessions with you before getting into age-regression hypnosis. But this is kind of a special situation. So let me tell you a little about the technique I'd like to try. I use it regularly with people who have lived through disturbing events they can't recall. Really, it's self-hypnosis. And I'm just there to guide you back in time and help you control the experience—so you'll feel more like an observer than a participant." When she'd gone into a bit more detail, she asked, "Do you have any questions?"

"No."

"Then make yourself comfortable," Abby said, pulling her chair closer. "Raise your eyes just a little and look up at the line where the wall meets the ceiling."

She obeyed.

"Now I'm just going to help you relax," Abby continued in a soothing voice. "Where would you like to go on vacation if you had the chance?"

Marianne had had enough of the beach. "The mountains," she answered.

"Good. Then imagine you're in a beautiful mountain forest, sitting next to a rushing stream. You can hear the water tumbling over the rocks, and you can feel the cool wind on your face."

She let the soothing sound of Abby's voice put her into the scene. Soon she felt herself drifting, relaxing, letting go of her anxiety.

"Can you talk to me?" Abby asked.

"Yes," she answered, although it was hard to get the word out.

"Good. Do you want to try going back to your childhood?"

She hesitated for a moment, then whispered, "Yes."

"Okay, imagine you're looking at a big TV screen across the room from you. It's got a calendar on it with this year. Can you see it?

"Yes."

"We'll start by flipping the calendar back to this time last year. Can you see that?"

When she nodded, Abby continued. "Now we'll go back farther, and instead of the calender you'll see *yourself* on the TV."

They stopped for a typical day in college, high school, middle school and her first year in Baltimore. Finally they reached the year of the fire, and she felt herself getting tense.

"You're going to relax more deeply. You're very relaxed.

Very peaceful," Abby reassured her. "On the TV screen you can see the little girl you were eighteen years ago. But it's like watching someone else. And no matter what happens on the screen, it can't hurt you. Duvalle can't hurt you. The fire can't hurt you. Understand?"

"Yes."

"Good. And remember, you can turn off the television any time you want to." She paused. "It's the afternoon of the fire. Where are you?"

"In my room. Mommy is upset. She's throwing things in suitcases. And she's shouting at Uncle Vance."

"Okay, let's come forward to the evening. Where are you now?"

"In an old broken house."

"Who's there?"

"Me and Daddy. Uncle Vance and Doo Valve."

"Duvalle?"

"Yes."

"Where is Tony?"

"His name is Nick. He and Mommy are getting medicine for Daddy." Marianne lifted her hand, stuck the edge of her finger in her mouth, and sucked.

"It will be easier to talk if you take your hand out of your mouth," Abby said gently.

"Big girls don't suck their fingers," she said, echoing her mother's words.

"Right. So where are you now?"

"I'm at the top of the stairs. But I'm scared. I don't want to be up here all by myself. It's dark. And the moon is so big outside the window. I want to come downstairs. But Doo Valve is shouting. Uncle Vance tells him to go take a hike, so he's going away."

"What do you do?"

"I go down to the room with Daddy and Uncle Vance

and peek in the door. Uncle Vance is talking about the
money.''

"The money from the robbery?"

"Yes. He says that Doo Valve wants to take it all and
run away. So he's hidden it."

"Where is it?"

"Under Daddy's sleeping bag. Daddy is lying on it. Uncle Vance says Doo Valve won't find it there."

"What happens now?"

"Uncle Vance has gone to get some food for us. And I
go in to see Daddy." She caught her breath as she looked
at her father's face. "He's glad to see me," she said, the
thrill of the memory capturing her. "His voice is always
soft and nice when he talks to me. But he got hurt. I'm
scared he's gonna die," she said, the last part choking off
in a little sob. Then she started to shake.

"What's wrong?"

"Doo Valve is coming back in. He's angry with Daddy.
They're fighting. I hit him, but he's hurting Daddy." Her
eyes widened. "No. Oh, no!"

"What?"

"Doo Valve kicked the lantern," she gasped. "It fell over
on the bandages. They're catching fire."

She cringed. "The floor is catching fire."

She was there again. With the little girl on the television
screen. As her terror grew, she and the little girl merged
into one person.

"Marianne, it's all right. Marianne! Wake up."

She began to scream then, scream in horror as the terrible
memory took control. Leaping off the couch, she started to
run from the flames that licked at her skirt, her legs.

Chapter Nine

"Marianne! Marianne!"

Tony's voice. She tried to lock on to his voice. Then his arms were around her, holding her, rocking her, telling her that everything was all right. That she was safe.

Her eyes blinked open, and she didn't know where she was.

"Marianne," he said again, bringing her back to the present. She was in Tony's arms. Safe in his arms. Lifting her into his lap, he cradled her trembling body against his.

With all her strength, she clung to him, as she tried to catch her breath.

"What did you do to her?" he demanded, tossing the angry question at Abby like a warrior hurling a spear.

"Don't," Marianne managed. "It's okay." She sucked in a breath and let it out in a rush. "She took me back to the day of the fire. I saw it. I know what happened. I didn't do it!"

His eyes were fierce. "Didn't do what? What are you talking about?"

She gulped. "Oh, Tony, I was afraid I was the one who knocked over the lantern. I thought I started the fire that killed Daddy! That's why I was so afraid to remember that night."

He stared at her, and she knew he was struggling to absorb her confession—and her vast relief.

"But it wasn't me," she sobbed out. "It wasn't me. It was Duvalle! He hit the lantern with his foot when he was fighting with Daddy!"

"And all this time, deep down, you were afraid you had done it?" Abby asked gently.

"Yes!" Tears stung her eyes, tears of relief.

"What you're describing can happen to sensitive children," Abby said gently. "When a parent or a sibling dies, the child thinks she's somehow responsible. In your case, you were afraid to deal with it, so you swept it out of your mind."

Marianne nodded, taking the words in as Tony's arms tightened around her.

"I didn't understand," he muttered. "I thought you were too traumatized by being caught in the fire to remember what happened that night."

"I was. But it was more than that." Raising her head, she looked at Abby. "Thank you for helping me."

"You had a very strong reaction." The psychologist spread her hands apologetically. "I'm sorry. I thought I could help you keep your distance from the experience."

"It was frightening. But it was worth it," she answered. "I saw my father's face," she breathed. "I heard him speak to me. He called me Lil' Bit."

"That was his pet name for you," Tony said softly.

"Yes. And I won't lose the memory of him again," she vowed. "He may have taken a wrong turn in his life, but he wasn't a bad man. He loved me."

"I know," Tony said, his voice thick. "I used to see the way you were together and envy you. My dad could never unbend that much."

She reached for his hand, twining her fingers with his,

longing to share the insights that the experience had given her. "Your father had flaws. But he loved you, too."

"I used to think he had a funny way of showing it."

"He was doing the best he could to take care of you—even if the way he did it was misguided. But the letter he left you says a lot about his character."

"Yeah. It says he didn't want to face me. It says he had to make sure I wasn't around to react."

She wanted to tell him she'd seen the same traits in the son. She knew it wouldn't serve any purpose. "A lot has been happening in the past few days," she said instead. "Too much to take in all at once. I understand, because I'm having the same problem as you."

He nodded.

In the silence that followed, she let her mind drift back over the scene, amazed that she could view it without the terror. "If you still want to hear about it, I found out about the money," she said in a low voice.

Tony's features sharpened, but all he said was "Okay."

"Your father and mine were talking about it—and I heard. It was under Daddy's sleeping bag."

"In the room where the fire started?" he clarified.

"Yes. It must have burned up..." She stopped, then forced herself to finish the sentence. "...with him."

Tony's fingers stroked her. "I'm sorry about your father."

"I know. But I lost him a long time ago." She spread her palms upward. "At least now I know what his face looks like. At least I know he loved me. And I know the fire wasn't my fault. Thank the Lord." She turned toward Tony. Maybe she'd come to terms with the past. But the present was still a mess. "You said you wanted to set a trap for Duvalle. We need to set things up so he thinks he's got *us* trapped."

"The Light Street Irregulars can help you," Abby interjected.

"Who are they?" Tony asked.

"That's the name we've given the group of friends who help each other when one of us is in trouble. Like last year, when Miguel and Jessie were being stalked by a killer."

Tony nodded. "I let Miguel use my house for a while, but I thought the guys from the barrio were hiding him."

"Light Street got involved later," Abby explained. "I can set up a meeting with them. A lot of the men work for Randolph Security now, but they ran covert operations for various government agencies. We don't advertise all this, for obvious reasons." She turned toward Marianne. "If you'd been at the foundation longer, you would have found out about us. I'm just glad we can help you out now."

Abby made a phone call to Randolph Security. When she got off the phone, she looked pleased. "They can meet with you this evening. Seven o'clock. Here."

"Good," Marianne answered, just as Tony's beeper went off. When he checked the number, it turned out the call had been made from his own house.

His face was wary as he used the special equipment that Miguel had had installed to prevent calls from being traced and phoned home. After hearing who was on the other end of the line, he relaxed a notch.

"It's Mike Lancer," he mouthed.

She knew him. He was a private detective who worked with her friend Jo O'Malley.

She could tell Mike was talking rapidly, and that Tony didn't like what he was hearing.

"What is it?" she asked.

He waved her to silence and gripped the receiver. "When?" he asked. Then, "I'll meet you there!"

Mike must have objected to the plan, because Tony came

back with a sharp insistence. When he hung up, his face was grim.

"What happened?" Marianne asked.

"I asked Mike to check up on Duvalle. He stopped by my house and found the place had been searched."

"I take it you want to go over there—and he wants you to stay put."

"He doesn't know what to look for. I'm the only one who can tell if anything important is missing."

When he started for the door, she raised her voice a notch. "You can't go over there."

"Why the hell not?"

"It could be a trap. Duvalle could *want* you to come. He could—"

He cut her off in mid-sentence. "In the first place, Mike says Duvalle is long gone."

"How does he know?"

"I left the air-conditioning on. The back door was open long enough for the heat to build up. Mike didn't find anyone inside. Probably Duvalle searched the place before he came to Paradise Beach."

The clipped sentences brooked no argument, but she mounted one, anyway. "I hope you're not thinking about driving yourself."

Tony moved his arm, concealing a grimace. "I'll be fine."

"Shall we ask your doctor?"

When he scowled, she relented. "If you insist on going, I can drive you."

"I don't want you out of this house until we know Duvalle is in custody."

"Why is it different for me than for you?"

"Mike and I can take care of ourselves," he snapped.

"I know you can. But you're not exactly in top shape.

You were wounded last night." As soon as she said it, she immediately regretted reminding him.

For several seconds he stared at her stonily, then sighed. "All right, you can haul me around!"

When he stalked into the hall, Marianne turned apologetically to Abby. "Sorry."

"It's okay. He's dealing with a lot of problems—and trying to figure out how to do the right thing by you."

"Exactly. Protect me."

Abby gave her a reassuring smile. "Trust me, it's more than that."

Praying it was true, Marianne joined Tony in the hall. He looked gray and fatigued, and she was certain that going over to his house was the wrong thing to do. For a nanosecond it flitted through her mind that she should simply tell him they were going to stay put and let Mike Lancer take care of any immediate problems. Instead she went to ask Jessie if she could borrow her car, which would be less recognizable than his.

Ten minutes later, they were on their way.

"I'm sorry I snapped at you," he apologized.

"It's okay. I know you're under a lot of pressure. We both are." She waited, hoping that might get them into a conversation, but he chose to pass up the opportunity.

When they reached his street of large brick two-story homes, Tony sat up straighter. "Drive around the block, I want to make sure our friend isn't lying in wait,"

She made a slow circuit of the streets as they both scanned the scene. When he was satisfied that the house wasn't under surveillance, he asked her to park in back of his next door neighbor's garage.

As soon as Tony stepped through the kitchen door, he made a low sound that was part anger, part surprise. "I guess Mike didn't want to give me the bad news," he muttered as he surveyed his well-appointed kitchen. The polished maple cabinets stood open and broken glasses, bowls and china were strewn across the granite countertops and the Italian tile floor.

Marianne drew in a sharp breath. "Oh Lord, what a mess."

"I've got a cleaning service. They can take care of it," he said with amazing calm as he guided her around the worst of the mess. Still, their shoes crunched on broken glass that ground itself into the surface of the expensive tile, and she knew it was going to take more than a cleaning service to set things to rights. Obviously Duvalle had taken out his frustration on the house. Hopefully, that meant he hadn't found anything important.

"Mike?" Tony called as he strode down the hall.

"Be with you in a minute," the detective called from upstairs.

Marianne drew in a breath, stiffening as she picked up Duvalle's scent.

"He was here. I can smell him," she whispered.

"Yeah."

The conversation came to an abrupt halt as the sound of running water reached them.

"What the hell?" Yanking open a door, Tony flipped on a light and peered down a flight of steps leading to what she knew was a plush recreation room and an office complex.

An oath tumbled from his lips as he switched on the lights and started down.

Marianne squinted over his shoulder and saw that the floor of the recreation room was covered with water.

"Either the bastard opened a valve, or he punched a hole in the water heater. No wonder Mike wouldn't tell me about it over the phone," Tony ground out. "The whole house is going to smell like mold before this dries."

"A pump and a couple of fans will work wonders," she said, hoping it was as simple as that.

"I hope." He looked around again and bellowed, "Mike!"

"In a minute," the detective called to them.

"Thanks for filling me in," Tony muttered under his breath as they sloshed their way to the office where modern equipment was juxtaposed with expensive antique pieces.

He squished across the oriental rug to several cardboard boxes on the floor that held letters and other papers. After shuffling through them, he opened a large antique armoire where more boxes were neatly stacked on shelves. After examining the contents, he let out a breath. "I'm glad I didn't leave any important business stuff on the floor."

"Good."

He stayed facing the shelves, his hands pressed to his sides.

Quietly she moved up behind him, aware that she had him cornered. The only way out of the room was around her—or through her. "Tony, before Mike gets down here, I want to talk," she said, knowing that there was hardly any chance of starting and finishing a discussion. But anything would be better than the tension she was feeling.

"About what?" he asked, still facing the shelves.

"About how we're going to be with each other from now on. Please don't shut me out."

He faced her.

She stood her ground, unwilling to back down now that she'd gotten his attention. "Are you feeling like I piled another obligation on you? Or are you just wishing things would go back to the way they used to be?"

"They can't go back. I've pushed you to remember stuff that you locked away. I've changed the whole structure of your life."

"Oh, Lord, Tony, is that what you think? It wasn't you

who did it. It was Duvalle. And…and even though it was hard to face the truth, I'm better for it. Don't you know that? Don't you know that what I need now is some honest communication with you? I want to know how you feel about us."

He made a low sound in his throat as he reached for her, hauling her to him as his mouth came down on hers. Startled, she gasped, and he took shameless advantage of her open lips—swamping her with a kiss that demanded surrender or flight.

Her only real choice was surrender, heart and soul, mind and body. She returned the kiss with a fierceness that seemed to stun him, then fuel his ardor.

When he finally lifted his mouth, her head was spinning.

"Do you have any better idea of how I feel?" he growled.

"I think so."

"Good." He looked around the office, then pulled her to the far side of the armoire, blocking them from view. With a deep groan of satisfaction, he drew her body tightly to his. She came willingly, unable to fight the need to be as close as possible.

Leaning his back against the paneled wall, he splayed out his legs and brought her between them, his good hand sliding over her hips and wedging her firmly against his erection.

He kissed her again, his lips lazy and warm, while his good hand began to do very provocative things to her breasts—things that would drive her over the edge if he kept them up.

"Tony. You shouldn't be doing this," she gasped, her knees so weak that she slumped forward against him. "Not until you're better."

"Well—maybe not standing up," he answered, his stroking fingers shifting to her back, drawing tiny circles. In her present state, the caress was only slightly less erotic.

"Do you know what it would have done to me if Duvalle had hurt you again?" he asked softly.

"Yes. The same thing it would have done to me if something had happened to you. It's no different."

He gathered her closer, and she listened to the ragged edge of his breathing and her own, her mind drifting.

Yet as she sucked in breath, an unpleasant scent wafted toward her, stronger, more immediate than a few minutes ago.

"What's wrong?"

"He's here!" she hissed, dread grabbing her even as she tried to tell herself it wasn't true.

"Mike. Yeah, we'd better cut this out before Mike catches us."

"Not Mike."

Whirling to the desk, she picked up the phone receiver. There was no dial tone. Frantically she pressed repeatedly at the button—with the same results.

"It's dead," she whispered, feeling the skin crawl on the back of her neck. "He took care of Mike. We're next."

"We've got to get out of here!" Tony climbed onto the desk, grabbed her hand, and reached to work the catch on the window high up in the wall. The mechanism wouldn't slide.

From the hall, she heard the sound of water sloshing, then an eerily familiar voice in the hallway. "If you're trying to open the window, don't bother. I nailed it shut from the outside. You're trapped. The way you were always trapped."

Marianne and Tony both froze—reacting to the voice as much as to the cruel observation. It sounded like Silvio Marco speaking. Only it couldn't be Silvio Marco. He was dead.

Tony's face had gone white, his body taut. "Dad?" he

gasped, starting to move away from the protection of the partition.

Marianne grabbed his arm and squeezed. "No."

"Look's like you're not free of me yet, kid" the mocking voice continued.

"That's not your father," Marianne whispered urgently. "It's Duvalle. He did this before—used your father's voice when he attacked me."

Tony blinked and straightened. Taking hold of Marianne's shoulders, he thrust her back so that she was behind him, and a protruding section of wall shielded them both from the door.

"What about Mike?" she whispered. "How can we get him downstairs?" *If he's still alive,* she thought.

Duvalle must have been straining to hear them, because he laughed again. "If you're waiting for your P.I. friend to rescue you, you're out of luck. It wasn't him who called you on the phone half an hour ago. It was me—pretending to be him."

"What?" Marianne breathed.

"Don't you get it yet?" their tormentor continued. "Lancer isn't here. He's off on a wild-goose chase to the Marco warehouse. It wasn't hard to figure out your boy-friend was working with him, once I got a line on your phone records from Paradise Beach."

Tony uttered a curse.

"How…how did you find us at the beach house?" Marianne stammered.

"Your credit card at the gas station. Then some old gee-zer in the local bar was bragging about seeing you."

When she made a low sound, Tony reached back and stroked her shoulder. "It's okay," he murmured.

Duvalle began to speak again. "If you're wondering how I learned his voice, all I had to do was listen to his an-swering-machine message a couple of dozen times. I can do anybody." To demonstrate, he switched voices—this time to Marianne's father. "Come on out, Lil' Bit," he crooned. "Come to Papa."

She felt her throat close. Tony's hold on her tightened, but he kept his face turned toward the door.

"So we're alone here," their stalker growled. "I've got a gun, and I bet you don't, cause you were expecting your friend Mike Lancer to provide the firepower. It's over. Come out in the open."

"You'll have to come and get us," Tony answered, as he bent and pulled gently at the cord on the desk lamp, stretching it to its full length. He unscrewed the bulb and set it gently on the back of the desk, then winced as he yanked at the socket.

There was complete silence for several seconds, then more sloshing in the water. Tony bent and picked up a glass paperweight. Pressing his mouth to her ear, he whispered in a barely audible tone, "When I squeeze your arm, throw it across the room so that it hits the door of the armoire. He'll think we're hiding inside."

She nodded her understanding, her whole body vibrating with tension, wondering if the ruse would really work. What was he planning? She wanted desperately to ask, but there was no way she could risk a question.

They waited on the desk, the seconds ticking by. Stealthy footsteps approached through the water. Finally, the shadow of a hand holding a gun appeared on the far wall, and Marianne had to clamp her teeth together to keep them from chattering.

"You can't hide from me," Duvalle growled with an undertone of smug triumph. "If you tell me where the money is, I'll only kill one of you."

Marianne felt a violent shudder go through her.

The gunman stepped cautiously through the doorway, his arm visible and then his shoulder. He was so close she could see his shirt was drenched with sweat—and the stench of him made nausea rise in her throat.

Still, Tony stood rigid, waiting.

Duvalle crept closer, closer, and she thought she could hear his rapid breathing as he turned first one way and then the other, looking for them.

"You're making me angry, kids," he growled, using Silvio Marco's voice again. "I get nasty when I'm angry. Maybe I'll keep the two of you around for a while—so I can have some fun with Miss Leonard and make Mr. Marco watch."

Marianne saw Tony bare his teeth in anger. Her own fingers clenched the glass ball, and it was all she could do to keep from hurling it at Duvalle.

But she willed herself to hold off.

The gunman crept forward. Then Marianne thought she heard footsteps on the stairs.

"Mike! It's Mike," she gasped. "He did come!"

"Duvalle. Up here," a raspy voice called. "Come and get me."

"What the hell?" the killer snarled, and Marianne saw the shadow on the wall whirl and turn in the other direction. "God—no," he wheezed, then began to fire the gun, the shots reverberating through the basement.

Tony leaned around the corner of the wall.

"Stay out of the water, Mike," he shouted as he tossed the lamp so that it fell over Duvalle's shoulder, the cord dangling down his back and anchoring the lamp to him.

The gunman screamed, his body vibrating wildly, and Tony pulled Marianne back, burying her face against his chest as a loud sizzling noise filled the air.

Abruptly, the lights went out, and the sizzling stopped. After several seconds, Tony peered cautiously around the corner of the wall. Although he tried to hold Marianne back, she squirmed forward. In the dim light coming from the window, she saw the man who had been stalking them. He lay sprawled on the floor, his body twitching.

"What did you do?" she gasped. The paperweight she was still clutching dropped from her fingers and crashed to the surface of the desk.

"Fried him," he said. "He was standing in over an inch of water. I exposed the wires on the lamp so the electric current would flow through him. The wooden desk kept it from getting to us."

She nodded, looking down at the body, then turned so that her face was pressed to Tony's chest again. "He would have shot us, or worse," she whispered.

Tony nodded, and she knew he had done what he'd had to do. When he started down from the desk, she tried to hold him back. "It's okay," he assured her as he splashed to the floor. "The lamp tripped the circuit breaker—but not before it zapped him." He reached for Marianne, helped her down, and guided her quickly past the body.

When they stepped into the hall, he stopped and listened, then called, "Mike?"

No one answered.

"Mike?" he tried again, then turned back to her. "Am I crazy? Or did I hear someone on the stairs just before Duvalle fired?"

"Yes. I heard it too."

"So where did he go?"

Cautiously he led her through the water, then up the steps. The back door was open, but when they called out again and searched the house, they found no one.

"Someone else was here," Tony muttered.

"I know."

"Maybe some kid tried the door, found it unlocked, and came in to help himself to the silverware."

She shook her head. "It wasn't someone off the street.

Whoever it was knew Duvalle's name.'' She shivered as a strange notion began to form in her mind.

"What?"

"I don't know." She gave an embarrassed laugh. "I was thinking it was like a ghost—or something. I mean, Duvalle sounded scared."

To her surprise, Tony seemed to take the idea seriously. "Your father or mine, coming to our rescue? To make amends after all these years? That would be poetic justice, wouldn't it?"

She flushed, turned her hand palm up. "It's pretty far out. I wish I could think of an explanation that makes better sense."

They were both silent for several seconds, then he reached for her hand. "Maybe we'll find out later. But whatever happened downstairs, we have to get to a phone and call the police."

"I know."

"But I want a few minutes with you first." He led her into the den.

One look at his haggard face, and she moved him toward the couch. "Sit."

He flopped down and leaned his head against the cushions. "We're in for a lot of explaining, I'm afraid," he said, his voice weary. "Miguel will get in trouble if they find out he treated a gunshot wound and didn't report it. So we'll skip that part—if it's okay with you. We don't need my arm to prove he tried to kill us. He made Swiss cheese out of the wall at the end of the hall."

"Yes."

He wrapped his good arm around her and pulled her close. "I'll feel better about dredging up the gory details of our childhood if you're beside me."

"Of course." Drawing up her knees, she snuggled close.

"But I need to say a few things first."

She tried to hide the sudden tension in her body, but she saw from his face that he'd picked it up.

"What are you worried about?" he asked, his voice husky.

She moistened her dry lips with her tongue, seeing his eyes follow the gesture. "That you can't change the way you've related to me since I was five. That you're still thinking of me as a fragile little thing who needs protecting—from the Rossi Gang…" She swallowed. "And from Vance Rossi's son."

He raised his chin. "Sure I want to protect you. I love you. I have for a long time, but for years I was afraid that acting on my feelings would be the wrong thing for you."

She felt as if the breath had been knocked from her lungs. "Oh, Tony, it's not the wrong thing for either of us. It's so right."

"I figured that out."

"You don't know how long I've waited to hear that from you."

"Good. Because I need to know—will you be my wife? I mean for real." His voice cracked. "Not just because you're running away from Duvalle."

"Your wife," she breathed.

"Will you?"

"Yes. Of course, yes. Tony, I love you so much." She laughed. "I've wanted to tell you forever. I wanted to tell you on…on our wedding night."

He leaned forward so that he could brush his lips against hers. "I thought of it as our wedding night, too. When I held you in my arms, I thought about how much I wanted it to be real. I always knew that if I made love with you, I couldn't let you go."

"You would have saved me a lot of insecurity if you'd shared that little insight with me," she murmured.

His finger stroked along her cheek, and his voice was

barely above a whisper. "Do you know how hard it is for a guy like me to talk about his feelings?"

"I think so. But that's part of sharing our lives. When I was trying to guess what you were thinking, it made me feel so uncertain."

"I'm sorry."

"Just so you remember we've got to be open with each other. Honest. You don't have to be Mister Tough Guy with me. You don't have to shoulder all the responsibility. I know you feel guilty about getting shot—but it's no worse than how I feel about using that stupid credit card."

"Don't."

"Then don't you do it, either. Okay?"

"Okay," he agreed too quickly. And she suspected she might have to keep reminding him that marriage meant a partnership. But that was okay, because now she knew she'd have all the time in the world to show him what a man and a woman could be to each other.

She leaned close to press her lips to his cheek. "One more thing. Tony, I know you're worried about being your father's son. But you're a good man. Honest. Honorable. Strong." She gave him a little smile. "And loving. That's who you are. That's why I love you. And you can count on my being here for you—whenever you need me," she vowed, the simple statement welling from her heart.

"Thank God." Finding her mouth with his, he sealed the bargain with a long, greedy kiss, then held her close, and she knew that the two of them had broken free of the past. They'd share the future instead, and it was going to be rich with love and warmth and all the things she'd longed for with this man.

Epilogue N.   [13]

Epilogue

The man in the new dark suit and the hat pulled low over
his face hadn't been invited to the wedding. But he'd slipped
into the Basilica of the Assumption to mingle with the large
crowd of guests at the ceremony.

He felt a surge of pride when he saw the groom standing
straight and tall at the altar, waiting for his bride. Tony
Marco. Once he'd been Nick Rossi—a great kid. He'd
turned into a very formidable man. An honest and upright
citizen, under his tough veneer.

As the wedding march sounded, the man stood and turned
to the back of the church with the rest of the congregation.
The sight of the bride standing beside the last pew, looking
a little nervous and very beautiful, took his breath away.
With a special pride he saw the way her blond hair was
swept up off her slender neck and her delicate figure was
enhanced by a high-waisted white gown with a train that
trailed gracefully behind her.

Her escort was a handsome dark-haired man, Miguel Valero. When the watcher saw her holding tight to his arm, he
felt a sudden jolt of envy as he imagined himself rushing to
her side. Then he pictured the wide-eyed fear in her eyes
and knew it was better this way—better to stay in the background where he belonged.

Marianne reached Tony's side and turned toward him.

The way they looked at each other made the watcher's heart swell with emotions he hadn't felt in more than twenty years. They were good together—the way it should be with a man and his wife.

He'd never had that in his own marriage. In almost every way, he'd made a wreck of his life. But he'd made the right decision this time. His daughter, Marianne, didn't need a ghost from her past to haunt her future. She was better off without him—better off not knowing that he'd gotten out of that fiery house and spent almost two decades searching for his family. He'd found them by tracking Duvalle—and he'd called out to the killer just at the right moment.

The priest began to speak the ancient words that joined two people in the sight of God. Tears blurred the watcher's vision as the bridal couple knelt and joined hands. Marianne and Tony. A man and a woman who had proved their love and their courage. A man and a woman who turned to the future with joy in their hearts.

CAROLINE BURNES

Familiar Stranger

To B.J. and Helmut—
cat lovers who go the extra mile
for the felines of Mobile, Alabama.

Prologue

August, 1991

Across the shimmering sand dunes the sun touched the earth and began its daily transition from golden ruler of the sky to a sinking orange ball. Molly Lynch stepped out of her tent and into the fading day. With the fall of night, the dunes would cool.

And perhaps Sulle would come to her.

At the thought of his touch, she felt her body shiver in the hundred-degree heat. She held on to the secret she had to tell him, afraid to anticipate his reaction. She knew so little about him. Nothing, really.

Except that in the twelve weeks she'd been in the Kuwait war zone, Sulle Alamar had shifted her world on its axis. She had come to do a magazine story on the women marines fighting in the Persian Gulf. She had collected her interviews and photographs, but she had lost her heart to a man of the desert. Now it was time for her to go home.

When she left Kuwait, she would take something with her that would forever tie her to this place and this man. Tonight she had to tell him that she was pregnant. Whatever his choice, her heart was already decided. She could only hope that Sulle would want the child as much as she did.

She turned to face the setting sun, and in the distance she

saw him, almost more dream and illusion than reality. Huge and red, the sun silhouetted him and cast a surreal glow over the sand. He was astride the enormous black horse that seemed his only friend and companion. He rode toward her through the waves of shimmering heat, a tall, dark figure in flowing robes who moved as one with the powerful animal.

"Sulle." She whispered his name, her hand going uncertainly to her abdomen.

She had never known a man could be both so masculine and so tender. She hadn't intended to sleep with him, much less fall in love. They had both been caught in a passion so intense that even now, with the consequences plain, she had no regrets. She had accepted Sulle Alamar as her fate.

As he drew nearer, her heart began to pound. He was riding hard, with urgency. Something was wrong. Without conscious thought she started walking toward him, then running, until she met him on the top of the next dune.

He swung from the saddle and swept her against him, kissing her with a need so great that Molly felt as if she had become a part of him.

"Come inside," she whispered, though there was no one near them. She'd taken great care to establish her tent away from the troops and other reporters. She drew away from him, leading the way with rapid steps.

"I've missed you," he said, stopping her and turning her around so that he could look at her. "Last night I dreamed that you were caught in a bombing, that you were killed. Molly, I can't stand the thought of you here, in such danger."

Hard lines showed at his mouth and Molly reached up and touched them. "I'm fine," she said.

"Hassan is targeting this area. You have to leave. Immediately."

Molly felt a rush of love and warmth. Sulle was telling her classified information. He'd come to warn her that the leader of one warring country would soon move against the U.S. Her heart pounded hard. Maybe he'd want this child as much as she did. Maybe he loved her enough to share the joys and heartaches of raising their baby.

"Come inside," she said, taking his hand and tugging at his arm.

He shook his head with a knowing smile. "Once inside the tent, I won't remember the urgency of my message." The smile faded. "You have to move to a safer location, Molly. Now. You know I shouldn't be telling this to a member of the press, but this place will become very dangerous in the next twelve hours."

"In twelve hours I'll be gone," Molly said. That was true, though she didn't want to believe it. Her magazine had called her to come home.

Sulle lifted her hand, kissing the palm with a passion that made her knees weaken. Then he turned to Tabiel and loosened the girth. "Wait for me, my friend," he whispered to the horse. "We have miles to ride tonight."

Tabiel lowered his head and pushed Sulle lightly in the chest.

Sulle removed the bridle. "Keep watch over us."

Molly watched in fascination. There was something between the man and stallion, a bond that defied anything she'd ever read about. Sulle placed his palm on the horse's neck before he followed her toward the tent.

She held open the flap and then carefully closed it after he'd entered. She watched him as he stopped just inside the doorway, taking in the candles and the wine.

"It looks like a celebration," he said.

"It is. You're here." She couldn't just blurt out her news. She'd planned the evening carefully.

He took a seat on the cot they'd shared with such passion, and she handed him a cup of wine. Taking her own cup, she settled in front of him.

"To us," he said.

"To us." She touched his cup and drank only a sip. She found that she couldn't look into his eyes. He was incredibly perceptive, and she was afraid he'd sense her news before she was ready to tell him.

"What's wrong?" he asked, cupping her chin so that she looked up at him.

"The magazine has called me home." She couldn't be certain if she imagined a split second of pain or not. Sulle smiled and leaned down to kiss her, a teasing of his lips across hers that for all of the gentleness was like a brush stroke of fire.

"The angels have intervened to keep you safe," he whispered. "I'm glad you're getting out of here. Hassan is a madman. I'm afraid of what he's doing, Molly. Though you may be out of reach of his missiles, there are other weapons in his arsenal that can kill and maim."

Molly felt the adrenaline jolt of a great story. "Chemicals? Is he using bio-warfare? Do you have proof?"

Sulle's smile was slow. "Even in the breast of a lover, there beats the heart of the reporter." He pulled her up into his lap and kissed her. "Bylines, headlines, your reputation growing and growing. This is what you dream of," he teased as he kissed her again. "And I dream of this." His hand slipped under the cool silk blouse she'd chosen because she knew it was his favorite color.

Molly wanted nothing more than to yield to the passion that swept over her. But Sulle was a man who came and went on the breeze. If he left before they talked, she might not see him for a week. And by then she'd be back in the states. This news couldn't be told long distance.

"Sulle," she said, putting her hand gently over his and stilling the exploration. "We need to talk."

Instead, he covered her lips with his. The kiss was so passionate that Molly almost forgot everything except the need to have him. She struggled to regain control and finally sat up.

"I don't know anything about you," she said. "I don't even know where you were born, or if you have a family."

For the first time since she'd known him, she saw all expression leave his eyes and face. The passionate man who'd been in the tent with her only seconds before was replaced by a creature of stone.

"Does it matter?" he asked with a coldness that made her want to withdraw the question.

"It doesn't matter, but it is part of getting to know who you are. And I'd like to do that."

He shook his head and picked up his wine. "We're given only the moment, Molly. There is no past or future. Only the moment."

It felt as if a giant hand was squeezing her heart. "That's not true. You don't believe that."

His dark eyes seemed to burn. "You ask about family. I was born in a small desert town on the border between Kuwait and Iraq. I was the youngest of a large family. Six brothers and sisters. They are all dead now. All of them. My parents, too. I was the only one left alive, and only because my mother hid me in a cupboard behind pillows and sheets. My parents had great plans for the future, for all of their children. And in one ten-minute span that lasted an eternity, it was all wiped away."

Molly felt as if she might fall forward, and she gripped the edge of the cot to maintain her balance. She put the pieces together fast. "No wonder you're working for the Americans." She'd never asked him why his allegiance to the United States war effort was so unflagging. She only knew that he risked his life behind enemy lines, and she strongly suspected that on the other side of the border Sulle Alamar led a very different life—that of a spy.

"I had hoped that our time together wouldn't be tainted

by my past,'' he said with bitterness. ''I should never have hoped for such a simple joy.'' His expression softened and he touched the corner of her mouth. ''You're so young, so unscarred by life. You almost made me believe that I could have such an existence.''

''I'm sorry for all you've lost, Sulle,'' she said, wanting somehow to erase the pain that was now so clearly revealed. Perhaps the baby would help ease the sorrow. For all that had been taken from him, there was so much still left in the future. Now was the time to tell him.

''I'm glad you're going home,'' he said, turning away from her suddenly. ''This is no place for you. No place for anyone. And it's only going to get worse. I came to tell you something.'' His hands grasped her shoulders. ''Tomorrow I go to Baghdad. I'll be away for a long time.''

At first Molly couldn't speak. If Sulle was going into the heart of enemy territory, it could only be for some dangerous mission. ''You can't,'' she whispered.

''I have to.'' His dark eyes locked with her green ones. ''This is my chance. If I can do this thing, many lives will be saved. Americans and those of my people, innocent victims.''

The first thing that leaped into Molly's mind was an image of Sulle, a darker shadow as he crept along the narrow alleys and walls of the old city. Assassin. Was he telling her that he was going into Baghdad on a mission of murder?

''You can't do this,'' she said.

He held her in his gaze. ''I can. And I will.''

''Sulle,'' she reached across what seemed to be a vast distance and touched him. ''You'll never get out alive.''

''The risk is great, but the chance of success is worth the risk. I am the only one who could possibly gain access. Think of the suffering that will be prevented. Think of the lives that will be saved—''

''Even if you survive this, you won't come out the same

man who went in.'' Molly understood the needs and sacrifices of war, but the order to assassinate was the harshest directive a soldier could receive.

Sulle rose quickly. He bent and placed a hand on either side of her face. ''Perhaps the greater truth is that you never knew the man I am.'' He bent and kissed her lips. ''For the time I lay in your arms, I was the man you thought me to be. A man far better than I really am. And that is a gift of exceptional worth, Molly. I'll always remember you.'' He kissed her again, this time on the forehead.

She knew he was leaving, telling her goodbye. Part of her wanted to reach out and catch his hand, to make him face her so that she could tell him that she carried his son or daughter. But another part, the larger part, kept her hands at her side and the tears behind her eyes as she watched him slip through the flap of the tent and disappear into the dunes that rolled like a silvery sea in the moonlight.

She went to the flap of the tent only when she heard Tabiel's hoofbeats, muffled by the sand. Sulle appeared on the top of the next dune, his robes streaming in the wind behind him and the horse's black tail a banner. And then he was gone.

Chapter One

August, 1999

It's hot as Hades here in the Big Easy, but a jazz funeral New Orleans style is the only way for a cool cat to be laid to rest.

I have to admit, I've never seen anything like this—a funeral that's also a celebration of music and a street dance. Pretty cool.

Not to mention that there are some fine-looking dames in the City That Care Forgot. They're on every street corner, and lots of them are watching me as I strut my stuff in the funeral procession. I can only say that Wade Ivory, a man who could tickle the keyboard with a style and talent this world won't see again, would love to be at his own funeral. This is something he would dig.

And to think that Peter and Eleanor were going to make me stay back in Washington because of my little escapade with the Gypsies! Hah, they should have known better. But once they discovered I was on the plane with them, they were gracious enough to get me a seat.

And look at little Jordan. She doesn't understand this is a funeral, but she's having a great time dancing in the streets. It makes a cat wonder why more people don't dance in the streets—whatever the occasion.

She is such a beautiful child, she is going to be a real heartbreaker.

Mama Mia! Or should I say, saints preserve us! Speaking of heartbreakers! Who is that woman with the camera? She should be on the other side of the lens. Green eyes, honeyed hair, and a complexion that looks like peachy cream. What a dish! In fact, peaches 'n' cream is a perfect name for her. P-n-C.

I think I'll sidle up a little closer. She's packing some serious camera gear, so she's not a tourist. She has that professional stance about her. And she's wearing press tags—Strong Currents. That's the magazine that specializes in current events that forecast change in today's society. Pretty high-caliber.

But something's wrong. She looks like she's been shot. She's photographing something up on the balcony there. It's a man. And from the look on her face, someone she knows and has strong feelings about. Not necessarily good feelings. She looks like she's seen a ghost.

Holy Moly! Who are these guys? Two men have just attacked P-n-C and they're trying to take her camera. These aren't New Orleans street hoodlums, either—they've got the moves of trained professionals. Time for a little Familiar Intervention.

Aieee!!! Ye-ow! And the claws sink into the tender neck flesh of one. As I expected, he screams and flees. Now the other. Aieee! His head is perfect for a four-claw dig-in. And he's taking off, too. I only hope that mounted policeman who just rode after them can bring them to justice. But now to make sure P-n-C is okay.

MOLLY HELD her camera in a death grip and turned to look at the black cat who'd begun to lick his coat back into place. She'd never seen anything like his attack before in her life. The feline had literally jumped out of the funeral procession and attacked the two men who'd grabbed her. Men who wanted her camera. In a reflexive motion, she tightened her grip on the Nikon.

"Kitty, kitty," she bent down and scooped the cat into her arms, making sure he wasn't injured. "What a brave kitty," she said, focusing on the feline and trying not to yield to the shock of what had happened in the last five minutes.

She took a deep breath and looked back at the balcony window. She couldn't have seen what she thought she saw. It had to be a trick of light or shadow or her memory. Perhaps it was her subconscious, reasserting the old dream, the old longing. Whatever it was, she intended to process her film, prove that she hadn't seen him, and then go on with her life as she'd been doing for the past eight years.

Sulle Alamar was a dead man. If that had even been his name. She felt a twinge of bitter frustration. She'd searched for the father of her child for four years before she'd finally given up. There was no record of Sulle Alamar working for the U.S. government in any capacity—and she had checked *all* the records. He was a nonentity, a shadow man who didn't exist. And after the bombing of Baghdad, it was almost certain he was dead. It was a fact she'd finally accepted—until today.

Sulle Alamar had seen her as the innocent twenty-one-year-old she'd been, and he'd taken advantage of her, feeding her hints and innuendoes about his work for the United States. And she'd fallen for his lines and for him. She'd been a fool, but one who had acted in good faith and from love. So the end result had been heartbreak *and* something so wonderful that she would go through ten hells of suffering again if it meant keeping her child.

The image that came to her mind was the smiling face of her seven-year-old son, Alan. He was her life, along with her work as a photojournalist. And whatever she had missed in the arms of a husband, Alan had made up for. He was her joy.

"Meow!"

The cat called her back to the present, and she went to speak to the mounted policewoman who was signaling her out of the funeral procession. The officer told her the assailants had escaped, and Molly agreed to stop by the station and give descriptions. A little shudder ran through her as she remembered the men with their dark eyes, hair and complexion. They could have been Middle Eastern. Or they could have been Italian or Spanish or a number of other nationalities, she reminded herself.

"Meow!" The cat struggled from her arms.

To her surprise, he appeared to be limping. "You poor thing," she said, scooping him up again. "We'll have to take you to a vet."

"Me-o-o-w."

The cat's cry was pitiful, and Molly hustled toward a small restaurant where she could sit down and fully examine him. He'd seemed fine a moment before. She sat down at a table and began to explore him. He didn't seem to have any tender spots, and he was purring and slapping at a menu. It wasn't possible, but— She held the menu up and the cat put a paw on a picture of crusted trout.

"Okay, Mr. Cat," Molly said, ordering it to go. "You can have the fish, but you have to go with me to the cemetery and let me take my photos. Then we'll decide what to do with you."

Familiar pushed his head against her hand and then lightly bit her fingers.

"You are one demanding devil," Molly whispered, laughing at him. "And something of an actor, I suspect. We'll see. If we can't find your owner, I think Alan would love to have you for a friend."

THE LIGHT FROM the floor-length window was almost too bright, but Sulle Alamar was captivated by the exotic procession that streamed below him on the hot New Orleans street.

It was a funeral procession the likes of which he'd never seen, and he'd seen a few burials with pomp and ceremony. But this was different—an occasion for mourning *and* joy. He'd read the newspaper stories about the musician who'd died. Ivory Wade was a blues piano player with an international reputation for talent and kindness. He'd helped hundreds of young musicians get a start, and they all seemed to be here, in the city of his birth and death. They'd formed a band behind the coffin and as they followed it, were playing saxophones and clarinets with a passion that took a man down into the sad depths of his heart. Then they switched to an upbeat ragtime tune that made feet tap and hands come together in joy. It was impressive to behold, and even though he was on edge about the meeting he was waiting for, he couldn't help peeking out the balcony window and watching.

His gaze landed on the beautiful honeyed hair of a young woman, and for an instant he felt the stab of old pain. Molly Lynch. He had long ago given up the idea that he would forget her. Like his parents and brothers and sisters, she was a casualty of the past that had left a cruel scar on his heart. No matter that her life was better because he didn't share it. That sentiment was balm for a philosopher's heart, not his. He'd never loved a woman so, or wanted one with such hot desire. And he never expected to again.

He stared at the mass of honeyed hair, waiting for the woman to look up and destroy the illusion of the past. But when her face lifted, Sulle felt a shock that seemed to echo in his bones. Molly Lynch looked up at him, and to prove the point, she lifted a camera and began to snap his picture.

For one stunned second, he couldn't move. Then his training kicked in, and he stepped back from the window. Risking another glance, he saw the two men attack her, and he knew sheer horror. They were his men, his protectors. And they were on Molly as if she were the enemy.

In eight years he'd stayed a continent away from her, and the one time they found themselves in the same city, by happenstance, she was in danger. Because of him.

He fled the small apartment where he'd been waiting to make contact with a dangerous international criminal and rushed down the stairs and into the street. He caught sight of Molly and his two guards—and a crazed black cat that was wreaking havoc on his men. Before he could lift a hand to do anything, the cat had dispatched his guards and sent them fleeing through the crowds, pursued by a mounted policeman.

Sulle couldn't help the tense smile that played at his mouth. Perhaps he, too, should find an attack cat to serve as his guard. He'd have to have a word with Jorge. That operation had been very sloppy.

An angry Molly stood on the sidewalk, cat in her arms, unharmed. As an antidote to the shot of pain he felt, he smiled again and then blended back into the crowds. He set off at a brisk pace in the opposite direction. He would have to reschedule the meeting with Victor Lolahta. Weeks of preparation and planning had been destroyed.

But Molly Lynch was unharmed—and she was even more beautiful than he remembered.

MOLLY SNAPPED ON the light in the darkroom and took a deep breath. It was time to confront her negatives and prove to herself that the man she'd glimpsed in the window only looked like Sulle Alamar. She had dreamed of him so often, had wanted to see him for so long. This vision was simply a manifestation of her still smoldering desires. And she had thought she was over him.

Right.

She unspooled the wet negatives and held them up to the bright light. Even as she examined her work, she felt an increase in her pulse. Whoever he was, he looked exactly like Sulle. Or, at least, how she imagined he would look after eight years.

She dried the negatives and prepared to print. An eight-by-ten would prove conclusively that she had a very active imagination.

She made the print, and even as the man's visage began to emerge in the developer, she felt her heart begin to knock at her ribs.

Beneath the liquid in the tray, the features of her desert lover began to emerge.

Molly felt her head grow light, and she gripped the edge of the sink as she finished developing the picture. She tossed it into the stop and fix, still unwilling to believe what was right in front of her.

Sulle Alamar was alive, and he was in New Orleans.

The next thought was bitter indeed. Since he was in the United States and not a prisoner of war or dead, he could have looked her up at any time. Her photographs had been printed in magazines and newspapers around the world. If he'd wanted to find her, he could have.

There was a light tap on the darkroom door. "Mama, are the pictures good? Can I see?"

"Alan." Her first thought was to hide the picture. She'd told Alan long ago that his father had died in the war—because that was what she'd believed. This news could do terrible damage to her sensitive son. "I'm coming out. The film is still drying. We'll print some together in a little while."

She debated destroying the picture of Sulle, but something held her back. Instead, she threw it into the wash and took off the apron that protected her clothes from the chemicals. "I think we need to go to the market and find some food for the cat."

"I've named him," Alan said, stepping back as the dark-room door opened and his mother emerged into the light. "He likes 'Familiar.' I said he looked familiar, like the cat on the next street. He liked that name a lot."

Molly smiled at her son's fancy. She knelt down so that she was on eye level with him. "You know he isn't our cat, sweetie. If his owners show up, we'll have to give him back. I'm sure someone loves him very much."

"But he loves me." Alan bit his bottom lip. "You said I couldn't have a dog because we travel so much. But a cat isn't any trouble. Not this cat. He's wonderful. Pauline said she'd help me take care of him."

Molly pushed back her son's silky dark hair. "Pauline's very thoughtful. We'll keep him if no one claims him. And we can call him Familiar. That's a great name for a black cat."

From the kitchen came a loud meow.

"See, he already knows his name," Alan said, satisfied for the moment. "And he wants shrimp for dinner. He showed me in the phone book. You could get some from the market."

"You and that cat have a real communication," Molly said, and then felt a streak of panic as she remembered another man who could communicate with his horse. Perhaps Alan had inherited more than his dark good looks from his father.

"When are we going back to New York?" Alan asked.

"In a week or two. I thought since we were here, we should see the city and some of the surrounding areas. Once I turn in my story, we can ride the riverboats and tour the plantations. There's a world of history here, Alan."

"I read on the Internet about the sugar plantations. Can we go to the aquarium, too?"

"We can do just about anything you want," Molly agreed, kissing his forehead before she stood. "I love you, Alan."

"I love you, too, Mom," he said, taking her hand. "Will you get Familiar his shrimp?"

"I'll get us all something to eat," Molly agreed.

SULLE ALAMAR STOOD on the brick-cobbled street and gazed up at the second-floor window of the apartment. He felt a thud of raw desire as the woman's dark shadow passed in front of the floor-length window. Even when he could only see her as a silhouette, he knew Molly Lynch. In eight years, she'd hardly changed.

"I followed her here," the man beside him said. "That place is a piece of cake. We'll climb up the wrought-iron supports and go in through the balcony." He laughed softly. "These old buildings weren't designed for security."

"Wait until she goes out," Sulle ordered. "I don't want her frightened or upset."

He felt his comrade's gaze turn on him. "Is there something I should know about this woman?" Jorge Mullah asked carefully.

Sulle avoided his direct gaze. He owed the man a truthful answer, and he also knew he wasn't prepared to give one. Eight years before, Jorge had risked his life to pull Sulle out of the rubble of a building destroyed by a bomb. Since that day, Jorge had been at his side, as his friend and protector. But Molly was something so personal, so emotional, that he couldn't share his feelings for her. Not even with Jorge.

"She's an American journalist. If you're caught breaking into her dwelling, it will be a big story. Our negotiations are delicate. We can't risk any public scrutiny." It was all accurate, but only a portion of the truth.

"She knows you, doesn't she?" Jorge asked.

Sulle sighed. "Sometimes you're too smart for your own good, except where cats are concerned."

"I saw the way she looked at you," Jorge said softly. "That mixture of hope and terror and anger only comes from deep feelings. I'll be very careful," he promised. "I'll get the film, and no policeman will find evidence that I was ever there."

Sulle nodded. He couldn't afford to leave the film Molly had taken behind. If his likeness should appear in a magazine, even as only a dim image in the background, his entire life would be a useless ruin. He was a man who came and went without leaving a trace of his existence behind. He had no choice but to get the negatives.

"There she goes," Jorge whispered. "I'll be back in fifteen minutes."

"Be careful," Sulle answered, but his gaze was on the woman who stepped out the double doors of the arched entrance. She wore shorts and a cotton T-shirt that revealed the firm, high breasts he well remembered. She was twenty-nine and still had the willowy grace of the college graduate.

From his vantage point in the alley, he watched her as she walked by.

He felt the strangest impulse to call out to her, to rush across the street and sweep her into his arms. As if she'd allow him to do so. He'd known when he deliberately disappeared from her life that she would never forgive him for that abandonment. She had loved him—and he'd known it. He'd seen it clearly in her eyes the evening he'd gone to tell her goodbye.

And he'd rejected her love and left her, alone, undoubtedly believing he'd been killed.

He felt the old familiar pain in his chest. Scar tissue stung by his emotions. He'd loved Molly Lynch, too. But he wasn't a man with a future or a past. He'd made his choices, but he wouldn't force Molly to live with them.

Instinct told him the man who'd killed his family was still alive, and Sulle knew that he couldn't rest until he discovered the man's identity and settled that old score. It was just taking a lot longer than he'd ever anticipated.

He saw Jorge's dark figure climb the ironwork that made the historic French Quarter of New Orleans so distinctive. He watched as the commando raised the window and eased into the house.

Molly had grown soft, living in a country where people of her class felt protected. Her windows weren't even locked. He felt a stab of pure happiness at the freedom she enjoyed—to live without fear. To live in a world where she could come and go without wondering if she'd be killed or disfigured by a car bomb or some other act of political evil.

He nodded to himself. When he'd left her in the desert, he'd made the right choice. For her, if not for himself.

Chapter Two

Sulle checked his watch. Five minutes had elapsed since Jorge went into the apartment. He should be out by now. Sulle resisted the impulse to pace. New Orleans wasn't the kind of city where men in suits paced in alleys.

The gunshot was so loud, so unexpected, that Sulle thought for a moment he'd imagined it. The enraged scream came next, and he couldn't ascertain if it was human or animal. One thing he knew, Jorge had not been carrying a gun when he went into Molly's apartment.

As he started across the street, the arched doors burst open and a hail of gunfire drove him back into the alley. He saw three dark shapes, one of them carrying a small bundle.

The scream of anger came again, and he watched in awe as the black cat leaped from the balcony onto the head of the man carrying the bundle. To Sulle's horror, a small arm shifted from beneath the blankets.

They had a child!

He ran forward, but another explosive shower of bullets forced him to throw himself to the ground and roll. One of the men flung the cat against the wall, and the feline sank to the ground and didn't move.

And then a van sped into the street. Sulle lunged out of the path of the vehicle and grabbed one of the attackers by the shin. To his surprise, the man looked down at him with amazement, faltered and then fell as the two other men threw the child into the van and reversed, roaring away into the night.

Sulle gained his feet. When he quickly checked the man beside him, he was shocked to discover he was dead. He'd been shot by his own comrades when he couldn't get to the van in time.

Leaving the body, he rushed to the cat. The creature was only stunned, and Sulle carried him in his arms as he hurried into the apartment, afraid now that the first gunshot had been directed at his friend and ally.

Molly's apartment door was unlocked, and Sulle rushed in to find a young woman, hands and feet bound, and unconscious. Beside her, Jorge lay bleeding from a leg wound.

"I was too late," Jorge said, gaining his feet. "They got the film and a young boy. I tried to stop them."

Sulle checked the pulse of the unconscious woman. "Did she see you?" he asked, putting the pieces together—the baseball glove on the floor, the small tennis shoes beside the sofa. The boy who'd been abducted was obviously Molly's son.

"No, she didn't see me," Jorge said, grabbing the hand that Sulle offered. "Let's get out of here before she comes home."

"Who is she?" Sulle pointed to the young blonde.

"Governess. She travels with Ms. Lynch and looks after the boy, does his studies. I heard them talking before they realized I had come in the window."

"Who were the men who took him?" Sulle asked as he checked the room to make sure they'd left no trace of their entrance.

"I don't know for certain, but I have some suspicions." Jorge limped across the room. "You're not going to like them, either."

Sulle checked the cat. He was breathing normally and seemed only to be sleeping. An incredible animal. Twice now he'd put himself in grave danger to protect a human.

"Let's go," Jorge said. "There's nothing we can do here. If we're caught…" He didn't have to finish. Sulle knew the consequences if he failed in this assignment.

"We have to find that boy," Sulle said as he helped Jorge down the back stairs and into an ally.

"I'm afraid you're right about that, and for many different reasons," Jorge said.

Sulle stopped. "What are you saying?"

"Those men worked for Victor Lolahta," Jorge said. "I'm almost positive I've seen dossiers on one of them before. The big one who had the kid."

"Why would Victor want to steal a magazine writer's child?" Sulle asked as he stepped into the street and flagged a taxi.

Jorge didn't respond as he got into the car. "I think I'd better see a doctor," he finally said.

"Take us to 1590 St. Charles Avenue," Sulle directed. It was an exclusive residential part of town, but after twenty years working for the National Security Agency, he'd developed a lot of influential friends, including some physicians. Now was the time to call in some favors.

MOLLY TURNED THE CORNER and froze. Police cars were parked on the curb, their blue lights flashing, and an ambulance was pulling away—all in an eerie silence that was worse than the ululation of sirens.

She felt the bag of groceries slip from her grasp, and she ran over the tumble of produce that she'd so carefully selected for their evening meal. She should have insisted that Alan go to the store with her. But he'd wanted to stay and play with the cat.

She ran to the first policeman.

"What? What happened?" she asked breathless.

He took pity on her fear. "A man was shot."

"Was there a child?"

He shook his head. "No, ma'am. Is there something you need to report?"

She didn't bother answering. She jerked open the front doors and felt a thud of fear because they weren't locked. Feet pounding on the old wood of the stairs, she hurried to her apartment and was met by Pauline's blue gaze of horror.

"They knocked me out and took him," Pauline sobbed, unable to move because her hands and feet were still bound. "They took him, Molly."

"Alan." Her son's name came out a whisper. "Alan!" Then a scream. "*Alan!*" She rushed to the back of the apartment, but she knew her son was gone. It was her worst nightmare come to life. Alan had been taken.

She ran back to Pauline, who was sobbing. "Who were they?" Molly demanded as she began to work the knots that bound the governess. "Did they say anything? What did they want?"

Pauline drew a ragged breath. "When I answered the door, they rushed us with guns pointed at us. Alan and I were playing with the cat, and they snatched him up. He struggled, and the cat attacked them, but they threw Familiar off. One of them laughed out loud and said something odd."

"What did he say?" Molly wanted to pull the words out of the girl.

"The man said, 'He'll pay dearly for this one, don't you think?' and he laughed again, and then they struck me, and I blacked out."

Molly felt as if the hand of death had brushed her heart. The words could have many meanings, but she knew what the man had been talking about. Someone had discovered that Alan was Sulle Alamar's son.

The man she'd photographed was Sulle. Even though

she'd tried to pretend it might be someone else, she knew it wasn't. He wasn't dead, but there was no telling who he really was or what he was involved in.

Eight years before, he'd slipped into one identity after another. And now those games had come back to haunt him—at her son's expense. She rushed into the darkroom and found that all of her negatives had been stripped from the hangers. Of course they'd taken them.

"Are you okay?" she asked Pauline as she came back into the room.

The young woman nodded. "I heard the police in the street. Did you tell the police about Alan?"

Molly hesitated. Calling in the cops might put Alan's life in danger. Whatever Sulle was up to, it was covert and secret. It crossed her mind that perhaps Sulle had learned of Alan and had abducted the child himself. It wouldn't be the first time one parent had done that to the other.

A cold anger took hold of her and she felt her thoughts clear. "No. No police."

"But, Molly, they have—"

"No police," she said in a voice she didn't recognize as her own. "We'll wait for word from them."

"And if it doesn't come?" Pauline asked.

Molly looked at her. "I know where to find the people who have my son." She saw the governess turn pale at her words.

"Don't try to force their hand, Molly. Alan's life may be at stake."

Molly shook her head and bent to pet the cat, who was pacing the floor. "Wait here, with Familiar. I'll be back soon."

"Where are you going?" Pauline asked, panicking. "What if they call about Alan? What should I do?"

"Promise them anything they ask for. Anything at all."

SULLE SETTLED BACK in the taxi and tried to relax. He'd left Jorge in the care of a doctor, and Kary was doing reconnaissance on Dumaine Street. Another meeting with Lolahta had been arranged. Kary had taken the call not half an hour after the boy's abduction. Clearly, they intended to use the child as a bargaining chip.

But why? That part didn't make a bit of sense to Sulle. Even if they knew about his long-ago romance with Molly, why would they assume that he would care about her now? Or about the child in her possession? Hell, he wasn't even certain it was her child. He felt a tingle of jealousy at the thought. Had she married and started a family?

He pushed aside his jealousy. It was natural for a woman to marry and have a family. He'd followed Molly's career, had assumed she was still single because her photographs and stories were credited to Molly Lynch. But it wasn't unusual for a woman to retain her maiden name, especially for professional purposes. He realized that he'd hoped she hadn't married. And then he accepted how selfish that hope had been, because he could never give himself to a woman and a family he had no right to want the same for her.

If the child was hers, he knew Molly would be frantic. For one crazy second he considered calling her, telling her that he'd find the boy and bring him home. But he couldn't do that.

He found his thoughts whirling around in the same tired pattern, and he tried to calm himself as the taxi turned down Dumaine Street. Kary had insisted on the same apartment for the ten-o'clock meeting. As the cab stopped, Sulle paid the fare and stepped out into the street.

He looked up to the second floor, alert to the movement of any shadows. Music from some of the clubs wafted to him, carrying the sounds of laughter on the sultry night. New Orleans was a city of sensual delights. A city that seemed to pulse with the promise of pleasures, some of them forbidden.

Again Molly came to mind, and Sulle stepped to the recessed doorway of the apartment. He could only hope he'd arrived before Lolahta—and that somewhere in the darkness Kary was protecting his back. He stepped into the doorway.

When a hand reached out of the shadows and grabbed his wrist, Sulle whirled instantly. His reflexes were so sharply honed that he grasped the person's arm and pulled his attacker into his chest, using his other arm to circle the assailant's throat.

It was only when his hand brushed down the chest of his attacker and found a mound of warm flesh that he faltered in his defensive maneuvers. He loosened the grip on the person's throat and was rewarded with a muffled curse.

"Let me go."

Though it had been eight years, Sulle remembered the throaty voice, made slightly rougher by the pressure he was applying to her neck. His hands slid away from her and he stepped back.

In the dim light that filtered into the recessed alcove, he watched as Molly Lynch turned to confront him. Her green eyes blazed in her pale face and she tossed her hair back.

"Where's my son?" she asked in a tone that accused him.

Sulle was unprepared for the fury of her gaze. "I don't know," he answered.

"Why did they take him? What are they going to do to him?"

He bit back his quick response. Even in the worst war conditions, he'd never seen Molly unnerved. Tonight, the least thing could push her over the edge. And if she lost it, now, in this place, it could cost her her life. Or her son's.

"I'm not certain why they took the boy," he said softly. "But I'm working on it, Molly. I'll get him back for you."

"What are you up to, Sulle? *If that even is your name.* What are you doing that would endanger my son?"

He took a breath and tried not to react to the savage tone of her voice. "It is my name," he said softly. "And I have no idea why your child has been taken."

He felt the palm of her hand, a burning sting on his jaw, before he caught her wrist. "Molly, get a grip on yourself." He pushed her back deeper into the shadows. "How did you find me?"

"I want my son." She ignored his question. "If he's hurt because of you—" Her voice broke and she turned to the wall. "If they ask for a ransom, tell them you'll pay it. Whatever it is, I'll get the money."

More than anything, Sulle wanted to draw her into his arms, to comfort her. But he knew that his touch was the last thing she wanted. It was as if his fondest wish had come true and turned into a nightmare. Molly was only inches away from him, and she hated him.

"Was the boy taken because of a story you're covering?" he asked, trying to make some sense of the turn of events.

She whirled on him. "It's because of you, Sulle."

In a split second, Sulle was transported back to the desert. He was in Molly's tent, aware of the candles and the wine, the symbols of celebration. "I have something to tell you," she'd said. But before she could give her news, he'd told her that he was leaving.

Now, he knew what her news had been.

"The boy is mine," he whispered. "My son?"

"Only in biological fact," Molly said angrily. "You're his father, but he's my child. And I want him back." She dashed the tears from her eyes.

At the sound of a car slowly approaching, Sulle pressed her against the wall with such force that he could hear her shallow gasp. She struggled against him, but he was far stronger and he held her in place. "Shush!" he warned her.

"You have no reason to trust me, Molly. None. But if you want to see our son, stay quiet." He felt her cease struggling and he eased the pressure on her. "There's a meeting here tonight. One that I must attend." When he felt her begin to struggle again, he leaned closer, so that he could whisper in her ear.

He caught the scent of her shampoo, a clean smell of herbs that triggered an explosion of erotic memories. He ignored them. "If these men have taken the boy, this may be my only chance to find out where he is." Instantly she went still. "You have to get out of here. If they realize you're here, they'll either kill you or refuse to meet. Understand?"

When she nodded, he released her. Looking out into the street, he saw that the car had driven past. It was Lolahta's men. He knew it. They were scoping out the meeting place.

He saw a sudden movement in a building across the street. It was nothing more than a brief shifting of shadows, but he knew it was Kary.

"Go over there," he said, indicating a quiet bar. "Go inside and wait. As soon as I know something, I'll come and tell you."

"Or maybe you'll just disappear into the night," she said bitterly.

Sulle didn't react. "Even if you hate me, I know you love your son," he said, his voice cool and professional. "Give me a chance to save him," he said. "What's his name?" He felt the strangest sense of loss as he asked the question. He had a son, a boy nearly eight, and he didn't even know his name.

"Alan," she whispered, her voice breaking as she spoke. "Alan Lynch." She gripped his arm. "He thinks his father is dead," she said slowly. "*I* thought you were dead, Sulle."

It was another blow, but one he knew he deserved. "I won't tell him any different," he said. "You have my word on it."

Chapter Three

Molly took a bar stool where she could glance out the door whenever it opened. She concentrated on trying to look normal and feel nothing. If she allowed herself to recognize the fear—or any other of the surging emotions—she knew she'd fall completely apart. She put on her professional attitude, distancing herself from everything, and focused on her surroundings.

The small bar was crowded with French Quarter residents. This wasn't a tourist place—the clientele was quiet, and there were games of backgammon and checkers going in different corners. At another time she might have found it charming.

Tonight it was hell. She was tough, but not tough enough.

Her son had been kidnapped and the man she'd loved and long ago given up for dead had stepped back into her life.

Sulle Alamar. Her body trembled at the thought of him. She felt his whisper in her ear, the hardness of his body as he pressed her into the recessed doorway. Surely if she closed her eyes for a moment, she would open them and find that she was asleep in her bed, Alan in the next room. She gave it a try and opened her eyes on the red neon of a beer light and the sharp laughter of a man who'd won his game of checkers.

"Alan," she whispered under her breath.

She got up and walked to the door, afraid to go outside and unable to stay inside. Alan needed her. He would be frightened. The thought of him suffering was almost more than she could stand. She started to go outside to force her way into the building across the street, but she stopped.

It was torture, but she had to trust Sulle and let him handle the situation. He seemed to know what was going on.

She turned to go back to her bar stool when the shots rang out in the night. Three of them, rapid and loud. She felt her heart nearly burst as she ran into the street in time to see a car turning the corner, headed toward her. She froze on the sidewalk and was completely unprepared when the car door swung open and a man jumped out and grabbed her.

The distinctive smell of chloroform came to her and she struggled with a strength she'd never guessed she possessed. The cloth was forced to her nose, sweet and pungent in her nostrils. She caught sight of two men rushing out of the shadows toward her before the drug took effect and she felt her mind roll into a tiny ball that seemed to swoop into darkness.

WHAT IS IT with this dame? Every time she gets out of my sight, trouble, and that with a capital T. In less than twenty-four hours I've been smashed and stomped so many times, if I weren't such a classy dresser, I'd be black and blue.

Thank goodness for the tall, dark stranger. He's the man she saw in the window. That guy across the street in the window with the scope and rifle must be his sidekick. I'm not certain they're the cavalry, but at least they weren't the ones who kidnapped the kid.

Hey, what's this? A car is trying to run P-n-C down. And now a man is jumping out and—hey! He's trying to abduct her. Time for less philosophizing and more action!

SULLE DARTED into the alley just in time to see the car wheel down the street. He knew from the sound of the high-performance motor, all revved up and roaring, and the squeal of the tires, that it boded trouble.

Just as he emerged from the alley, he saw the man leap out and grab Molly.

"Hey!" Sulle shouted, hoping to break the man's concentration and give Molly a chance to get away. When he saw the white cloth at Molly's nose, he knew it was useless. She'd been drugged.

As he sprinted forward and launched himself at the abductor, a small black shadow hurtled through the air. This time he wasn't even surprised to find the black cat on the scene.

As soon as the man released Molly, letting her tumble to the cobblestone street, Sulle scooped her into his arms and ran for the safety of the building where Kary had begun a covering ground fire.

"Come on, cat," Sulle called over his shoulder as he gained the doorway of the building. The black cat was right on his heels as Kary slammed the door.

"What went wrong?" Kary asked.

"It was a setup," Sulle said tersely. "The door was rigged. As soon as I opened it, three guns fired. I was lucky I'd dropped to the floor. The bullets would have caught me in the thigh, chest and head."

"They don't want to negotiate," Kary said, his face drawn into a frown. "Jorge was supposed to make that meeting, before he was injured. They intended to kill him as a warning to you that they play hardball."

"We're coming up to bat next," Sulle said. He eased Molly down on the bare and dust-covered floor. She was so pale. He did a cursory check to see if she'd been hit during the gunfire. There was no sign of a wound, but he found his hands lingering on her, his fingers remembering the feel of her skin, the curves of her body.

"We have to get out of here, fast," Kary reminded him. "What are we going to do with her?"

Sulle hadn't given it a lot of thought, but he knew the answer. "We'll take her with us."

"She's a magazine writer," Kary said in disbelief. "We can't risk that. If she ever writes a word about us, all of our power is gone. We'll never be able to pull off a deal again. Our cover will be ruined."

"We can't let her loose. They have her son and they want her," Sulle said.

"That's ridiculous," Kary snapped. "It's clear as a bell this woman means something to you, but we can't take her with us, Sulle. She'll be in the way." He gripped Sulle's shoulder. "She'll be in danger."

"They've taken her son," he said.

"We can try to get him back, but that isn't our mission," Kary reminded him.

Sulle stood up slowly. He put a hand on Kary's shoulder. "It might not have been our mission, but getting the boy back is now our first priority."

"Sulle, what about the thousands who'll die if we mess this mission up? You can't just go off half-cocked and—"

"The boy is my son," Sulle said, his dark eyes burning in the dim light of the room. "He's been abducted because of me. I have no choice but to get him back."

Kary stepped back. "Now I understand," he said slowly. "What are we going to do with her? She's a wild card."

"I have a plan," Sulle answered carefully. "She isn't going to like it, but it'll keep her safe and out of the way until we can find Alan and bring him back to her. We'll kidnap her ourselves."

Kary paced the room slowly, glancing down once at Molly and the black cat who sat serenely at her side.

"If she goes missing, every cop in New Orleans will be looking for her."

"I know," Sulle said. "It's perfect. It will draw Lolahta out and force him to come to the table with the boy."

Kary looked at him long and hard. "Jorge is going to have a fit," he said, then smiled.

Sulle lifted Molly into his arms. She was warm and soft, just as he remembered her. "I know just the place to put her," he said. "Bring the cat."

"Funny how it works out that you get the woman and I get the cat," Kary said good-naturedly.

THE SOUND OF A BIRD singing outside her window awakened Molly. She opened her eyes to a pale green mist that seemed to be draped around her, a beautiful shimmer of color and light that made her smile. Until the headache pounded down on her.

She groaned out loud. It felt as if someone was hitting her skull with a mallet. But it was morning and time for Alan's breakfast. She rolled to her side and found that the bed was enclosed in the pale green material. It puzzled her, and she reached out and swept it aside. The room was like a fairy tale. It was furnished with antiques that gleamed from polish, a huge tapestry that had to be worth thousands on a wall, plush curtains and a chaise longue designed for luxurious reclining.

She raised up slowly, and to her surprise she saw a huge window, and outside an enormous oak tree draped with Spanish moss. In the distance were sugarcane fields.

She had the disoriented feeling that she was dreaming, but not asleep. Her headache was fierce, and she got up and stumbled to the huge window to look out.

It was clearly morning, and she was awake, but she had no idea where she was. Or where Alan was. She felt a clutch of terror and whirled. To her surprise her suitcases were neatly stacked by the wall, her cameras lined up on the dresser. She was staying in this place, and yet she had no idea where she was or how she'd gotten there. The headache pounded a warning of disaster.

A robe had been tossed across the bed and she put it on, trying to remember how she'd undressed and gotten into the strange, draped bed that looked like something fit for a princess. Or better yet, a Southern belle. With that thought she finally realized where she was. The ornate furnishings of the room, the cane fields in the distance—somehow she'd been transported to one of the old plantations along the Mississippi River. But how, and why? And where was Alan? Her heart pounded as she began to remember her son's kidnapping and her own abduction.

She went to the door, determined to find someone to answer her questions, but when she turned the knob, she found it locked. The first surge of true panic hit her. To her surprise she felt the handle turn beneath her hand. She stepped back as the door swung open and she saw a man she recognized. He limped into the room and closed the door.

"You tried to take my camera," she said accusingly.

He nodded. "My job is to protect the man you were photographing. My name is Jorge."

"Where is my son?" she demanded.

"Sulle is trying to find him now," Jorge reassured her.

"Good," she said, determined not to show how terrified she actually was. "I won't waste time asking for explanations of how I got here. I'll just get dressed and you can take me to Sulle."

"I'm afraid that's impossible," Jorge said easily. "You will remain here, where you're safe. In case you don't remember, you were almost abducted last night. Sulle can't afford for them to have two hostages. It will be difficult enough to rescue the boy."

Molly was numb with shock. "The boy is my son," she

said slowly. "You can't keep me here. I'm an American citizen."

Jorge's smile showed grudging admiration. "Sulle said you would be difficult. He also said that he would shoot me if I let you escape."

"What is this place?" Molly asked. It didn't look as if it would be hard to leave. She'd seen people working in the fields. The place was elegant, civilized. There were bound to be other people in the house, people who would help her if she explained to them what was happening. She glanced down and saw that Jorge, for all of his casual ease, was armed.

"It is Beau Monde Plantation," he said softly. "It is a working plantation that is open to the public for tours."

"I'm a prisoner in a tourist attraction?" Molly almost didn't believe her luck. She'd be out of this place in seconds.

Jorge nodded, but his smile was deadly. "Sulle knows the owners, Ms. Lynch. You're ideal for the role that has been hastily created for you."

"And what role might that be?" she asked.

"Everyone here has been told that you're an actress who is playing the insane cousin. They expect you to concoct wild stories of abductions and to scream and beg to be released. They will treat you with gentle kindness and bring you right back up to this room and lock you up—everyone will think it's all part of the act."

Molly felt her mouth drop, and she snapped it shut. "That's insane. No one would believe that."

Jorge's smile was self-satisfied. "I think they will," he said. "There is only one restriction. If you leave this room you must wear the period costume. Otherwise I'll be forced to bring you back up here and lock the door. Kick and scream as you wish—it only adds to the charm of your character."

"I won't participate in this. I won't—"

Jorge looked at his watch. "Breakfast is being served. I suggest that you hurry. The staff here is trained to present a certain image to the public." He stepped back into the hallway and closed the door, locking it.

Molly considered testing him. She was tempted to throw herself against the door and kick and scream and demand that someone help her. But he had been too cool to be pretending. Sulle had designed this prison with the intelligence and wit of the master spy—one thing she knew him to be. She was a prisoner without being locked away. How perfect.

Her best chance was to go downstairs, act her part, and find an avenue of escape that would require no help from anyone.

"Meow!"

Molly turned to the chiffonnier in a corner of the room. The black cat nosed the door open and hopped out.

"Meow!"

"Familiar," she said, rushing to the cat and picking him up. As she hugged him, he purred against her chest and rubbed his head on her chin, reaching up to nip and nibble. "I won't ask how you got here, I'll only say thank goodness you did," she said, stroking him all over. "It seems you're the only one I can trust in the whole world. You'll help me get Alan back, I know."

The idea of her son being held captive by cruel and brutal men, made the tears start to her eyes. Crying was useless, so she turned her thoughts to Sulle Alamar. When she saw him—and she would very soon—he was going to pay a high price for making her a prisoner. A high price indeed.

SULLE EXAMINED the black leather riding boots. They were of excellent quality and craftsmanship. And he'd seen some of the horses in the stables. They were magnificent animals. Not the Arabians he'd grown up riding, but Tennessee

Walkers. Big horses with an easy, single-footed gait, a man could ride all day without getting the least bit tired.

He left his room, nodding to Jorge who sat outside Molly's door. In his planter outfit, Jorge almost didn't recognize him.

"How's she taking it?" Sulle asked, a hint of excitement in his eyes.

"Too quietly," Jorge said. "No protests, no arguing. That means her mind is working and she's trying to think of a way to escape. She's going to want to take your head off, Sulle. And I can't say I blame her. If this plantation weren't the perfect exchange point, I'd say you had lost your mind with this scheme."

Sulle laughed. "If I could tell her that Beau Monde is the perfect place to stage a rescue of Alan, she might feel differently. But Molly isn't the kind of woman to sit back and do what she's told. That's why we can't risk telling her anything. Keep her in the dark, no matter how furious she gets."

"It's your head she wants, not mine," Jorge said, adding under his breath, "Thank goodness for that."

Sulle entered the dining room and found a dozen men and women, all dressed in Southern costume, seated at a table that gleamed with heavy silver. The aroma of bacon, ham and biscuits made his mouth water.

"This is Mr. Belton, a new player," the lady at the head of the table said as she rose. "As I told you earlier, we've been joined by Mr. Belton and a young woman named Molly Lynch, who will play the insane betrothed of Mr. Belton. It should add a certain…intensity to our little family."

Sulle smiled at Maria St. Claire. Her family owned Beau Monde, and they had opened the doors of the plantation to him once he explained his need. They were an old French family that he'd helped long ago, in another part of the world, and their dock on the Mississippi River would provide the perfect place to stage the upcoming exchange—Alan for the chemicals that Victor Lolahta wanted. If only he could tell Molly... He forced his mind back to the present.

"Is Ms. Lynch coming down?" the hostess asked sweetly.

"I'm here and I resent every second of it."

All heads swiveled to the doorway where Molly stood in a beautiful morning dress of watered silk.

Sulle felt his heartbeat increase to a dangerous high. The apple green silk heightened the highlights in Molly's hair and made her skin look like peach perfection. But the fire in her green eyes had nothing to do with her dress or coloring. It was aimed at Sulle, and he felt the heat of it across the room.

"Have some breakfast, darling," he said in a perfect Southern drawl. "Our journey last night was difficult for you."

Molly started across the room, but the tiny slippers that had been set out for her forced her to take the small, mincing steps of a belle. She made it to the sideboard slowly. "I'm starved," she said sweetly, but her eyes belied her tone.

Sulle watched with amusement as she began to fill her plate with eggs and grits and fresh jam.

"Okay, the first tourists are here," Maria St. Claire said to the group at the table. "Everyone into their parts now. We must present a typical Southern breakfast."

Sulle's gaze left Molly long enough to glance into the doorway where a guide was ushering a group of bedazzled tourists up to the red ropes where they could watch.

"A typical Southern breakfast comprised of ham, bacon, eggs, grits, jam, gravy, biscuits and coffee," the guide was saying.

Sulle caught movement on the edge of his vision. He was

completely unprepared for the plateful of food that slammed into his face with enough force to make him stagger backward.

"You can't hold me prisoner here!" Molly shouted. She turned to the gaping audience. "Help me. Please help me. This man is holding me here against my will," she protested.

Sulle wiped the food from his face and controlled the urge to shake Molly. Hard. Instead, he swept her into his arms. "Oh, darling, the doctor said you might have another attack." He kissed her forehead as he held her, pinioning her with his strong arms and whispering savagely into her ear. "Settle down, Molly, or you'll regret it."

Before she could respond, he carried her across the room. "I'll call the doctor," he said, playing to the tourists. "You're my heart and soul. Surely we can find a way to help you back to sanity."

To loud applause, Sulle rushed up the stairs with Molly in his arms.

"Open the door," he commanded Jorge as he got to the top of the third stairwell.

Jorge opened the door and Sulle carried Molly into the room. He kicked the door closed behind him and carried her to the bed.

Pushing her down into the soft comforter, he held her shoulders as she gave him a defiant green stare. The impulse to spank her vanished, and Sulle found himself in the grip of another, more powerful compulsion.

She was breathing through parted lips, her eyes flashing.

"Go ahead. Do your worst," she challenged.

It was the last straw. Sulle's discipline slipped. He kissed her with a passion that he hadn't felt in eight long years. At first he didn't care that she wasn't responding. Until he felt her mouth begin to open, her tongue to welcome him. And then he knew that no matter what else happened between them, for this moment in time, he was lost to her.

Chapter Four

Molly didn't trust a single thing she thought. She felt like Alice—fallen through the looking glass into a world where nothing was as it seemed.

Her first impulse had been to bite Sulle, to do some physical damage to him that would force him back and away.

And then his lips had closed on hers, and despite the terror of Alan's disappearance and her fury at Sulle for making her a prisoner after eight years of silence, she felt herself responding to his kiss.

It was not the response of a sane woman. Nonetheless, she could not deny herself the pleasure of his kiss. Eight years. Certainly she'd kissed other men in that time, but none had kindled the blue-hot flame that only Sulle could ignite. And she'd given up hope that she would ever taste his kiss or feel his touch again.

Yet here he was, over her, in a bed that seemed to be part of a fantasy world.

Her arms moved up to his shoulders, and her fingers found his hair. It still had the same thick, luxurious texture that she remembered.

His mouth moved over her chin and down her neck, slowly working the delicate flesh that made her quiver at his touch. The beautiful gown was low cut, and the corset pushed her breasts up so that they mounded at the top of her neckline. As Sulle's lips began to explore that territory, Molly admitted to herself that she was lost to all reason.

She felt his fingers at the small buttons of her gown and she wanted him to hurry. Her own hands began to work open the buttons of the brocade waistcoat he wore. Her lips curved into a smile, a soft chuckle escaping, as she wondered how Southerners had ever survived the heat—of summer or of passion—wearing so damn many clothes.

Sulle's head lifted. "This amuses you?" he asked with that old familiar teasing glint in his eye. His fingers dipped into the neckline of her gown. "What should I do to make you take me seriously?"

Molly was unprepared for the surge of emotion she felt for this man. He had disappeared from her life, leaving her to raise his child all alone. Had allowed her to believe him dead for eight years. And yet… "Sulle," she whispered.

The buttons of the dress popped and fell into the plush comforter as he tugged at the material, releasing her from the tight confines of the garment. But the corset she wore was an even more formidable barrier.

"How did you get into this thing?" he asked as he fought with the strings that tied the heavy material and whalebone. At last he untangled the knots and freed her.

For a long moment he looked down at her, and Molly felt as if she would catch fire from his gaze. She reached up to him, but he resisted, his hand skimming over her body.

"You're even lovelier," he said. "I tried to convince myself that I'd imagined you. That I'd turned you into a fantasy that no flesh-and-blood woman could ever live up to. The truth is the opposite. My memory didn't do you justice."

Molly felt the question rise to her lips, but she didn't ask it. The last eight years had taught her the consequences of romantic foolishness. This time, when she accepted Sulle Alamar into her bed, she would have no expectations of tomorrow or the next day. No foolish dreams that what they shared could last longer than the moment. But it was enough.

She rose to her knees and reached out to him, unbuttoning his clothes as fast as she could and helping him shed them on the floor. There were traces of breakfast on his coat, and she hid her smile.

When his chest was bare she ran her hands over the sculpted muscles. He had changed. He was a mature man now, not the young man of the desert.

She pulled him down to her, wanting only to make the connection that would tie them to the past, would somehow anchor her to something familiar, would give her hope that this man might save her child.

A knock came at the bedroom door, sharp and commanding.

She felt Sulle tense.

The knock came again. "Sulle, we've made contact." Jorge's voice was filled with excitement and tension.

Sulle slowly stood, his hand sweeping the floor for his clothes.

Molly sat up, clutching the skirt of her dress to her chest and watched him. "It's Alan, isn't it?"

Sulle nodded. "My men have found something." He turned to go to the door.

Molly was out of bed and across the room in a flash. She backed against the door. "You're not leaving me here," she said. She could feel the hammering of her heart. "Alan needs me." But even as she spoke she could see that the passion in Sulle's eyes had been replaced by hard resolve.

"You can best help by staying here," Sulle said. He tucked in his shirt. "They tried to abduct you, Molly. You're safe here at Beau Monde. This place is like a fortress and no one would ever think to look for you here." The coldness thawed for a moment. "Not even your magazine."

Molly acknowledged the truth with a twist of her mouth. If she didn't check in with her magazine, they'd begin to wonder, and to worry, and to phone the authorities. "I don't care about the magazine. I care about my son."

The expression in Sulle's dark eyes seemed to soften. "Our son," he said gently.

Molly knew in that moment that Sulle would do whatever he had to do to save Alan. But it wasn't enough. She was his mother, the parent who'd raised him for seven years. Alan loved her, and he would be afraid and would want her.

"I'm not staying here," she said, not hiding her defiance.

"You don't trust me to save him, do you?" Sulle asked the question with some objectivity, but she knew him well enough not to be fooled by the dead calm of his expression. She saw the twitch of muscle at the corner of his mouth.

"It isn't a matter of trust. I want to be there."

She was surprised when his hand came up and caressed her face. It was an unexpected gesture of tenderness, something the younger Sulle might not have done.

"I'll return him to you safely," he said. "It would have been better if I'd never known he was my flesh."

His words, and the cool delivery of them, were as sharp as a stiletto. Before she could recover from their cruelty, Sulle had slipped through the door. The lock clicked into place and she heard his footsteps departing down the hallway.

SULLE PUSHED Molly's pale face and pained green eyes from his memory as he set a brisk pace for the limping Jorge. "Where is he?" he asked.

"He's still in the city. They're holding him captive in one of the better sections in town. It's an area that gives them a lot of advantages."

"What does Lolahta want?" Sulle asked.

"He hasn't named a ransom."

Sulle almost stopped, but he kept moving, down the servants' stairs and out into the morning heat. Outside the air-conditioned plantation house, the humidity was impossibly thick. The air felt liquid. "How do people live here?" he asked Jorge.

"They ask the same question of our home," Jorge answered.

Sulle nodded, remembering again the hot desert days and the cold nights. But that conjured up another image of Molly, her hair a nimbus of fine chestnut silk in the candlelight of a tent. She was sitting on him and leaning forward, her mouth preparing for the kiss that was in her eyes.

"Sulle?" Jorge asked. "You okay?"

He shook his head. "How did Kary find them?"

"He has some contacts among the dock workers. Lolahta has been in New Orleans a long time. He's grown incautious. His men are too casual and easily identified, and his shipping business is well-known among men who make it their business to know who's bringing illegal goods into the country."

Sulle got into the car and started the motor. "Does Kary think this is going to endanger the mission?"

Jorge was silent a moment. "Although no ransom demand has come in, it's obvious Lolahta believes he can use the boy to force a better deal." He shrugged. "Except for the danger the boy is in, and the pressure that it puts on you to protect him, I don't see how it's harmed the mission."

Sulle gave a nod, and a tight smile played across his handsome features. "But Lolahta has an edge on me now, one no man has ever been able to attain." He didn't have to be more specific. Jorge knew about his past, the murder of his family as a form of political revenge. Jorge had grown up in the same small desert village and had known the Alamar family. Since that time Sulle had allowed no one to come close to him, and Jorge knew the reason why. Sulle—

and the rest of the organization—could operate far more effectively when there was no one or nothing that an opponent could use for blackmail.

"The woman only claims that he's your son," Jorge said, trying to inject a note of doubt.

Sulle shook his head. "Eight years ago, Molly tried to contact me. She left messages with the people I'd been working for. Messages that I understand now. She tried to tell me, and when I didn't answer, she assumed, rightly, that I didn't want to be involved with her. So she took on the burden of raising the child without a father. The child is mine." He maneuvered the car around a sharp curve in the winding road that followed the deep currents of the Mississippi River.

Jorge reached across the seat and touched Sulle's arm. "The boy is dangerous to you only if you allow him to be."

Sulle nodded. There was hard truth in those simple words. It was only the idea that Alan was his flesh that gave him a connection. He'd never laid eyes on the child. And there were thousands of children who would suffer and die if he didn't stop Victor Lolahta from shipping chemicals to the Middle East. He had to stay focused.

But he knew that his entire world had changed. Walking away from Molly had been emotionally the hardest thing he'd ever done. Their relationship had been brief, but intense and passionate. He'd never doubted that he had grown to love her. There had been women in his life, and he had cared for them, but never with the intensity of his love for Molly. And now she was back in his life, the danger of his feelings for her more real than ever before.

And she had brought with her his son. Alan. Sulle wondered if she'd remembered that his favorite older brother had been named Alan. He'd told her stories of his childhood, of the handsome young man who'd carried him on his shoulders and taught him to survive in the sparse landscape surrounding his village. Those skills had saved his life after the murder of his family. Her choice of name had to be deliberate. And it touched his heart with raw pain.

Jorge spoke softly, his voice almost lost in the whir of the tires on the asphalt as they hurtled toward New Orleans. "Our biggest advantage has always been our willingness to risk all, Sulle. If you go into this meeting and show even a hint that the boy means something to you, you'll lose him and everything else."

Sulle's immediate reaction was anger. The fact that what Jorge said was the truth made him angry. Beyond the anger was reason. "I know," he said. "I'm worried."

"I can meet with Lolahta."

Sulle felt a rush of emotion for his lifelong friend. "Your leg is wounded. You'd be at a disadvantage if you needed to move fast."

"Your heart is wounded," Jorge said with a sad smile. "I believe your wound is far more dangerous."

Sulle laughed softly. "You were always the poet. No-wonder the women prefer you."

"I was always a second choice, because you seldom saw the women who wanted you. Your eyes were already filled with a green-eyed tigress."

Sulle laughed out loud. "Molly. I never thought to see her again."

"You've done your best to avoid her," Jorge agreed. He sighed. "Perhaps we should consider retiring. Once this is over and your son is safe…"

Sulle knew that Jorge was planting seeds of the inevitable. Since Lolahta knew of Alan and Molly, all of his enemies would soon know. Retirement was a nice way of saying he'd be forced from the international game once his enemies were aware of the powerful weapon that could be used against him.

Sulle changed the subject. "Did Kary mention a plan to

rescue...the boy?'' He had to put some distance between himself and Alan or he would never be able to function effectively.

"Now that we know the location, you should call Lolahta and set up a meeting. Even though he knows about the woman and the boy, he still believes you to be an international broker in biochemicals. He wants those deadly agents to sell. Kary and I believe he'll use the boy to try to get a better price, so we believe we must force the meeting as soon as possible. The more time he has to prepare, the more dangerous it will be for us.''

"And I must not indicate that Alan is worth even a percentage point.'' Sulle knew he spoke the truth.

In the grim silence, Sulle picked up the cell phone and dialed a number. The man who answered spoke pleasantly with a hint of a foreign accent. "Hello.''

"Tell Victor I'm on Canal Street,'' Sulle said briskly. "I want a meeting in ten minutes at a place of his choice. I have another buyer for my shipment of goods.''

"And he has something he wants to trade,'' the man almost purred. "A smart little boy, that one. Worth a lot, I'd guess.''

"Worth nothing,'' Sulle answered coldly. "Trade him back to his mother. She has some excellent photographs, something to decorate your home.''

There was silence. "Mr. Lolahta is not a man to be toyed with,'' the accent said.

"And I'm not a man to be blackmailed,'' Sulle answered. "You have nine minutes left. If I don't receive a call by then, I'll sell to the other buyer.'' He hung up the phone before he could change his mind.

MOLLY RETIED THE CORSET, fuming at the idea that Sulle had left her. The dress she settled over her head and shoulders was made from yards of lightweight muslin, a beautiful dress of white, patterned with lavender and mint.

She had tried pounding on the doors, begging, telling the passing tourists outside her chambers that her son had been kidnapped, that she was being held prisoner. Just as Sulle had said, no one believed her. Her frantic attempts to gain help had only garnered applause.

"She's terrific," she'd heard more than one tourist say as they continued on the tour.

"Damn." She tapped politely on the door. "I have my costume on," she said sweetly. "I'd like to go downstairs."

The door opened immediately and a man she didn't recognize smiled at her. He was a tall, muscled redhead who also wore a costume. He fell into step beside her, offering his arm as if he were a planter and she a belle. It was almost more than she could force herself to do to take his arm and smile up at him. But if she wasn't willing to go along with the game, she'd end up stuck in her room for the rest of the day—and she intended to escape the plantation and somehow get into the city.

She passed another group of tourists and felt her heart beat harder. Where there were tourists, there was a bus. And she forced herself to concentrate on that so she wouldn't think about her child. Or her anger at herself.

Once again she'd fallen victim to Sulle's charms. After eight years she'd acted like the naive twenty-one-year-old girl who'd welcomed him into her bed without asking a sensible question.

He was gone again, and she didn't know who had her son or why Alan had been abducted—except that he was a bargaining chip to be used against Sulle in whatever game of international intrigue he was playing.

Just as she would have been, if she'd been taken.

Which was exactly her plan.

She'd get into New Orleans, make it known that she was

looking for her son, and then allow the men who'd taken Alan to catch her. At least she'd be with him and be able to protect him.

That it would throw a kink in Sulle's plans was beside the point. Had he cared to share his plans with her, she might have been more understanding. As it was, she had to take care of Alan, just as she'd done since the day he was born.

She descended the staircase on the arm of the man who guarded her. Liam was his name.

"How do you know Sulle?" she asked sweetly as they crossed into the parlor where another cluster of tourists squealed with delight at the sight of them.

"We work for the same purpose," Liam said guardedly.

"And that would be?"

"Peace," he said simply. "I come from a land that's seen enough tragedy, as has he."

She detected his accent then, a slight brogue. "Do you know where Sulle is now?" she asked.

"In the city." Liam looked down at her and smiled. "You won't escape me, Miss Lynch. Your questions may satisfy your curiosity, but it won't put you any closer to the action. Sulle wants you here, and here you'll stay."

She only smiled, but in her mind she was determined to show him that she was not so easily thwarted.

They strolled through the house and out onto the front porch. "I'd love to see the gardens," she said, hoping that would take them by the place where the tour buses parked. There would also be private cars. Out of the corner of her eye she saw the black cat slip out behind them. He was stalking them, and Molly felt a rush of gratitude to the feline.

"As you wish," Liam answered, leading the way.

The estate was magnificent, and even in her agitation Molly could appreciate its beauty. Far off in the fields she heard the sound of singing as the delicate cane plants were hoed and tended, all by hand.

"This would be a fascinating place," she said, "if I weren't being held here as a prisoner."

They had made it to the rear of the garden when she spotted a modern brick structure tucked in a grove of pecan trees. Beside the building were three charter buses and at least twenty cars. She had hit pay dirt.

"There's a water fountain over there. I'd like a drink," she said.

"We're not supposed to go past the garden," Liam said amiably, "but a drink wouldn't hurt. But I think it's the buses that have drawn your interest, rather than the water."

His amusement made her angry, but Molly knew when to hold her tongue. She went to the fountain and drank deeply, examining the buses and vehicles from beneath her lowered lashes. This was the way to escape, if she could only shake her watchdog.

"Meow!"

She understood completely and bent down to pick Familiar up. "He's a brilliant animal," she told Liam.

"Aye, cats are smart," he agreed, but took no particular notice of Familiar. He was watching the vehicles with a cool speculation, his hand resting easily on a bulge under his jacket.

Molly felt a chill. Liam was making sure that no one around them meant to harm her. He was there as much to protect her as he was to guard her. Her life could be in danger, as could his because he chose to follow Sulle and guard her.

She whispered softly into Familiar's ear. "He's a nice man, don't hurt him too badly, but we need to make an escape. We have to find Alan."

When she looked up at Liam, she took a breath. Without any warning Familiar leaped onto the man. Liam was so startled he stumbled and Molly stuck out a leg and tripped him. He hit the ground hard, the breath rushing out of him in a whoosh.

Molly picked up a drink bottle a tourist had left and brought it down hard on Liam's red hair.

"Sorry," she said as she rushed toward one of the cars. The tourist had climbed in, started it and then gotten out to retrieve her playing child.

"Sorry," Molly said again under her breath as she slid behind the wheel, the hoop skirt threatening to spring over her head. She forced the skirt into submission as the cat leaped into the passenger seat. She put the car in reverse and burned rubber as she tore away from the tourist center and headed for New Orleans.

Chapter Five

Sulle walked into the dimly lit restaurant and paused long enough to allow his eyes to adjust. All the tables were empty except for one in the back. An elegant, white-haired man sat there, alone, napkin tucked in his collar and a plate of barbecued shrimp before him.

"Mr. Alamar," the man said, rising and removing the napkin to reveal an expensive suit. "Please join me. The shrimp here are excellent. A messy dish, but well worth the trouble. I keep a residence in New Orleans strictly for the pleasure of its food."

Sulle took the indicated chair and watched as Victor Lolahta resumed his seat, retucked his napkin and began to peel one of the shrimp.

"Your son is a very precocious young man. It's a shame he believes you to be dead." Victor bit into the four-inch shrimp.

"I'm not a man who enjoys mixing business and relatives," Sulle said in a tone that could not be misunderstood.

"You don't seem to want to mix with your relations at all," Victor replied, pushing the platter of shrimp toward Sulle. "Eat. Once you taste this dish you'll have to return here at least once a year."

"I have the material you want. The only question we must settle is if you're willing to pay the market price for it.'' Sulle sat back in his chair, ignoring the food. ''If you aren't, I have another buyer. I do you the honor of giving you first choice. And I know the boy will be returned to his mother, whatever we should decide to do in our *business* negotiations.''

''That's an interesting assumption,'' Lolahta said, peeling another shrimp and biting into the tender pink morsel. ''And very wrong.''

Sulle had his feelings under tight control, but he felt a wave of anger. He struggled to master it. ''How unfortunate for the boy, then,'' he said, rising. ''You know my price. I'm tired of games, Mr. Lolahta. I have business in other parts of the world. I will call you to set up the exchange. The materials are on a ship, already crated and with false papers that approve them for export. Except for the necessary transfer to an oceangoing vessel, we've done all of the work. You have only to buy the goods and sell them for a handsome profit.''

Victor nodded. ''Why is it that you don't sell them yourself?'' he asked in a casual tone. ''Why are you willing to share the profit with a middleman?''

''Long ago, when I was younger, I was forced to take action against some political factions in the Middle East. If I should happen to return there and be apprehended, my life would end in a very unpleasant way.''

''Ah, so you retaliated against those who killed your family,'' Lolahta said, ''and with typical Middle Eastern temper, you let it be known you'd retaliated.'' He nodded. ''Your pride works to my advantage in this case.''

Sulle gave a tight smile. ''I'm not a greedy man. I demand a certain profit, but I don't mind others dipping into the pie.''

Lolahta stared at him. ''Where is Ms. Lynch?''

Sulle shrugged.

''Her disappearance—and her son's—is all over the papers and television. Her employer is making a very big noise. It has brought scrutiny to my city, which I do not enjoy.''

''I have no hand in this,'' Sulle said.

''I don't believe you're telling the truth,'' Victor said with a wolfish smile. ''You have the woman and I have the child. In my younger days, I would have preferred the woman. But the child amuses me. He has told me many interesting things. As I said he's very precocious and quite accomplished in mathematics and computers.''

''Perhaps you should keep him. You have no son of your own,'' Sulle pointed out in a move that was guaranteed to anger Lolahta.

''You have no regard for him at all?'' Lolahta asked.

''None. I have never laid eyes on him. I never knew he existed, and should he cease to do so, it will leave no void in my life.'' Sulle stared directly into Lolahta's eyes.

''You're a cold man,'' Victor said.

''Remember that,'' Sulle said, rising. ''I will be in touch to name a place of exchange. Your money for the transfer of ownership papers for the cargo. The ship will sail by 10:00 a.m. tomorrow, and someone else will own the cargo. Whether it is you or my other buyer, I don't care. Just remember, if that Lynch woman isn't found soon, they may begin searching the docks. We both have things we'd prefer were not found, Victor. Make your decision and make it fast.''

Sulle stood up and walked out of the restaurant without looking back. He didn't have to. He knew that men had stepped out of the shadows and that the muzzles of their guns were trained on his head and spine.

I'VE RIDDEN with some wild drivers, but Molly Lynch is a danger behind the wheel of a car. I hope the owner of this little Mustang has good insurance. We've made it into the city limits, and soon she's going to have to stop.

Jeez, we're going back to the apartment. Not the smartest move, but one I understand. Yes, P-n-C's abduction is news. There's crime tape up all over her building. Hold on. She's a resourceful woman and is going to the alley to use the fire escape. All I can say is that I'm probably going to have to make Eleanor start taking me to the gym. In my younger days I could leap and tumble and run with the best of them. But I'm feeling a little stiff today. No matter. I'm following P-n-C up the fire escape and into the window of her old apartment.

Ah, so now I see. She's dragging a laptop computer out of a neat little hiding spot in the closet. I'm surprised that Sulle's men missed it, but Molly is delighted with this turn of events. She's opening her E-mail. Technology at its most provocative. And she's gasping and beginning to cry. I suppose I'd better check out what's got her cranked up now.

MOLLY HADN'T DARED to hope for a message from Alan, so when she saw it she was overwhelmed with relief and terror. The note was hurried.

Mama,
Three men have taken me. I don't know where I am, but I am not hurt and they are treating me very well. I hope they didn't hurt Pauline when they tied her up. The man who has me is named Victor, and he has talked to me a lot. I got him to let me use the computer to play games, and I'm afraid they'll find I know how to E-mail. We are still in New Orleans, I do know that. It's an old building with tall white columns outside, big gardens, but I can't go into them. And a streetcar runs by the front of the house. People walk on the sidewalks, and there are many big trees. I can also hear

a church bell tolling the hours. Every hour, even at night. I'm not so afraid, Mama, but I want you to come and get me. I will listen and look and try to send more clues. Please come soon. I haven't cried.

Love, Alan

Though her son had not wept, Molly could not stop her tears. He was such a brave boy. And so smart. She noted the E-mail address and then hurriedly typed out a note to the magazine stating that she was fine. Before she could send it, she heard a noise at the window she'd entered.

She immediately shut down the computer and picked up a piece of Alan's clothing.

The blond head of the governess appeared in the window, her expression changing from grim determination to shock when she saw Molly. Pauline climbed in as Molly had.

"You're here! Every policeman in New Orleans is looking for you," Pauline said. "I've been worried sick. Have you found Alan?" She did a double take at the antebellum dress. "Where did you get that outfit?"

Molly brushed her tears aside. "No, I haven't found Alan, and the dress is part of a disguise," she said. "What are you doing here?" she asked. "I thought you went back to Maryland."

"I couldn't leave without knowing you and Alan are safe. Where have you been?" Pauline asked, her eyes red with worry and her makeup smudged. "I've been hunting everywhere for you."

Molly hesitated. "They had me, but I got away from them," she said. "We have to find Alan. Can you tell me anything about the men?"

Pauline bit her lip. "It all happened so fast, and they knocked me out. When you disappeared, I had to tell the police. They questioned me for hours." She sniffled.

"Where could Alan be? Where could he be?" Her question ended on a wail.

Molly went to the younger woman and hugged her tight. "We'll find him, Pauline. We'll find him and then we'll leave this city."

"Have you any plans?" Pauline asked, wiping her eyes.

Once again Molly hesitated. "I need to contact the magazine and let them know I'm okay."

"Everyone has been searching for you," Pauline agreed. "I spoke with Mr. Briggs, and he was terribly worried. I told him a lot of your things had disappeared, including your cameras." She took a breath. "Did they take your film and everything?"

"My equipment is replaceable," Molly said quickly. "Alan is not." She got up and began looking around the apartment.

"What do you need?" Pauline asked. "Tell me something to do to help."

"I need a streetcar schedule," Molly said.

"Why?" Pauline's face showed puzzlement.

Molly started to tell the truth, but she stopped herself. If Pauline figured out what she was doing, she would try to prevent her. So would Sulle. "It's a long story, Pauline. Too long to go into. Find me the schedule, please. I want to change into something else."

Before the governess could ask another question, Molly picked up shorts and a blouse, two of the few items left in her bedroom, and began the process of getting out of the dress.

"Sure," Pauline said, handing over a streetcar schedule. "I'll come with you."

"No," Molly said. "Stay here, in case Alan calls."

Pauline nodded. "Where can I get in touch with you?"

"I'll be back," Molly promised. She slipped into the casual clothes. "The rent is paid here for another week. If there're any problems, call Mr. Briggs at the magazine. Tell him to extend the rent until I contact him."

"Okay," Pauline agreed with some hesitation. "At least tell me what you're planning. I'll be worried sick."

Molly patted her shoulder. "I'm a lot smarter than any of them believe. I'll be fine." She looked at Pauline's purse. "I could use some cash and a credit card. I'll pay you back."

Pauline dug in her purse and came out with the requested items. "I only have the money you gave me for groceries."

"Thanks." Molly climbed out the window. "If anyone asks, you haven't seen me."

"Not even the police?" Pauline asked nervously.

"Especially not the police." Molly jumped onto the fire escape and climbed down into the street that was sweltering with midday heat.

SULLE PACED the plush carpet of the hotel room that gave a spectacular view of the Mississippi River and the busy tourist places that comprised the Riverwalk.

When the telephone rang, he snatched it up. "Yes?"

"Sulle, it's Liam. She got away."

Sulle's knuckles tightened on the phone. "How did this happen?" he asked. His first reaction was to lash out at his man, but he knew Liam too well to believe it was negligence on his part that allowed Molly to escape.

"It's hard to explain. There was a black cat. He attacked me and then she tripped me and knocked me out. She took a car from the tourist center."

Sulle had a terrible vision of Molly forcing her way into danger.

"I'm afraid she headed for the city," Liam admitted. "She asked where you were and that's what I said. I never dreamed a woman could get the best of me. I'm sorry on all accounts."

"Molly Lynch isn't an ordinary woman," Sulle answered. "I should have given you better warning."

"I'm headed back," Liam said. "I'll find her, and she won't have a chance to trick me again."

"Come on in," Sulle said, replacing the phone and looking at Jorge.

"Don't tell me she's on the loose," Jorge said, but there was a hint of appreciation in his eyes. "She's a tigress, Sulle. Whatever else happens, I wouldn't discount this woman. You may have found your match."

"I've found another worry," he said. "The exchange is set tonight on the river. The landing at Beau Monde was a brilliant idea. If she shows up there, she could ruin everything and endanger the boy as well as herself."

"Lolahta isn't to be trusted, on any account," Jorge warned him. "If he knew we had the woman, he'd kill the boy outright."

"I know." Sulle took a long breath. "You've contacted the federal authorities?"

"They'll be in position."

"Then we've done all we can do. We must wait until dark when we meet with Victor." Sulle began to pace the room again, and then went to stand at the window. It was going to be one of the longest days of his life.

MOLLY WIPED the sweat from her forehead and leaned back against the wooden seat of the streetcar. This was her fifth ride, and she was beginning to lose hope that she could find a location that contained the clues Alan had sent her. She felt the tears threaten—her son was trying so hard to help. She closed her eyes and concentrated on the babble of voices around her.

Even in the ninety-degree-plus heat, the residents of New Orleans kept up lively chatter and rich laughter. Alan would love riding the streetcars, she thought.

The St. Charles car made a slow turn and all at once she found herself headed down a boulevard that was lined with huge houses set back on lawns filled with trees hung with Spanish moss. She felt the skin on her neck prickle. She was getting close. She knew it. Her boy was somewhere nearby.

The streetcar rocked down the street. At stops people got on and off, and Molly felt her certainty grow. Alan was close. The houses got larger, the yards worthy of an estate. The car had stopped to collect an elderly woman dressed in an elegant style when Molly heard the church bell toll.

The rich, somber tones of the bell marked the hour at noon, and by the time it finished, Molly was on the sidewalk rushing toward a house that was set back far from the street. It was a massive structure with huge white columns supporting a portico.

The limestone house was surrounded by beautiful grounds and what looked like a park in the back. Molly halted her forward assault and forced herself to consider her options. If Alan was in there, she didn't want to do anything stupid that would endanger him. Yet she meant to be with him.

She examined the yard and gave her options careful thought. If Alan could see the garden in the back, see the streetcar, and hear the church bell, it stood to reason he was being held in one of the upstairs, corner rooms.

But which one? She hadn't a clue. And she couldn't afford to make a mistake. Finally, she chose the northeast window because an ivy vine offered her access to the second-floor windows. As she started up the vine, she realized how dangerous her position was. Guards could be watching and reporting her arrival even now. But her son's safety was far more important than her own. She kept climbing.

As she reached the second-floor window, she peeked over the ledge into a spacious room. Her gaze swept over the neatly made bed and finally settled on the young boy sitting with his head bent at a desk. Molly felt a rush of love that made her tighten her hold on the vines. "Alan," she whispered.

She forced her gaze away from him and checked the rest of the room. He was alone!

She tapped lightly at the window and almost cried out as he looked up, saw her and rushed to the window. Together they forced it open enough so that she could crawl in.

"Mom!" Alan ran into her arms and hugged her so tight that she gasped.

"Are you hurt?" she asked.

"I'm okay." He glanced toward the door and put a finger to his lips. "There's a man outside the door. Be quiet."

Molly knelt by Alan. She forced herself to be calm, confident. They had so little time.

"Alan, I think we can climb down the vine outside the window," she whispered. "We can get away." For the first time in two days, she felt her hope rising.

"It's a long way down," Alan said, his face showing his fear of heights. He looked at her with terrified eyes. "I can't do it, Mom. I can't."

"Sure you can. We can do it together," Molly reassured him. She was too close to saving him to allow anything to stand in her way. She kept talking, soothing him, leading him closer to the window. "I can't believe our luck that they haven't sealed the windows. We're going to get out of here."

Alan's face registered his own small hope. "Can we?"

"Sure. Like I said, we'll do it together. You know anything we try together, we can do."

"Of course we can," Alan answered, his voice firmer.

Molly felt more than heard the bedroom door swing open. She looked up into the face of an elegant older man.

"Ms. Lynch, how nice of you to join us," he said as if she'd stopped by for tea. "I knew you wouldn't be able to resist joining your son. That's why we allowed him to E-mail you on the computer.''

Molly looked back at the window and realized with a sinking heart that she'd been a complete fool. They'd let her get to Alan. She'd left Beau Monde with a plan of getting caught by Alan's captors. Now that she had, she realized the stupidity of that action.

And even worse, she might have left a trail for Sulle that would guarantee his death.

Chapter Six

Sulle swallowed the last bite of the crab po'boy, too stressed and worried to enjoy the rare treat. He walked out on the balcony of his hotel room and stared out at the busy Mississippi River. New Orleans was swarming with tourists. It was a city where someone could easily get lost. And that was what Molly had done.

Where was she? What was she doing?

When his mind should be on setting up the perfect trap for Victor Lolahta, a major player in the underground world of illegal weapons trading, he was worried about a woman. Sulle knew that his lack of focus could cost many lives, including Molly's and his son's.

''Hey, Sulle, there's a special delivery for you,'' Jorge said, bringing the packet out on the balcony. ''Come inside.''

Sulle took the letter that had been delivered by courier and glanced at it. There was no return address. Dread touched his heart. It was in this type of package that men received the worst news.

He ripped it open and pulled out the single sheet of paper and the Polaroid snapshot. He didn't need to read the letter. The photo told it all. Molly and Alan stood against a large window that gave a view of magnificent grounds. She was holding a copy of a newspaper that was clearly the most recent issue of the *Times Picayune*. Molly's disappearance was headlined in the paper.

Molly had been taken as a hostage. She had gone straight from Beau Monde into the hands of the enemy. Sulle wordlessly handed the photo to Jorge.

"Damn," his friend said under his breath.

Sulle read the demands. Victor Lolahta would release the woman and the child if the ship with the cargo of chemicals was turned over to him without any strings attached. There would be no money exchanged. The hostages for the biochemicals. Lolahta would call with a new meeting place.

Sulle handed Jorge the letter and waited for him to read it.

"What are you going to do?" Jorge asked.

"I don't know," Sulle answered slowly. "I won't risk Molly or my son."

Jorge's smile was tight and slow to come. "I'd already guessed that much. What should I do about the feds? They aren't going to want to cancel this deal. They've been trying to nail Lolahta for years."

"Call them and tell them the deal is off. Tell them Lolahta got cold feet and we'll work with him to reschedule in three days."

Jorge put a hand on Sulle's arm. "You might need those agents, Sulle. There's only me and Kary and Liam. You're going to need more backup if you intend to take Lolahta on. He has a small army."

Sulle's face was bleak. "I'll give him the chemicals, if it comes down to it."

Jorge's eyebrows drew together. "I know you care for this woman. It's obvious to everyone. And the boy, he's your son. But think, Sulle. Think of the thousands who'll suffer and die if these chemicals are used as weapons. Think!"

Sulle turned angrily away. "You ask too much of me,

Jorge. My life is mine to risk. But not Molly's. Not Alan's. I can't allow them to die, no matter the consequences.''

''The others are innocent, too,'' Jorge said softly.

Sulle whirled on him, anger flashing. ''You ask the impossible.'' He stalked out the door, slamming it as hard as he could.

I NEED A TELEPHONE and a platter of crusted mahi-mahi. Something with horseradish. And a bowl of chilled cream. This heat is killing me. No wonder Southern gentlemen chose white linen suits. Black, though always stylish and classic, is a little hot for this climate.

I checked the hotel where Eleanor and Peter were staying, but they weren't in the room. I left a little kitty paw print in the middle of Eleanor's book, so she'll know I've been there and gone. I'm positive they'll remain in New Orleans until they recover me.

They aren't extremely happy with me, but what else is new? Once they discover that I'm on the trail of a worldwide weapons dealer who has been involved in nefarious plots in every trouble spot in the world, they'll be a little forgiving.

Far more forgiving than I should be toward Molly P-n-C Lynch. And I thought journalists were supposed to have some sixth sense that warned them of a trap. She went right up that vine and into that house without a thought that no one would leave a young boy with such an easy means of escape. I mean, the entire scenario screamed setup to me.

I would have stopped P-n-C, except for one thing. She'll be more useful inside Victor Lolahta's operation than outside. And she will give Alan some comfort. He is an extraordinary little boy, and children aren't my favorite life-form.

So with this rescue attempt, P-n-C has moved into the place I want her. Now to see if the mysterious Sulle Alamar will also be so agreeable.

He won't risk the woman or the boy. I saw his face when he looked at P-n-C. He's more deeply in love with her than anyone will ever know. For a man who's lost everything, she is his chosen love. Even if he has denied it to himself for all of these years.

The trick to this tense little situation is to keep P-n-C and Alan safe and put Lolahta behind bars. My objective is clear, but it's the getting there that's a little troubling.

If humans weren't so unreliable, this would be much easier. But for every direct course, there are a million indirect ones. And humanoids seem to love those twists and turns. It has to do with bipedism—my word. Standing upright and balancing on two legs has messed up the neural pathways in the humanoid brain.

But give credit where credit is due—love that prehensile thumb!

Of course an elegant tail would add a lot of character, not to mention balance, but that's something they'll never have.

Time to move to a new place to set up my watch. The sun has shifted and my shade is fast disappearing. Thank goodness Victor Lolahta has a fondness for trees. Otherwise I think I might faint from the heat.

I do feel that I'm going to deserve a very large compensation for all of this work. I hope the U.S. government isn't opposed to making out a check to a black feline who simply refuses to have a social-security number. I'm thinking of at least six digits.

Ah, and right on schedule, here comes Mr. Tall, Dark and Handsome. He obviously knows P-n-C is now a hostage, and he's come to save her.

Of course he's going to need my help, which is why I've been sitting here waiting.

SULLE TUCKED the cell phone back in his pocket and made sure his gun was in the holster under his arm. He would have no chance to use it, but it would add authenticity to his plan.

It had taken him several phone calls to locate Victor's residence, a magnificent home purchased under one of his many pseudonyms. Sulle's plan had many holes, but he had to believe that it would take him to Molly and Alan.

He scouted the perimeter. He was only slightly shocked when the black cat came out from under an azalea bush and meowed at him. The cat had an amazing ability to show up everywhere Molly went. He was like her guardian angel—only black and without wings.

"So Molly is here," he said to the cat.

"Meow," the cat answered, golden eyes blinking.

"And you are guarding her."

"Meow," the cat agreed.

He scratched the cat's ears and knelt to whisper to him. When he stood up, the cat gazed at him with keen intelligence. "Meow."

"Let's go, then," Sulle said, darting across the lawn as he moved from cover to cover. He immediately saw the half-open window and the ivy. It was clear that Molly had found her son and a way into the house—and that was how she'd been captured.

He was aware that more than likely he was walking into a trap, but he also knew he had no choice. He rushed the house and started up the vine. He climbed fast, and in less than a minute he was scrambling over the sill.

He heard a sharp intake of breath and then he saw Molly. Standing behind her was a man with a gun, the barrel trained right at his heart.

"Mr. Lolahta has been expecting you," the man said with a smile. He twisted his fingers in Molly's hair and used the gun to motion Sulle into the room. "Toss your gun over here."

"I'm sorry," Molly said. She reached out to him but the man prevented her from moving closer.

"Where's Alan?" Sulle asked. He removed the gun and pushed it across the floor to the guard, who kicked it away to the far side of the room.

"Mr. Lolahta has taken him to the zoo," the man said with a cruel smile. "He likes the boy. Perhaps he'll keep him for his own."

A sob escaped Molly and Sulle saw that his haphazard plan had already begun to fall apart. He'd counted on Molly and Alan being together. If they were separated, he didn't have a chance of saving them both. He could never allow Molly or the man to see his concern, though.

"I'm certain the boy will enjoy the zoo," Sulle said, dusting his hands. He tried to signal Molly with a look but failed to catch her eye. "So I suppose we'll wait for his return." He motioned out the window. "It's a hot day. Could we have some water?"

"Certainly," the man replied. "And a cool place to stay." He pushed Molly toward the door. "Go on, and if you make one small move, I'll shoot you both."

"I have no doubt you will," Sulle said as he walked to Molly. He touched her shoulder briefly, hoping that he could communicate to her that all was not lost.

"Down the stairs," the gunman ordered. "Through the kitchen."

When they'd made their way across the large, empty kitchen, the guard opened the door to an old icehouse.

"There is no escape," he said, "but entertain yourself trying to get out if you like. If I were you, though, I'd make my last hours count." He laughed as he pushed them down the stairs and into the darkness of the unused room.

Sulle heard the door slam and a heavy bolt shoot into place.

THE ICEHOUSE was dark and damp, and Molly felt along the wall until her fingers hit a light switch. She flicked it on, though the dim bulbs did little to illuminate the vast space.

Sulle was behind her, so close she could feel the heat from his body. She'd led him to this trap and they would both die.

"I'm sorry," she whispered again. "I should have stayed at Beau Monde."

"You only wanted to save our son," he answered. "It is I who should be sorry to have brought you both to this danger."

"What's going on, Sulle?" she asked. "Can you tell me? There's no point keeping secrets now," she said, and her voice broke.

Sulle lifted a hand to her cheek and touched her tenderly. "You have a right to know. I should have told you at Beau Monde."

He looked beyond her and then led her down into the center of the room. Molly looked around at the bed and sofa, a table and chairs. Her gaze went to several glazed windows high on the walls, but even through the frosted glass she could see the iron bars.

"We're truly prisoners, aren't we?" she asked.

"I suspect so," Sulle said, but he made an examination of the walls and windows. "Victor Lolahta is a thorough man. I was allowed to penetrate his home. As were you."

"I realized that as soon as I was inside," Molly said. "I had hoped to rescue Alan." She took a breath. "My only consolation is that Mr. Lolahta seems genuinely fond of Alan. And though he may well kill us, there's no reason for him to hurt Alan."

"That's true," Sulle reassured her. "In all of this, Alan should remain safe. Victor now has you and me. He has everything he wants."

Molly took a seat in one of the chairs and looked up at

Sulle. She had expected to hate him, but she found that she didn't. She didn't feel much of anything at all. "What's this all about?" she asked again. "I want to know."

"My work has taken on many facets," Sulle said slowly. "When I met you I was working for this country, as I am now. I know you tried to trace me, to find evidence of who I was. I also know that you met with a dead end. I could have contacted you, but I thought it would be better, safer, for you to return to your old life. Without me or any way to reach me."

Molly listened, his words confirming the long years she'd searched for him. All along he'd known she was looking for him and he'd chosen not to respond. He had received her notes and queries, the one showing her growing desperation as the child inside her grew and she had no way to reach him. He had chosen not to contact her. For her safety? Who was he to make such a judgment?

"I can see by the color in your cheeks that you're angry," Sulle said. "You have every right to be."

"You made my decisions for me," Molly said, the words painful in her throat. "You treated me as if I didn't have a say. You knew I was looking for you and you chose to ignore me. You still aren't giving me a full explanation."

"Because your safety is the most important thing to me."

"And yet I'm not safe. And neither is Alan," Molly shot back. With each second she felt her anger grow. The soothing numbness had evaporated. Pain seemed to well up inside her. All of the lonely nights, the days when she'd felt certain that Sulle had never cared for her, that she'd been a young and foolish girl who'd fallen under the spell of a master seducer. How much those hellish moments had cost her— in self-respect, in the passing of time, and in her unwillingness to risk her heart again.

"I have failed you, and my son," Sulle said.

In the dim light his dark eyes seemed sad, but Molly was

too angry to care. "One word, Sulle. One word and I could
have gotten on with my life. But to allow me to live in
doubt for all of that time—" She stood up. "And then I
almost jump right back into bed with you again." She made
a sound of disgust and strode away from him.

She leaned against the wall and tried to control her temper
and her emotions. Though she railed at Sulle, she was also
aware that her feelings were far more complex than simple
anger. She could not look at him without remembering. And
there was much to remember.

She could never forget the joy Sulle had brought into her
life. She had given herself so completely to him, heart and
soul. He had marked her, and no matter how mad she got
at him, she couldn't undo it.

She did not hear him move behind her, but she felt his
hands on her shoulders. Strong hands that held her but didn't
restrain her.

"You have every right to hate me," he said softly.

Molly whirled on him, furious. "Of course I have every
right to hate you! The problem is that I don't! I want to
hate you. I want the satisfaction of hurting you and hating
you. And I can't even have that because...because I—"
Horrified at what she had almost said, Molly caught herself.

"Ah, Molly," Sulle said. He didn't move closer, only
held her in hands that offered light support and the tenderest
caress. "If I told you that I longed for you during the lonely
nights, would that reduce your anger? If I said that no
woman held my interest, that I dreamed only of you, would
that help? If I could have led another life, I would have
begged you to share it with me. It wasn't because I didn't
care, it was because I cared so much," Sulle said, almost
whispering into the back of her neck.

Molly put out her hand and leaned against the wall. Sulle
made her knees weak. She tried to deny that she still loved

him. She fought against the emotion, but she knew it was futile.

The timbre of his voice, his scent and heat, the memory of his touch were all working against her. And she was afraid. For herself, but most especially for her son.

She struggled to fight back the tears, but her emotions were too volatile. She felt Sulle's arms move around her, turning her and pulling her against his chest so that she could hide against him as she cried.

"It's okay," Sulle whispered to her again and again. "Alan will be okay. Don't give up, Molly. You can't give up now."

Molly fought the tears back down, and for a moment she leaned against Sulle to regain her strength. The feel of his chest beneath her cheek was so familiar, so dear that she closed her eyes and tried to shut out her fears. Sulle's heart-beat was steady, and his arms, which moved around her to hold her safe, were strong.

Behind her closed eyelids she remembered another embrace, another moment of tense emotion in the fading heat of a desert dusk.

"Promise me you'll save our son," she whispered, finally looking up at him.

"I promise," Sulle said. His handsome face showed worry and fatigue, but also an iron resolve. "Alan will return to you, safe and unharmed."

Molly knew it was foolish to believe Sulle. No man could guarantee what he promised. But she did believe him. And she so desperately needed to believe in someone.

Staring into Sulle's eyes, Molly felt her breath catch. She saw the shift from determination to desire, and she felt her body respond. Whatever else had changed between them, this had not. She could not look at him without wanting him. And she saw in his parted lips and shallow breathing that he, too, felt the hot flames of passion.

Instead of turning away from him, Molly lifted her chin, inviting the kiss. His lips came down on hers with such force and passion that she clung to his broad shoulders.

Sulle lifted her and carried her to the bed. The casual clothes she wore came off much more easily than the antebellum dress, and soon Sulle was beside her, naked also.

"Sulle," she whispered, her voice rough with emotion as her hand slid over his muscled body.

"Molly," he answered, lifting her so that she straddled him. "I've made mistakes in the past, but none so tragic as thinking that I could live without you." He pulled her down to meet his lips.

Molly cast aside her doubts and fears. It would be time enough to face the future when Victor Lolahta and Alan returned. For now, she wanted Sulle, even if it was only for the moment.

Chapter Seven

Molly awakened from a sleep induced by a combination of sated desire and the closeness of the old icehouse. Outside the window she saw the wheels of a car roll by and heard the sound of people getting out of it. Beside her Sulle stirred, and she slipped out of the bed without awakening him completely.

Stacking several old crates, she climbed up to the window. She was level with the driveway of the house, and she felt a rush of joy at the sight of thin legs climbing out of a big black car. Alan. It had to be him, and he was okay! The car door slammed and she saw his shoes, recognized his knees, the right one with a scrape mark where he'd made a crash landing on the sidewalk outside the apartment while learning to roller-skate.

She heard his voice, listening closely. There was no fear in the tone, only a general discontent.

"You said if I went to the zoo you'd let me call my mother," he said.

Molly forced herself to remain quiet.

"Don't worry, little one." Victor Lolahta's voice was warm and easy. "Your mother will join you shortly. If all goes as planned, the two of you will be on a plane and headed for your mother's next assignment by this evening."

"You said that we'd be gone by lunchtime. It's after lunch," Alan insisted.

There was Lolahta's chuckle. "You're much too aware of time for a young man. I did say lunch, but the plans had to be changed. Besides, you would have missed the albino tigers at the zoo. Now that was worth seeing, wasn't it?"

Alan hesitated. "I guess. But I want my mother."

"And you shall have her," Victor promised. "Sooner than you think. Now come inside and let Cook give you some cookies and something cool to drink. It's very hot today."

Molly watched Alan's legs disappear from view. She wanted to call to him, but she kept silent. To see her, a prisoner, would only agitate him. She would be free soon. And Alan would be safe. Sulle had promised her. The best thing would be to protect Alan from the danger he faced.

"Molly?"

Sulle's voice called to her from the shadows of the bed.

She went to him and sat beside him on the rumpled sheets, knowing that of the many images of Sulle she kept in her mind, this would be a favorite. "Alan is back," she said.

Sulle sat up slowly. "Our time together is over," he said. "So soon. I had hoped we could have another hour."

The poignancy of his tone went straight to her heart. They had stolen another few hours together, much as they had done during the long nights in the desert. There had never been much hope that they would share anything but stolen moments because of Sulle's life, his work. In the future, she would miss him with the same familiar ache that had been part of her life for the past eight years. But now there was Alan.

"What are we going to do?" Molly asked, eager for action, yet afraid of what results it might bring.

"Alan is in the house," Sulle said. "That makes things much simpler. We only have to get out of this cellar."

"How are we going to do that? Maybe I should pretend to be sick. It always works in the movies," Molly said, aiming for a bit of humor.

"Show me sick," Sulle said.

"What?"

"I mean it, let me see how good an actress you are. And remember, Alan's life could depend on it."

"Sulle, I—" Molly stopped the protest before she could finish it. She'd never tried to act. That didn't mean she couldn't. And for Alan, she'd try anything.

She fell over on the bed and began moaning and thrashing. "My stomach," she cried out. "My stomach!" She grabbed her abdomen and curled into a ball on the bed. "Get a doctor!" she screamed. "Get a doctor! I'm dying!"

Sulle wasted no time rushing up the steps and pounding on the door. "Molly's sick!" he called. "She's in terrible pain! Something serious is wrong!" He pounded harder. "She's going to die if she doesn't get a doctor."

Molly's wild scream echoed off the rafters.

There was the sound of a lock being thrown back and a gun muzzle pointed in the door. "Step back," the man commanded.

Sulle moved to the bed and lifted the thrashing Molly in his arms. In the clammy room she was covered in sweat, and he pushed her hair back from her damp forehead. "She's very, very sick," he said. "She needs a doctor. Look for yourself."

Molly gave a pathetic moan and rolled her eyes, showing the whites.

"She was fine three hours ago," the man insisted, shifting down the steps and walking to the bed, his gun trained on Sulle.

"It could be her appendix. If it ruptures, she could die." Sulle held Molly as she began to thrash again.

Molly let out a moan, her face twisting into a mask of agony. She threw herself out of Sulle's arms and began to thrash on the bed.

"I'll get Mr. Lolahta," the man said, and for one brief instant he turned his back on Sulle.

Sulle leaped from the bed, his hand descending with a deadly force that caught the guard on the neck. The man dropped to his knees and fell face forward onto the stairs.

"Molly," Sulle said. "Let's go." He bent to retrieve the gun that the guard had been carrying.

Molly jumped up, rearranging clothes that had become twisted with all of her thrashing. She was halfway up the stairs when Sulle overtook her and moved into the lead. The open door to the kitchen was like a portal to freedom—a path to Alan. And she intended to find her son and remove him from Victor Lolahta's clutches.

She followed Sulle across the empty kitchen, wondering how much longer their luck could hold out. Lolahta wasn't a careless man. When they entered the back hallway, she saw Sulle head toward the exit. She looked right, toward the staircase. "Alan is upstairs somewhere," she said.

Sulle shook his head. "I'll come back for him, Molly."

"I'm not leaving without him." She had no intention of taking another step without her son. The idea that Sulle was suggesting that she leave him behind was stunning.

"I'll find him," Sulle said, motioning her out of the house. "You have to get away from here."

"No." Nothing could make her leave Alan behind. Nothing. Not even the grim determination and cold eyes of Sulle Alamar.

"Molly, trust me. I'll get him back. But you need to be away from here. If we go after Alan now, Lolahta has enough men to take us prisoner again."

There was reason in Sulle's words. Cold reason that went against every instinct she had as a mother. "I can't," she said. She turned and started to run up the stairs that led to the second floor.

She felt Sulle's hand on her shoulder, felt the pressure he applied to her neck, a sharp pain exploding like lightning behind her eyes. And then she fell backwards into darkness.

SULLE SCOOPED MOLLY into his arms and ran from the house. He caught the chauffeur lounging against the side of the car, smoking a cigarette. Pointing the gun, he ordered the man into the car. He stowed Molly in the back and climbed in behind her.

"Take me to the Riverwalk," he said through the open window that separated the passenger section. He pressed the gun barrel into the driver's neck. "I won't hurt you if you do what I say. I want a ride and I want to get out of this car. Then you can do whatever you have to do."

"You got it," the driver said. "I work for Mr. Lolahta, but I'm not in a hurry to die today."

"Good," Sulle said as he glanced at Molly. Her face was pale, and he regretted having to take her forcibly. But she would never have left Alan unless he'd made her. By physically abducting her, he'd forever destroyed any future they might have had. He knew that. Molly would forgive him many things, but never leaving their son behind.

The action he'd taken was irrevocable. Even when Alan was safely returned—and he *would* be released unharmed—Molly would not forgive this moment. He brushed a strand of golden-brown hair from her face and savored her soft skin. He'd been a fool in many things in life, but never for loving Molly. Walking away from her was his only regret.

Through the years he'd accomplished some good for a world that abounded in greed, avarice and corruption. His reward had been personal satisfaction. But the cost had been high. His was a life of solitude, of pretence and shadows and a grim determination never to care too deeply for another living creature. Had he been a different man, he could have loved Molly, and his son, every day for the past eight years.

The limo made a sharp turn and Sulle glanced up to check their location. The driver was headed straight to the most crowded part of the tourist center in the old French Quarter in New Orleans. Perfect.

Sulle gently shook Molly, bringing her out of the unconscious state he'd put her in when he'd pinched the delicate nerve on her neck. He prepared, ready for her to come up spitting and fighting.

She swung out with one hand and he caught it, unable to stop the smile. She was a tigress. Jorge had been right about that.

He saw her eyes widen and she pushed herself up in the seat—as far away from him as possible. Her gaze roved wildly about until she got her bearings—and then he could see the events of that afternoon come rushing back at her.

"I had to do it," he said without a hint of apology in his tone. "For Alan's sake. I didn't want our son to lose his mother."

Molly's cheeks, so pale only moments before, flushed brightly. "You had no right. None!" She spat out the words, and even as she spoke she started clawing at the door handle. Sulle caught her, pulled her to his chest, and held her there.

"Molly, listen to reason. You would have been recaptured. Think it through. If Lolahta wants your son, what stands in his way from keeping Alan?" He gave it a pause. "Only you. And me." He felt her struggle lessen.

When he knew she was listening, he continued in a soft voice. His lips were pressed against her hair and he was struck with a sense of loss and longing so keen that he almost couldn't speak. But he forced himself to go on. "I'll get Alan. I promise. But if you'd gone up there and been recaptured, he would have had you killed. You're an impediment now. You were a bargaining chip, but if he truly wants the boy, you're in the way of his ambitions. Think about it before you try to kill me or yourself."

"I trusted you," Molly said, pushing away from his chest.

Sulle released her so that she could shift back and away from him. Her face told its own story. Hurt, fear for her son, bitter anger.

"I haven't betrayed your trust," he said. "I was only protecting you. Protecting our son." Out of the corner of his eye he saw the chauffeur glancing into the rearview mirror, following the scene in the back seat. The driver would attempt to redeem himself in Lolahta's eyes—a juicy tidbit would perhaps save his life. And Sulle wasn't averse to giving the man such a bone—as long as it suited his purposes. Molly shifted to face him, her voice rising.

"You made a decision you had no right to make." Molly's chest heaved. "I hate you," she said, crowding as far as she could into the far corner of the car. "I'll never forgive you for this."

Sulle nodded. He felt as if he'd been shot in the chest, but he allowed none of his emotion to show. There was a larger game at stake, one that might work to Molly's benefit in the future. "I know this already. Nonetheless, I have no regrets about what I did."

"You may not have regrets, but I give you fair warning that when I get Alan back, he will never know that you're his father. He won't know a thing about you. Nothing."

Sulle looked at her long and hard. She was a strong woman, someone who meant what she said. He had never met her equal, and expected he never would again. And in her strength he saw the only possible answer to the future. His smile was deliberately tight and amused. "Once your son is safe and you are both out of my way, I have no desire to see either of you again. You seem to think that I've stepped back into your life to make trouble. The exact opposite is true. You and the boy showed up at the wrong moment in my life. You've complicated a very important operation. I've tried to help you, but after this, understand that I won't risk my life or my men to help you. You and the boy are on your own.''

He saw the shock and pain in her eyes, but only for a split second. Fury replaced the pain, and he knew he'd done the right thing. Once Molly and Alan were safe, the only security they had was in not caring for him—and Molly wouldn't hesitate to make that very clear to everyone who crossed her path.

MOLLY CAUGHT the watchful eye of the driver. She felt her face burn with a combination of anger and shame. She glanced at the man who shared the back seat of the car and saw only the profile of a stranger.

Though she'd shared the most intimate acts with this man only hours before, she realized that his tenderness or generosity or passion were all part of a cold and calculated technique. The truth was so painful that she felt as if she couldn't breathe. Eight years she'd wasted on this man. Eight years she'd fantasized and dreamed of finding him again. She'd compared every man she met to him and judged them lacking. In her mind he'd been the most wonderful of lovers, a man who matched her soul. And now she understood it was all technique.

It was almost more than she could accept. But the fact that this man had abducted her, had manhandled her into abandoning her son, that was the one thing she must force herself to accept. Because she had to fight—or she might lose Alan forever. Sulle was capable of trading Alan for something he wanted. A weapons deal or some other international plot where one young boy's life didn't matter. Even if it was his own son.

The limo pulled to the curb in front of an open café where a lone saxophone player dipped low into the blues. The notes seemed to run down her spine, speaking of sorrow and pain and heartbreak. Molly knew them all.

When Sulle got out of the car, she considered trying to talk the driver into speeding away, but she knew it was useless. Her door opened and Sulle handed her out of the car. For a moment, Molly stared into the eyes of the saxophone player, saw the sweat beading on his forehead as he played his heart out for the tips the tourists threw into his hat. So this was New Orleans, the city that care forgot. Another empty illusion, just like her fantasy of Sulle.

"Don't try anything stupid," Sulle said in a voice colder than the Arctic.

Molly didn't dignify that with an answer. She was his prisoner, and there wasn't any point trying to sugarcoat the situation. "What are you going to do with me?" she asked.

"Keep you safely out of the way." Sulle stepped away from her, as if contact with her was unpleasant.

"You have to let me go after Alan," she insisted, her voice rising in anger. Several tourists stopped to stare at them.

Sulle grasped her arm and propelled her down the sidewalk. At first Molly didn't resist, but after a hundred yards, she put her brakes on. "I'm not going to make this easy for you," she said through clenched teeth.

"Don't make it hard," he said, his voice soft and deadly.

"Who are you?" Molly asked, and she knew the question was as much for herself as for him. Who was this man who, even in his absence, had been such a big part of her life?

"I'm the man who long ago gave up the hope of having family and friends. I'm the man who made a mistake eight years ago with a woman who drew him like a moth to a flame.'' For a split second, Molly thought she saw a flare of dark pain in his eyes, but it was gone before he spoke again. ''I fear I'm the man who will bring you sorrow and suffering. It gives me no pleasure, but it is also something that I can't change.''

''Can't or won't?'' Molly asked.

''It doesn't matter. The cards are on the table now. You'll come with me, and quietly. My men will guard you, and do a much better job than the last time. Tomorrow, I'll let you go.''

Molly swallowed. ''And Alan? Will he go with me?''

''I make no promises.''

Molly clenched her teeth to keep from crying out. They were on a public street with tourists rushing past them by the dozen. There was a carnival air in the afternoon heat of the city. She looked around and composed herself. Her only hope was her own wits and determination. They would work to her advantage if Sulle underestimated her.

He was waiting and watching. She dropped her head as if her spirit was broken, and when he put his hand on her elbow, she walked beside him without protest. Several times he glanced at her, but she kept her eyes down and on the sidewalk. Let him believe her the meek lamb. As soon as a reasonable opportunity presented itself, she would show him another side.

SULLE SHIFTED HIS GAZE to Molly. It wasn't like her to give up, but he was grateful for her docility as they hurried along the street to the hotel. He'd had the limo drop him a mile from the place he was staying, a necessary precaution. Now he wanted to get Molly safely locked in a room and he wanted to go forward with his plans to meet Lolahta.

He felt that Alan was reasonably safe, for the moment. Lolahta's interest in the boy was chilling, but it wasn't predatory. He wouldn't kill Alan unless absolutely forced into it. And Sulle didn't intend to give him reason or opportunity.

As he guided Molly through the lobby of the hotel, he looked at her again. She was like a whipped dog, and he felt a pang of remorse. But it was better for Molly to believe him a villain. It would give her the cloak of safety that might allow her to lead an ordinary life. A cruel necessity, as so much of his life had been.

He punched the button to call the elevator, and used the key to access the top floor. Molly seemed indifferent to where they were going. Perhaps she'd lapsed into a place where she could endure no more. It might be better for her.

As the elevator opened, he expected to see Jorge or Liam, but the hallway was vacant. He opened the door to his suite and let Molly enter. She went to the center of the room and sat down on the sofa, her gaze on her shoes.

He did a quick check to make sure everything was secure, his concern growing when he found no trace of his men. He didn't know where they had gone, but he knew it was unusual for them to leave. Very unusual.

He went to Molly. His greatest temptation was to draw her into his arms and reassure her that everything would be fine. In his mind, he knew he would save Alan, return him to Molly, and then disappear. She would hate him and she would take her son and find a new home, a safe life. And it would be for the best.

But to achieve that end, he needed to take action. Where were Jorge and Liam? He couldn't leave Molly alone. He looked over at her and realized that it was almost as dangerous for him to remain with her, alone. Desire for her swept over him. He went out on the balcony and stared toward the river. Dusk was settling down over the city, and the heat had waned, leaving a lush warmth in the air that was tempered by a breeze. The desert nights came back to him with a rush of remembered sexuality that made him half turn toward Molly. It wasn't too late. He could explain what he intended to do and at least leave her with a shred of hope—and not hating him.

But it was her safety that was at stake. If his enemies thought he cared for her, she and Alan would be constant targets. No, he'd made the right choice, for all of them. He'd never expected it to be so hard to make her suffer.

"Sulle?"

Her voice was like a ripple of sensual fire that traveled down his body. It was the heat of the desert sun commingled with the fire in his blood. He ached for her, and it took reserves of strength he could not spare to hold himself rigid and unmoving.

"Sulle, please let me go. Once I get Alan, I'll vanish. I'll get as far away as I can and I'll never resurface."

Her voice broke and Sulle nearly gave in. He caught himself at the last second. "You and the boy are chips in a much larger game." He couldn't help himself. "I would change all of this if I could," he added.

"Would you?" she asked in a voice clearly begging for some shred of hope.

Sulle clenched his jaw. "I would, if it were possible. But it isn't. The hand is dealt, the cards must be played."

"And what is the death of one seven-year-old boy?"

He knew she was trying to make him see Alan as a person, not a statistic to be counted as a casualty. What she couldn't know was that the boy was as much a part of him as her. Only he couldn't allow himself the luxury of showing it. Not now, and not ever. "Many children die in desperate countries all over the world, Molly. You've been there. You've seen it. I—"

Her touch on his arm was so powerful he broke off in midsentence. He could no longer avoid looking at her, so he faced her. Her green eyes were liquid with tears.

"I'm begging you," she said. "Save Alan. Bring him to me." The tears slipped down her face and she ignored them.

Sulle could not. His hand trembled as he brushed a crystalline tear from the corner of her mouth. The dusky tones of the setting sun burnished her honeyed hair with fire. The same sunset colors suffused her pale skin with a golden warmth, and Sulle remembered their evenings in the desert. Stolen time for him. Hours of pleasure and love that he'd never allowed himself again.

Because he'd fallen in love with Molly Lynch. He'd been a weaker man then, unable to deny himself the wonders of her touch, her presence. And now he found that he was no stronger. He bent toward the sun-warmed lips and felt his control slipping. He would tell her the truth—that Alan would be saved at all costs. That he loved her and the boy. That he couldn't endure a future without them. His lips captured hers and he tried to pour all of his feelings into the kiss.

The door of the suite opened and there was the clatter of footsteps in the front room.

"Sulle? Are you here? We have to go now!"

It was Liam, and Sulle stepped back from Molly, both of them breathless and flushed. The dazed look left her face, suddenly replaced by worry and fear.

"Sulle—" She held out her hand to him. "Promise me—"

Liam found them on the balcony. Sulle saw him register the tableau and ignore it. "We have to go," Liam said, guarded in front of Molly. "Now."

Sulle knew his man well enough to realize that Liam was not one to exaggerate. He looked at Molly. "I have to run an errand," he said. "I'll be back shortly. Jorge will be here soon. If you need anything, ask him."

"Sure," she said in a flat voice. All the life had gone out of her.

"Molly—" He didn't finish. He had to hurry. He left the suite with Liam beside him, taking care to lock the door from the outside.

Molly couldn't escape. There was no way. He could at least continue with his plan with the assurance that she was out of danger, for the moment. It was a small assurance. The elevator came and a young maid pushed a cart of laundry out.

"Sir, I need to leave fresh linens," she said, looking from one to the other. "Could I use your key?"

"Leave them in the hallway," Sulle said. "I'll get them when I return."

"Yes, sir." She nodded and pushed the cart past.

Chapter Eight

Molly heard the gentle tap on the door and knew instinctively that it wasn't Sulle. He was never tentative about anything. "What is it?" she called through the locked door. As if she could do anything about it. She was a prisoner, held while her son was used as a bartering chip. She paced to the door and listened.

"Molly?"

She recognized the female voice. "Pauline?" It was impossible.

"Are you alone?" Pauline asked in a whisper.

"Yes, but the door is locked, and I can't open it."

There was the sound of a key sliding into the lock and the door swung open. Pauline stood in the maid's uniform, a set of keys in her hand.

"Hurry," she said. "If you want to escape, let's get out of here now."

"How—" Molly stopped herself. This was not the time for questions. She broke into a run toward the elevator with the nanny at her side. "I don't know how you managed this, but a million thanks. They have Alan. We have to get to him." She spoke in spurts as she skidded to a halt in front of the elevator, her finger relentlessly pressing the button. Sulle could return. Or Jorge. She had to get away.

The elevator doors opened and they stepped inside. As

soon as the doors shut, Pauline began stripping out of her maid's uniform to the shorts she wore beneath. By the time they reached the lobby, she looked as much like a tourist as Molly.

"Walk across the lobby very casually," Pauline said. "Don't draw attention, just in case they've left someone to watch you." She handed Molly a pair of dark sunglasses. "Put these on."

Molly took the glasses but stared at the young woman who'd been her son's companion, teacher and nanny for the past six months. This was not the mild-mannered young woman she'd come to know.

She felt Pauline's grip on her arm as they started across the lobby.

"The seafood is delicious at this new place," Pauline said with a lilting laugh. "And the drinks are killers. They have one called a mudslide that's like a dessert. You'll love it," she said in bright tourist chatter as they ambled across the lobby and out into the street.

Molly instinctively turned right, toward a taxi stand. The grip on her arm stopped her.

"This way," Pauline said.

Molly felt the first true flush of trouble. "I have to go to Alan." She tried to tug away and felt something in her ribs. Without looking, she knew it was the barrel of a gun.

"You've made enough trouble for all of us," Pauline said in a cold voice. "Now come with me and don't make a scene."

NOW WHERE, oh where could my little gal be? The night lights are coming on and the stars are beginning to twinkle. At last a little relief from the oppressive heat. If it weren't for air-conditioning, I wouldn't survive in this neck of the woods. I'd love a tiny little nap, but I can't abandon Alan. He's a brave little boy—and smart as a whip. He acted as if he didn't recognize me when I sauntered into his room. He caught on quickly that he had to pretend. And what a job he did! That boy soon had the old man convinced he couldn't live without me for a pet.

Surprise, Lolahta, you've been infiltrated.

I'm in place but where are Sulle and P-n-C? I thought when they got out of the cellar they'd be right up here to get Alan. I was poised on the stairs to offer assistance, but they retreated. Strategic on Sulle's part, but I'll bet P-n-C is fit to be tied.

And time is growing short. I overheard Mr. Lolahta saying that he would finish Sulle off tonight. Mr. L., as I prefer to call him, seems to have learned a great deal about Sulle and his background. There's this long-standing feud between them that goes back to Sulle's childhood when his entire village was killed. Unfortunately, Sulle isn't aware of this. In fact, I get the impression that this entire exchange of biochemicals for money has been a setup. Sulle has been the target all along, not chemical weaponry. Mr. L. wants the biochemicals to sell for a profit, but he wants to kill Sulle more.

P-n-C and Alan are pawns in a master game of revenge.

But how did Mr. L. find out about Alan? I gather P-n-C has never told anyone. And Sulle never knew, so he couldn't talk. I suppose that P-n-C, as smart as she is, had a rash moment of sentiment and probably put Sulle's name on the birth certificate or something like that. Perhaps named him as legal guardian in the case of her death.

In the world of humans, there is no anonymous past. There's always a paper trail, and Big Brother is getting better and better at keeping documentation on the humanoids. I wish I could make Eleanor and Peter watch the sci-fi channel with me. Call me a paranoid cat, but I'm not fond of the idea of having my entire existence documented.

Enough rambling—time for action. I'll give Sulle another

*ten minutes. If he doesn't show up, I'm going to have to
talk the boy into climbing out a window. Lolahta is nobody's
fool. Alan has already told him of his deadly fear of heights.
Mr. L. feels certain the boy won't try to escape from the
window. But he hasn't counted on the slick persuasiveness
of a black feline.*

SULLE STOPPED ABRUPTLY, forcing Liam to halt. The Irish-
man squinted at him.

"What's wrong?" He looked around, alert and wary.

"The maid. Something isn't right." Sulle's dark eyes
seemed to narrow. He looked at his friend, and in the same
instant they turned and began to run back toward the hotel.
They were at the corner that gave a clear view of the gold-
and-glass front door when they saw Molly and the blonde
come out of the hotel. Sulle saw Molly try to go toward the
taxis, and he saw the woman halt her. He didn't have to see
the gun to realize what was happening.

"Get a cab," he said to Liam as he darted behind the
bumper of a car. He was careful to stay hidden as he
watched Molly being forced into the back of a black sedan.
The blonde got in behind her.

Sulle had memorized the license plate of the car when
Liam's taxi pulled up beside him. He jumped into the back
seat and held on while the driver peeled out, intent on keeping the black sedan in sight to earn the hundred-dollar tip
Liam had promised.

Sulle wasn't surprised when the black car glided out of
the old French Quarter and headed uptown, toward the pa-
latial estates of the rich. Lolahta felt no need to be overly
cautious on his own turf. He'd snared Molly, and he didn't
care that Sulle would figure out where he'd taken her. Sulle
knew that didn't bode well for Molly.

"Hurry!" He instructed the driver.

Although the cabby drove with the skill of a NASCAR

pilot, they could never get close enough to effect a rescue. Sulle's hopes plummeted when the sedan turned into the gates of Lolahta's drive. Molly was out of his reach, for the moment.

"What's next?" Liam asked.

"Let me out here," Sulle said. "Go back for Jorge. Call the emergency number and tell them the deal has gone sour."

"You want the feds swarming in here?" Liam asked, surprised.

Sulle nodded. "I want tanks, bombers, whatever it takes to get my boy and Molly out of there safely."

"What about Lolahta?" Liam asked.

"He may escape this time, but I'll see him in hell much sooner than he anticipates."

Liam nodded, his face a puzzle of concern. "You sure you want me to leave you?" he asked.

"If anything happens to me," Sulle said, stepping out of the car. "Make Lolahta pay. And take care of Molly and Alan. Tell her…" He looked up at the estate where he knew she was being held prisoner. "Tell her that I always loved her—that I never stopped."

Before Liam could say anything, Sulle stepped back from the car and slapped the hood, signaling the driver to take off.

MOLLY STARED into the dark gaze of the man who sat behind his desk. Pauline had removed the gun barrel from her side, but the former nanny stood at the ready only three steps away, the deadly weapon as natural in her hand as a geography book had been.

"Your son is an extraordinary young man," Victor Lolahta said, the smile never reaching his eyes. "You're to be commended for the job you've done raising him. Especially since you've always put so much time and effort into your career." He chuckled. "I'm an old-fashioned man. I believe the woman should be at home with her child."

The man's insufferable arrogance was just the tonic Molly needed. Along with her temper came a jolt of adrenaline. She had been stupid to open the door to Pauline. Foolish not to question the nanny's miraculous rescue scheme. But she wasn't beaten. Not by a long shot. Not when Alan's safety was at stake.

"Your views on child-rearing don't interest me," she said. "Your opinion of Alan, though flattering, is of no consequence."

She saw the thunderclouds in the man's eyes and knew he wasn't used to such treatment, especially from a woman. Too bad.

"My opinion counts far more than you know," Lolahta said with force. "The boy's life hangs on it."

Though his words made Molly quake down to her toes, she affected a bemused smile. "How can you be so certain that my abduction isn't part of the plan?" Though he recovered fast, she saw his eyes dart to Pauline's.

The nanny instantly left the room, going to alert the perimeter guards, Molly guessed. She gauged the distance to the door. Victor Lolahta was an old man. He couldn't move fast. Perhaps this would be her best chance to try and escape. Alan was somewhere in the house, and she had to find him.

"Don't think about it," Victor said softly. "Your son is secured with a guard. He is adjusting nicely. Should you find him and upset him, it would only mean that I'd have to kill the boy. A true mother's love would protect her child from the knowledge of her death."

Molly knew the words weren't an idle threat. She hesitated. As she turned to face Victor again, she caught a movement outside the window. The black cat leaped gracefully down the limb of an old oak. The cat turned to face her. He nodded his head twice and then looked up.

Molly glanced up and saw the dangling legs of a young boy, and before her face gave her emotions away, she turned from the window and fell to her knees in front of Victor.

"Let Alan go and I'll do anything you want," she said, desperate to keep Lolahta's attention on her rather than the window. Alan was getting away! The cat was helping him escape. And it didn't matter what happened to her as long as her son was free.

Lolahta put a hand on her head. "Such devotion. It makes me want to keep you around, my dear. But your value is only to Mr. Alamar. Once you draw him back to me, I'll kill you both. And finish what I set out to do years ago. It will be the perfect revenge. His line is destroyed, and I will raise his son as my own."

"You're making a mistake," Molly said, looking up at him. "Sulle cares nothing for the boy, and he certainly won't risk anything to save me."

"You're an amusing liar," Victor said, "but unconvincing."

Molly rocked back on her heels. "I wish I was lying. This is the truth. If you expect Sulle to rush here to save me or Alan, you'll be disappointed. He won't help us. He told me so himself. He has no feelings for anyone. He's a man who doesn't allow himself tender emotions."

Victor eased his chair back and stood.

Terrified that he might walk to the window, Molly grabbed his hand. "I'll help you catch him. I owe Sulle nothing. I overheard his plans." It was an outrageous lie, but she saw a flicker of interest on the older man's face.

"What do you know?" Victor said.

"Let Alan go." Molly was walking a narrow line. She could no longer ask to see her son—Alan was easing down the tree. She chanced a look outside and saw his terrified face. He was staring at her. For a heart-stopping second, she was afraid he'd call out to her. But the black cat reappeared, batting him on the chin with a paw and they slowly began to move down the tree.

"Tell me what you know." Lolahta demanded.

"Not until you tell me your plans for my son." She laced her voice with defiance. She had to play for time.

"You aren't in a position to bargain," Lolahta said angrily. "Don't make me use force."

"I won't talk," Molly said. "Sulle Alamar has a trick up his sleeve, and you'll find out soon enough what it is. I won't tell until I have assurances that Alan will be safe."

Victor was fast. He grabbed her hair and pulled her head back. "I don't have time for foolish bravery. You'll talk." He looked to the door. "Mitch! Bobby! Come and get her."

The door burst open and the two men rushed forward, grabbing her arms.

"Miss Lynch claims to know the plans of our old friend Mr. Alamar. I wish to find out what she knows." He nodded. "I'm sure you can convince her to cooperate."

"It won't take long," the bigger of the men promised.

Molly felt herself being lifted between the men. Her feet never touched the floor as they hauled her out of the room and down the stairs. Her only satisfaction was that Alan's head had disappeared from the window before she was taken.

SULLE CIRCLED THE HOUSE. Lolahta had again neglected to post a perimeter guard. Sulle made his way to the back, suspecting another trap, and stopped dead when he saw the cat leap to the ground. Familiar. The sight of the feline made his hopes surge. The cat was like a talisman. He was always there to protect Molly and Alan.

Sulle missed seeing Alan until he swung from a lower limb and also hit the ground. Sulle didn't wait. He rushed to the boy, tumbling with him and rolling across the ground to the protection of a hedge.

He was rewarded with a strong punch to the stomach, followed by a jab to the jaw. Alan had inherited his mother's ability to fight.

"Easy," Sulle whispered. "I'm here to help you."

Alan drew himself up and gave Sulle stare for stare. "Who are you?"

Sulle felt his heart contract. Alan didn't look exactly like the older brother he'd lost to violence, but there was a marked resemblance. He put a hand out and brushed Alan's dark hair back from his face. "I'm a friend of your mother's," he said softly. "Trust me, Alan. I'm here to help."

"Meow!" Familiar came forward and brushed against Sulle's leg.

"See, the cat knows I'm a friend."

Alan looked from Familiar to Sulle. "If Familiar says so, I guess you're okay." His brave facade began to crumble. "They've got my mom. Inside. Mr. Lolahta has her. And I think he's going to hurt her."

Sulle cupped the boy's face between his hands. "He won't hurt her. I won't let him."

"I'm coming too," Alan said.

Sulle saw more of Molly in him. "You have to listen to me, Alan. I want you and the cat to get away from here." He pointed west. "Go in that direction. Start walking and keep going. After five blocks you'll come to 128 Wisteria Lane. Knock on the door and ask for Mr. Alamar. Tell the owner that you're his guest. He'll keep you safe. As soon as I've rescued your mother, we'll both come for you."

Alan frowned. "I don't want to leave her in there."

"Listen to me, Alan. If I have to worry about you, I won't be able to put all of my attention on helping your mother. Can you understand that?"

Alan nodded slowly. He looked down as the cat snagged his pants leg and tried to pull him away. "I understand."

Sulle smiled. "In some ways, you're smarter than your mother. Now go." He pushed the boy gently in the direction he wanted him to go. "Hurry!" He watched with satisfaction as the boy and cat began to run to his old friend, the doctor's, house, a place where he knew they would be safe.

With Alan safe, his plans changed. There was a possibility now that he could save Molly and still nail Lolahta and put him behind bars for the rest of his life. It would be tricky, and he would have to count on Molly's trust. That was something he couldn't be certain of at all.

But the plan was a good one. Instead of going into the house, he backed up and hurried to the street. When he was two blocks away, he pulled his cell phone from his pocket and dialed Lolahta's number. In a matter of seconds he was speaking with the man.

"Do you still want the chemicals?" he asked.

There was hesitation on Victor's end before he spoke. "I have something you want, Alamar."

"That's where you're wrong," Sulle said.

"The woman is very tough. She's made the claim that she overheard your plans, yet we can't convince her to speak."

Sulle almost abandoned his plan at the thought of what Lolahta might do to Molly to make her speak. "She can only tell you that the meeting place is still the river. There's a landing dock at the Beau Monde Plantation. My boat is there, loaded with the goods. Bring the money and the boat is yours, just as we said."

"And the woman and boy?" Victor asked.

"Whatever. I'm sure she's told you that I have no feelings for them. She speaks the truth." Sulle had to keep his voice level.

"No feelings for your own blood?" Lolahta waited several seconds. "How unusual for a man who has spent his entire life seeking revenge on the killers of his family."

Sulle felt his mouth go dry. Lolahta had opened the door to the past with an implication that was hard to ignore. The old man was throwing down the gauntlet, but Sulle knew better than to accept the challenge. Not now. His pride would have to suffer for Molly's safety.

"The search for revenge can be detrimental to profit," he said coolly.

"Your son reminds me a great deal of your older brother. They were about the same age when my men paid a visit to your village."

Sulle felt the effect of Lolahta's words like the jolt of an electric shock. "You admit this?" he asked. "Why?"

"I warned your father not to try and stop me. I had organized a small army, mostly thieves and cutthroats, but they served their purpose. I was poised for a considerable reward from one of the more anti-American factions. When your father found out what I was doing, he tried to talk me out of it, and then he turned me in. My men were crushed while they slept."

"And in return, you destroyed an entire village." Sulle found it hard to accept, and even harder to control his temper. He wanted to rush to Lolahta's house and lace his fingers around the man's throat. But he had to play the game. "You murdered innocent women and children, families who knew nothing of your dirty political game."

"They were disposable, a million more where they came from. And your father had to pay. He also had to be silenced. My only mistake was in letting you escape. And now I'm going to rectify that. I'll kill you and raise your son as my own. He'll hate your bloodline. He'll spit on your name." Lolahta laughed. "It is perfect."

"How did you know about Alan?" Sulle gripped the phone. He might find Lolahta's weakness in some detail.

"Oh, I went to a lot of trouble to find out about Alan."
There was cruel humor in Lolahta's voice. "Once I knew
of his birth, I had to wait. It was difficult to place Pauline
as the nanny. But once there, she did fine work."

"And all for nothing," Sulle said. "You should have
guessed that a man like me wouldn't allow sentiment to get
in the way of profit," Sulle said, determined not to give
Lolahta the emotional edge.

Victor laughed again. "Nice try, but I think you should
speak the truth. I should have warned you that you were on
the speakerphone. I'm afraid that declaration has caused Ms.
Lynch more pain that anything I could think of."

Sulle gritted his teeth but kept his voice cool. "I'm afraid
Ms. Lynch's suffering is of little interest to me. Bring the
money. What you do with the woman and the boy is up to
you." He broke the connection.

Chapter Nine

Molly couldn't believe the pain she felt at Sulle's words. How convenient that Victor Lolahta had arranged for a speakerphone in her prison.

Sulle had sounded so cold, so untouched by her plight. And Alan's. And when she thought of all he'd lost, she came to the terrifying conclusion that he really didn't care about his son. Couldn't care. Losing so much, so young, had undoubtedly crippled him.

She hadn't quite believed him when he'd told her that he didn't care about her and Alan. Some tiny corner of her heart had refused to let go of her love for him. It was there that the pain was most excruciating.

Her only consolation was the memory of Alan sliding down the tree, his face white from his terror of heights. But Familiar was with him. Thank God for that black cat.

The door burst open and Victor Lolahta stood in the opening, his chest rising up and down with anger. "He's gone!" he said. "Where is he?"

Molly didn't say anything, just went to the window and stared out into the falling darkness. Alan had escaped. Her family would take care of him if anything happened to her. He would be okay. That was the best she could hope for.

She felt Lolahta's eyes on her and she summoned all her self-control.

"Sulle Alamar will pay for this," he said.

"Sulle had nothing to do with this. I told you," she said. "He doesn't care. He isn't capable of caring. Your foolish scheme has been a wasted effort." Whatever the words cost her, they were devastating on Lolahta. His face darkened and twisted.

"We'll see how brave you are," he said. "Mitch, put her in the front window. Put the gun to her head. When she begs for her life let's see how cold our Mr. Alamar really is."

LITTLE ALAN is eating cookies and drinking milk with the good doctor and his wife—a pastime that this black kitty could get into. Chocolate macadamia nut. Sounds like heaven, but I don't have time for a snack. Thank goodness for the darkness. I can slink all over the place without being seen.

I get the feeling that I'm thinking like a humanoid as I head back to Mr. L.'s palace/prison. I have a bad feeling in my gut that retribution is going to fall on P-n-C's head when Victor discovers the boy is gone.

Holy Moly! The front of the house is lit up like there's a party going on, and P-n-C is standing in the big front window. One of Mr. L.'s baboons has his gun right at her temple. I'd better get a move on, and fast.

SULLE PICKED UP the phone on the first ring. He was prepared for the angry voice of Lolahta.

"There will be no exchange, no deal. But there will be something better," Lolahta threatened. "A public execution. Ten o'clock. I'm sure you'll be there."

Sulle listened to the dial tone for a moment and replaced the receiver. When he looked up he saw intense worry on the faces of Liam and Jorge.

"The federal agents are in place at Beau Monde," Jorge

said. "They have the expertise and equipment to take them all out."

"But not before he kills Molly," Sulle pointed out.

Jorge and Liam looked away. It was Jorge who spoke first. "This isn't your fault."

"Perhaps not," Sulle answered. "But it certainly isn't hers. Lolahta never wanted the chemicals. He wants revenge, on me. And Molly and Alan are his tools."

"The boy is safe," Liam threw in. "That's something."

"More than something," Sulle agreed. "But he needs his mother."

"What are you going to do?" Jorge asked, apprehension in his voice.

Sulle stood up. "He doesn't want Molly. He wants me. So I'm going to pay him a visit."

"He wants your son, too," Jorge hurried to say. "You know that revenge is handed from father to son. He can't allow the boy to live, to grow to understand what was done to his family. Alan is safe, for the moment. But eventually Lolahta will find him again."

"Lolahta won't be alive to worry about Alan. You seem to forget that he murdered my family. And boasts about it. I can't forget that."

Jorge and Liam exchanged glances. "Do you have an idea?" Jorge asked.

For the first time all evening, Sulle smiled. "I do. And one that may work. Let me tell you what I'm thinking."

MOLLY'S LEGS trembled, but she straightened her back and stood taller. The man holding the gun to her temple had to be as tired as she was. They'd been in the window for over an hour. It was after nine o'clock, and she'd heard Lolahta set the execution for ten. She almost laughed when she realized she was hoping the time would pass faster. An irony—wishing her life away.

At first she didn't believe the vision of Sulle walking toward the house was real. He strode with such confidence that she thought she was imagining things. And right beside him was the black cat, Familiar. Her heart took a violent lurch until she forced herself to remember that he was merely doing his job.

She focused on details, becoming the reporter she'd always been. Sulle had a small briefcase tucked in his hand. The doorbell rang, and she heard Lolahta's surprised curse when Sulle was announced.

At Lolahta's order, she was dragged from the window and at last allowed to sit. She sank into a chair with relief, and with a pounding heart. Sulle had not come to save her. He had made that clear. So what was he doing in the enemy's lair?

"You are a very foolish man," Victor said to Sulle as he led him from the front door into the room where Molly sat. Five armed men surrounded Sulle, weapons at the ready. She looked up and saw no emotion on Sulle's face. He lifted the small briefcase, and she recognized that it was a laptop computer.

"You brought a gift?" Lolahta said in a mocking voice. "Such good manners for a man who's about to die." He eyed the black cat, but otherwise ignored him.

"Open it," Sulle said easily. "There's something you should see. I have no use for Ms. Lynch, but there are others who feel differently." He snapped the lid open and booted it up.

Molly had no view of the screen, but she saw Lolahta's face. It went from stunned to outraged. "What kind of game is this?"

Sulle's face showed the tiniest hint of victory. "No game," he said. "Ms. Lynch's magazine is very widely read. Once this issue hits the streets, you're ruined."

"They have no proof—no documentation for these lies."

"They have everything they need. I gave it to them," Sulle said. "And once this story breaks, there's not a place in the world that will hide you. You've left a wide path of suffering behind you. No port will be safe. You will be a man without a country. And once your money runs out, a man without a friend."

Lolahta looked over at Molly. "How did she learn all of this?"

Sulle shrugged. "All along you thought she was a pawn. That was never the case. She was always investigating you. And she had information about you from years back."

Molly stifled the desire to speak out. Sulle was lying through his teeth. She'd gone to New Orleans in all innocence. Her goal had been to photograph and write about the death of a jazz musician. Instead of speaking, she watched the handsome man she'd loved for so many years lay out the cards that would decide her fate.

"How can I stop this from happening?" Lolahta asked, pointing at the computer screen.

"Release Molly. I'm still willing to sell you the chemicals." Sulle lifted one shoulder in a dismissive gesture. "They're loaded on the *Mary Jane.*"

Lolahta paced the room, ignoring the worried looks of his men. "How do I know you'll stop the magazine story?"

Sulle looked at Molly. She felt a flicker of something in his eyes, but she couldn't be certain what it was. His voice gave no hint of what he was thinking. "Ms. Lynch wants to be left alone to lead her life. She wants her son to be safe. If you don't bother her, I'm sure she won't print the article. But remember, it's already written, documented and ready to go. If she even suspects that you're trying to hurt her or Alan, she's the kind of woman who won't hesitate to set the presses in motion."

Molly saw the spark in Sulle's eyes again. Everything he said was one big lie. Her magazine wasn't running a story.

Sulle had somehow engineered it to make it look as if it were true. He was taking a tremendous gamble.

"I thought you didn't care for this woman," Lolahta said angrily. "Yet you risk your life to save her."

"My life is my work," Sulle said. "If you read the article, you'll see that she can also destroy me. You and I live in the dark shadows of the world, Victor. We can't afford exposure. I want my revenge on you, but I will seek it out in a private time. Not when it will make headlines." He walked to Lolahta and stared directly into his eyes. "We'll settle this when there's no one between us."

Sulle checked his watch. "My men are waiting to transfer the goods. If you leave now, you can still make it. If you aren't at the dock by ten o'clock, they have orders to get underway. There's still another buyer. One who is less troublesome."

Lolahta looked at Molly. "You haven't won, you know." He turned on his heel.

"Victor," Sulle called. "The money?"

"It's in the train depot." He reached into his pocket and pulled out a key. He tossed it across the room to Sulle. "By the time you get there, I'll have my merchandise and be on the way to the Gulf." He started to leave, then turned back. "This isn't over." Then he was gone.

Molly felt all her strength melt. She'd been tense for so long that she thought she might faint. Only the idea of Sulle staring at her kept her in her chair. She wouldn't look at him. What was there to say? He'd saved her life, that was true. He'd risked his own, another indisputable fact. None of it mattered. He'd done what he was trained to do, what he lived for. Neither she nor Alan was personally involved in the outcome. They were pawns. So they'd been saved in this game. Another time, another place and they would be expendable.

Sulle broke the silence. "Alan is with an old friend of mine. He's fine. He wants his mother."

Molly forced herself to stand. "Where is he? I have to go to him."

"I'll take you."

"I'd prefer if you didn't." Molly intended to get her son and get out of New Orleans as fast as possible. She didn't want Sulle in her future—not in any way.

"Lolahta won't be troubling you again."

"You think the idea of a magazine story will stop him? He's probably calculating a way to kill me, Alan and the entire staff of the magazine." Molly clenched her hands at her side.

"He won't be free much longer," Sulle said in an undertone. "Federal agents are waiting at the boat. As soon as he boards her and tries to leave, they'll arrest him. The string of charges will put him in jail for a thousand years."

Molly listened to Sulle calmly describe Lolahta's fate. He would be jailed. Her future looked much brighter, except for the unknown equation of Sulle Alamar. "So Alan and I can return to our lives." It was almost as much question as statement.

"Just as before," Sulle said. He stepped toward her.

"Just as before," she said, walking to the door, wondering why she felt no great relief at the obvious fact that Sulle was withdrawing from her life. She went past him and out into the night without even saying goodbye. At the steps she bent to retrieve Familiar, but the black cat darted from her grasp and went into the bushes.

"Familiar," she called, looking around. "Kitty, kitty."

Sulle walked to the door. "Leave him. Go and get Alan. I'll bring the cat to you tomorrow."

Molly nodded and then began to run down the sidewalk toward a car that was waiting with a red-haired driver she recognized.

So my services weren't needed in the final shoot-out. It's a good thing. This heat has me moving kind of slow. But I'm definitely going to have to do something about this romantic standoff. These two are so in love, and both too stubborn to admit it. Mysteries are my forte, but I'm also handy in the cupid department.

They don't call me the Furball of Love for nothing. Here comes Mr. Masterspy now. I'll hitch a ride down to the Mary Jane *and make sure the feds clean up properly. Then I'm going to give this big hunk a lesson in the fine art of life. Running around the world snaring criminals is all well and good, but there's a seven-year-old boy and a beautiful woman who need Sulle. So I guess he's going to have to give up his gallivanting life-style and try something a little more sedate. He won't do it willingly, but I have my ways.*

As for me, I haven't had a decent meal since I got involved with P-n-C. I want to settle their hash and then find something a little more gourmet for a late supper.

Sulle checked his appearance in the mirror one last time before he picked up the cat and started toward Molly's apartment. The federal agents had done a thorough job of cleaning up Lolahta's operation. His men, and Pauline Duprey, the pretend nanny, were all behind bars. The money had been collected from the train depot and turned over to the authorities.

Sulle was due in Washington in a week for reassignment. Something in the Balkans. He was determined to deliver the cat and leave without a word of explanation. It was the right decision. His instincts for protecting Molly and Alan were correct. They would have a better life without him.

"Let's go," he said to the cat.

"Meow," Familiar said agreeably, jumping into his arms.

He found a taxi and was at Molly's in less than ten minutes.

He wasn't prepared for the young boy who threw open the door and greeted him with a hug around his hips. "You saved my mother," Alan said, squeezing as hard as he could. Then he lifted Familiar from Sulle's arms. "And he saved mine. He made me climb down the tree."

"That's one smart cat," Sulle agreed.

He dreaded seeing Molly, but he walked inside. She was standing at a window, backlit and more beautiful than he remembered. "Goodbye, Molly," he said. "I won't be troubling you."

She nodded, and because of the lighting he couldn't see her face clearly.

The phone rang and Molly rushed toward it as if it were a lifeline. "Yes," she said. She looked at Sulle. "Yes, I know of the article, but—" She looked at Sulle again. "Yes, but—" She lowered the phone and handed it to him.

"It's for you." She stepped back, but not too far away.

Sulle took the phone and spoke into it. He never got another opportunity to speak again. After five minutes where he could only listen, he replaced the receiver. He took a breath and walked past Molly onto the balcony.

"What happened?" she asked, following him.

Sulle shook his head. "I don't know. No one knew about that story but Lolahta and us. My men never read it. I wrote it so quickly that I…" He shook his head again. "My cover is blown. I'm essentially fired."

Molly went to him. "I didn't do this, Sulle. I hope you believe that."

He stared into her green eyes. "There have been lies between us, Molly. All from me. I believe you."

"What will you do?" she asked.

"My work has always been my life. I never considered what I might do if I didn't have it." He felt a sharp prick on his shin and looked down. Familiar was standing on his back legs, pawing the air like a dog.

"What?" Sulle said.

With a growl, Familiar bit his shin in a not-so-gentle nip. Then he ran into the apartment. In a moment, Alan called out to his mother.

"Mom, Familiar is playing with the computer!"

Sulle looked at Molly. "The cat?" he asked, wondering if he was losing his mind along with his career. And the strange thing was that he wasn't upset about it. He actually felt as if an enormous weight had been lifted from him.

"He is extraordinary," Molly agreed. "But why…?" she didn't have time to finish before Familiar came out onto the balcony, Alan in tow. Hissing and growling, the cat herded them all together.

"Meow!" Familiar cried, swatting Sulle's leg. "Meow!"

Sulle looked at Molly and saw awareness dawn in her eyes. He looked into the expectant face of his son. His life had come to a crossroads, and it was up to him to make a choice. He felt the cat's claws in his calf and he bent down to scoop Familiar into his arm. "Easy, boy, give me a chance," he said, and his brown eyes seemed to mesmerize the cat.

He turned his attention to Molly. "I lied to you," he said. "When I told you I didn't care about you or Alan, it was the worst lie I've ever told. I did it to protect you. I wanted you to hate me so that you'd be safe."

Molly put her hand to her lips. Her eyes filled with tears. "I've always loved you, Sulle. Always. Even when I wanted to hate you. Even when you took me prisoner and made me leave Alan behind."

The young boy rolled his eyes. "If you two are going to talk mushy, I'm going inside to play with Familiar." He grinned at his mother and then ran into the apartment, taking care to close the door behind Familiar.

WELL, IT'S UP TO THEM now. I've done all I can. I wrecked his career and set up a confession. Not one of my more subtle moments, but time is running out. Eleanor and Peter only had a hotel booked for four days. I'd better hustle to the room and catch a ride back to D.C. and my eternally beautiful Clotilde.

Perhaps there's time for one meal here in sin city. Something Cajun and spicy and seafood. Something elegant. I do believe room service is in order. I'm sure Eleanor and Dr. Doolittle will gladly indulge me. Now that I'm through playing cupid, I can take on my favorite role—prodigal cat.

INTIMATE MOMENTS™

Sparked by danger, fueled by passion!

Passion.
Adventure.
Excitement.

**Enter a world that's
larger than life, where
men and women overcome
life's greatest odds for
the ultimate prize: love.
Nonstop excitement is
closer than you think...in
Silhouette Intimate Moments!**

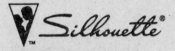

Visit Silhouette Books at www.eHarlequin.com

SIMDIR104

Emotional, compelling stories that capture the intensity of
living, loving and creating a family in today's world.

Modern, passionate reads that are powerful and provocative.

Romances that are sparked by danger and fueled by passion.

SILHOUETTE *Romance*

From today to forever, these love stories offer
today's woman fairytale romance.

Action-filled romances with strong, sexy, savvy women who save the day.

Visit Silhouette Books at www.eHarlequin.com   SILGENINT04

eHARLEQUIN.com

The Ultimate Destination for Women's Fiction

Visit eHarlequin.com's Bookstore today for today's most popular books at great prices.

- An extensive selection of romance books by top authors!

- Choose our convenient "bill me" option. No credit card required.

- New releases, Themed Collections and hard-to-find backlist.

- A sneak peek at upcoming books.

- Check out book excerpts, book summaries and Reader Recommendations from other members and post your own too.

- Find out what everybody's reading in Bestsellers.

- Save BIG with everyday discounts and exclusive online offers!

- Our Category Legend will help you select reading that's exactly right for you!

- Visit our Bargain Outlet often for huge savings and special offers!

- Sweepstakes offers. Enter for your chance to win special prizes, autographed books and more.

Your purchases are 100% guaranteed—so shop online at www.eHarlequin.com today!

INTBB104R

eHARLEQUIN.com

The Ultimate Destination for Women's Fiction

Your favorite authors are just a click away
at www.eHarlequin.com!

- Take a sneak peek at the covers and
  read summaries of **Upcoming Books**

- Choose from over 600
  author **profiles!**

- Chat with your favorite authors
  on our **message boards.**

- Are you an author in the making?
  Get advice from published authors
  in **The Inside Scoop!**

**Learn about your favorite authors
in a fun, interactive setting—
visit www.eHarlequin.com today!**

INTAUTH04R

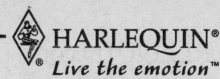

HARLEQUIN®
Live the emotion™

AMERICAN *Romance*®

Upbeat, All-American Romances

flipside

Romantic Comedy

Harlequin Historicals®
Historical Romantic Adventure!

HARLEQUIN®

INTRIGUE

Romantic Suspense

HARLEQUIN®

HARLEQUIN ROMANCE®

The essence of modern romance

HARLEQUIN®
Presents
Seduction and Passion Guaranteed!

HARLEQUIN *Super* ROMANCE®

Emotional, Exciting, Unexpected

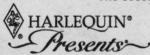

Temptation

Sassy, Sexy, Seductive!

www.eHarlequin.com   HDIR104

HARLEQUIN®
INTRIGUE®

WE'LL LEAVE YOU BREATHLESS!

If you've been looking for thrilling tales of
contemporary passion and sensuous love stories
with taut, edge-of-the-seat suspense—then
you'll love Harlequin Intrigue!

Every month, you'll meet six new heroes
who are guaranteed to make your spine tingle
and your pulse pound. With them you'll enter
into the exciting world of Harlequin Intrigue—
where your life is on the line
and so is your heart!

THAT'S INTRIGUE—
ROMANTIC SUSPENSE
AT ITS BEST!

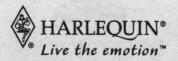

HARLEQUIN®
Live the emotion™

www.eHarlequin.com   INTDIR104

eHARLEQUIN.com

The Ultimate Destination for Women's Fiction

The eHarlequin.com online community is *the* place to share opinions, thoughts and feelings!

- Joining the community is easy, fun and **FREE!**

- Connect with **other romance fans** on our message boards.

- Meet your **favorite authors** without leaving home!

- **Share opinions** on books, movies, celebrities…and *more!*

Here's what our members say:

"I love the friendly and helpful atmosphere filled with support and humor."
—Texanna (eHarlequin.com member)

"Is this the place for me, or what? There is nothing I love more than 'talking' books, especially with fellow readers who are reading the same ones I am."
—Jo Ann (eHarlequin.com member)

Join today by visiting
www.eHarlequin.com!

INTCOMM04R

W9-BPI-747

"Come down here," Wes called to Anna, making no effort to lower his voice.

"Are you mad? Papa's in the next room. He'll hear—"

"I don't care. If you don't come down, I'm coming in after you."

Anna wasted no more time trying to reason with him. She could see it would do no good. Why had Wesley come here, risking discovery like this? Was he drunk? She pulled the back door open. He was there.

Before she could say a word, he thrust her back against the doorjamb and crushed his mouth down on hers. Unprepared for his assault, still she knew a thrill of sheer pleasure. There was no taste of whiskey in his mouth, just the familiar hot sweetness she always tasted when he kissed her. Every part of her body was telling her to cling, but reason warned of the danger.

Twisting against him, she pulled back and gasped, "What are you doing?"

"I want you, Anna," he said. "I want you now." He pulled her outside and away from the building. He was a different man tonight, all civilized restraints had dropped away somehow.

"This isn't the way to your house," she protested, fear and excitement mingling in her voice.

He led her quickly toward the woods. "It would take too much time to get to my house. You're mine, Anna. And when I want you, I'll take you...."

The Thirteen Books in the Delaney Dynasty Series
Ask your bookseller for the books you have missed

The Shamrock Trinity:

RAFE, THE MAVERICK
by Kay Hooper

YORK, THE RENEGADE
by Iris Johansen

BURKE, THE KINGPIN
by Fayrene Preston

The Delaneys of Killaroo:

ADELAIDE, THE ENCHANTRESS
by Kay Hooper

MATILDA, THE ADVENTURESS
by Iris Johansen

SYDNEY, THE TEMPTRESS
by Fayrene Preston

THIS FIERCE SPLENDOR by Iris Johansen

The Delaneys, The Untamed Years—I:

GOLDEN FLAMES
by Kay Hooper

WILD SILVER
by Iris Johansen

COPPER FIRE
by Fayrene Preston

The Delaneys, The Untamed Years—II:

VELVET LIGHTNING
by Kay Hooper

SATIN ICE
by Iris Johansen

SILKEN THUNDER
by Fayrene Preston

THE DELANEYS, THE UNTAMED YEARS
II

Silken Thunder

Fayrene Preston

BANTAM BOOKS
TORONTO • NEW YORK • LONDON • SYDNEY • AUCKLAND

SILKEN THUNDER

A Bantam Book / November 1988

All rights reserved.
Copyright © 1988 by Fayrene Preston.
Cover art copyright © 1988 by Rino Daeni.
No part of this book may be reproduced or transmitted
in any form or by any means, electronic or mechanical,
including photocopying, recording, or by any information
storage and retrieval system, without permission in
writing from the publisher.
For information address: Bantam Books.

ISBN 0-553-21979-0

Published simultaneously in the United States and Canada

Bantam Books are published by Bantam Books, a division of
Bantam Doubleday Dell Publishing Group, Inc. Its trademark,
consisting of the words "Bantam Books" and the portrayal
of a rooster, is Registered in U.S. Patent and Trademark Office
and in other countries. Marca Registrada. Bantam Books,
666 Fifth Avenue, New York, New York 10103.

PRINTED IN THE UNITED STATES OF AMERICA

O   0 9 8 7 6 5 4 3 2 1

Silken Thunder

THE DELANEY DYNASTY

Shamus Delaney m. 1828 Malvina Kelly

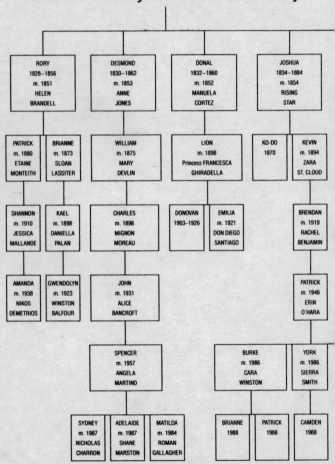

RORY
1828–1856
m. 1851
HELEN
BRANDELL

DESMOND
1830–1862
m. 1853
ANNE
JONES

DONAL
1832–1860
m. 1852
MANUELA
CORTEZ

JOSHUA
1834–1884
m. 1854
RISING
STAR

PATRICK
m. 1880
ETAINE
MONTEITH

BRIANNE
m. 1873
SLOAN
LASSITER

WILLIAM
m. 1875
MARY
DEVLIN

LION
m. 1898
Princess FRANCESCA
GHIRADELLA

KO-DO
1870

KEVIN
m. 1894
ZARA
ST. CLOUD

SHANNON
m. 1910
JESSICA
MALLANDE

KAEL
m. 1898
DANIELLA
PALAN

CHARLES
m. 1898
MIGNON
MOREAU

DONOVAN
1903–1926

EMILIA
m. 1921
DON DIEGO
SANTIAGO

BRENDAN
m. 1919
RACHEL
BENJAMIN

AMANDA
m. 1938
NIKOS
DEMETRIOS

GWENDOLYN
m. 1923
WINSTON
BALFOUR

JOHN
m. 1931
ALICE
BANCROFT

PATRICK
m. 1946
ERIN
O'HARA

SPENCER
m. 1957
ANGELA
MARTINO

BURKE
m. 1986
CARA
WINSTON

YORK
m. 1986
SIERRA
SMITH

SYDNEY
m. 1987
NICHOLAS
CHARRON

ADELAIDE
m. 1987
SHANE
MARSTON

MATILDA
m. 1984
ROMAN
GALLAGHER

BRIANNE
1988

PATRICK
1988

CAMDEN
1988

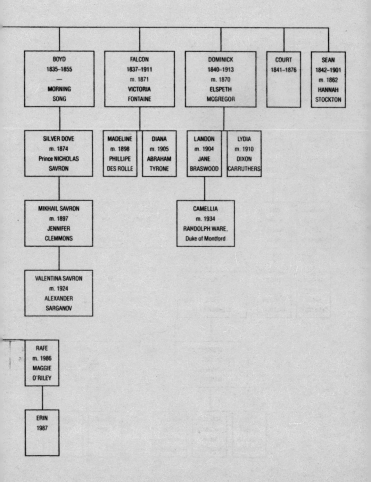

1

1873, Territory of Colorado

Oh, God, Sloan was dying.

Brianne's hands clenched slowly until her nails cut half circles into her palm. Just yesterday he'd smiled at her and spoken of their future together. She'd been so sure he was on his way to recovery. But in the night he'd grown steadily worse, and at one point had gone into convulsions. Frantic to help him, she'd jammed a stick into his mouth and held him while his powerful muscles twitched and jerked. The seizure had lasted only a few minutes, but it had seemed a lifetime to her.

Now he was unconscious, mumbling incoherently and thrashing about. She'd never been so scared in her life. She'd never felt so helpless in her life.

Damn Dan Cummings. She should have killed him when she had the chance. By the time she'd been

able to get to the tent city, he and his men had
beaten Sloan almost senseless. That had been early
Sunday morning. She'd set fire to the whole place
and gotten Sloan out of there. Their ride of escape
had been grueling for both of them and, in addition,
torturously painful for Sloan.

It had been late that afternoon when she'd come
across this box canyon inside the butte. It had offered what she'd been searching for—concealment
and shelter. At that time she'd believed that Sloan
needed only to rest. Now she knew he needed much
more. He was gravely ill and suffering terribly. She
had to help him. But how?

Only she stood between Sloan and death, but, dear
Lord, she knew so little about nursing. Rising Star,
her aunt, had taught her the rudiments of herbal
medicine, but how could she find the necessary herbs
here in Colorado, in territory that was unfamiliar?
Only with luck. And hers seemed to have run out. Or
with time. And she had precious little.

Sloan moaned and threw out his arm, hitting her
across the chest. She gasped at the pain of the blow,
but didn't recoil. She placed his arm at his side and
bent forward to touch his forehead. He was on fire.

The need for more water was desperate. At the far
end of the meadow there was a creek of fresh, clear
water that meandered through a stand of willows
and cottonwoods. She had their horses picketed there,
and by now they needed tending. But could she leave
Sloan alone for the length of time it would take her
to collect the water, see to the horses, and return? If

he got to thrashing about, he might injure himself even more. On the other hand, she reasoned, if she didn't get water into him and on him to lower his fever, he was going to die.

How could she leave him?

How could she not?

She bent close to his ear. "Sloan, I'm going down to the meadow. I'll try not to be gone long, but you've got to stay still."

His head turned toward the sound of her voice, but his eyes remained closed and his mutterings unintelligible.

"I love you, Sloan," she said, but the tears and fears that were clogging her throat broke her words into soft, disjointed pieces.

Their shelter was a shallow cave carved into the side of the box canyon about twenty-five feet above a meadowed floor. A shelf edged the cave's mouth and curved downward to the meadow.

Brianne followed the path, surprised to find her legs so leaden. Putting one foot in front of the other was suddenly a major chore. When her rifle slipped from her hand, clattered to the rocky ledge, and then slid off to fall some twenty feet to the ground below, she was forced to stop and lean against the canyon's wall.

A shroud of weariness clung to her like a soggy cloak, weighing her down. She shook her head and took several deep breaths, trying to chase away the dull-witted numbness she was feeling. She couldn't allow herself to falter. More from instinct than from thought, one hand dropped to the butt of the gun that was resting in its holster on her hip. She was all too aware that she had to be constantly on guard. All her senses were telling her that menace was not far away.

Once on the floor of the canyon, she retrieved the rifle. Frightened that it might have been damaged, she looked it over, then levered a bullet through the chamber. It was a relief to find that it still worked.

As she crossed the meadow, trying her best to hurry, the natural beauty of the riotously blooming wild-flowers and the long grasses escaped her. Instead, she took wary note of the deeply carved arroyos and the huge rocks and boulders that would make excel-lent cover for Cummings and his men if—no, when . . . no, *if*—they managed to discover where she and Sloan were hiding.

The horses seemed to be in good shape. Impatient to get back to Sloan, she watered them quickly and moved them to a new grazing area. Then she filled the two canteens and half ran back to the cave.

She heard birds chirping as they fluttered from tree to tree, and the soft rustling of the wind as it stirred through the grass, and the scurrying of small, unseen animals as they darted out of her way. The creek babbled as it meandered through the canyon. There was life and movement all around, but she felt only death and an ominous stillness.

Never had she been so alone. Her family had al-ways surrounded her, protected her, loved her. And even now she knew they were trying to get to her.

But this was Tuesday and their help was still days away. By the time they arrived, it might very well be too late.

She was halfway up the path that led to the cave when the full force of what she was thinking hit her. She could depend on no one but herself! She felt a smothering moment of blind panic. No.... She couldn't do this.... She *couldn't* save the man in the cave, so terribly hurt and ill. She *couldn't* protect them both from the men searching for them with such deadly intensity. Not alone.

Lord, what was she thinking? There was no question that she would have to do it. There was no one else. She had to pull herself together. From somewhere deep inside she was going to have to find a well of courage and strength that she'd never had to tap before. She prayed she could find it.

She skidded to a stop, and her eyes widened in horror. "God, Sloan, what are you doing?"

He was standing up just inside the cave, swaying unsteadily. Pain and confusion glazed his eyes, but when she called his name, he took a step toward her. Instinctively she jumped to help him, but she wasn't quick enough. He fell, striking his head against a rock, and what seemed like a river of blood came gushing out.

"Oh, God." Fear rose like bile in her throat. He couldn't be dead. He couldn't be ... but he was lying so still, his head at such an odd angle.

She scrambled to him and groped for a pulse at his neck. It seemed like an eternity before she managed to make out a faint beat and she went weak with relief. "Sloan, I need you to be all right," she whispered. "Please wake up now." She was only vaguely aware of the tears that had begun to stream down her face. "You've got to wake up, or I'm not going to be able to help you." She reached a trembling hand to his forehead and her fingers came away wet with blood. Then she saw that his blood had already stained a spot on the ground.

Flying into action, she rummaged through the contents of their two saddlebags and came out with a rag Sloan used to clean his guns. The cloth was filthy, and she tossed it aside. Without another thought she reached down and withdrew the knife she kept sheathed in her boot. Lifting the hem of one leg of her riding skirt as much as it would allow, she cut clear around the leg of the pantalets, then made a long downward slit. Soon she was folding a large, clean white piece of material into a pad and pressing it against his wound.

When she had stemmed the bleeding as best she could, she threw a glance over her shoulder at the makeshift bed she had put together from pine needles and leaves. She gauged he was lying about two feet away from it. Somehow she had to get him back there.

She positioned herself above his head, grasped his arms, and pulled. She couldn't even budge him. His body was dead weight. She dug her boot heels into the ground and tried again. An aching crept into her back, but she kept at it until she had moved him an inch, then two, then three.

The movement and pulling on his arms brought him around, and he groaned. "No!"

The pain was thick and an unendurable agony. He was swimming through its thickness, using all his might, but it seemed to be no use. He couldn't break free of the fiery waves. They were endless. And the sun was making it so much worse. He remembered how hot that West Texas desert had been, but it had never hurt like this. This was like being cooked alive.

Leaning over him, Brianne stroked his face. The heat of his skin nearly scorched her fingers. Dear God, she was causing him even more pain, but what else could she do?

Her heart felt as if it were breaking. She brushed at the wetness on her face. The need to make him understand what she was trying to do was very important. "I know I'm hurting you, Sloan, but I've got to get you back into the cave."

"No," he said, this time quieter.

"I'm sorry," she murmured, "I'm so sorry." Her tears broke free again, but she took hold of his arms. She'd managed to move him only another inch or so when he began fighting her. As weak as he was, he still remained a powerful man by anyone's standards.

At first she could only try to keep him from hurting himself and her. "Sloan, stop. It's Brianne. Stop."

But he couldn't hear her. His eyes were wild and

he was mumbling words that were unconnected and muddled.

She was aching and sore. Every time his hand connected with some part of her body, he inflicted a new bruise, but it was nothing to the inner pain she was suffering. She couldn't seem to make him understand who she was and what he was doing. His delirium had taken him beyond her reach.

Her chest hurt with the exertion of her efforts, and her throat was tight with anguish. Tears overflowed her eyes, and she had no energy to arrest them. "Sloan," she cried, "please . . . don't do this."

Someone was calling to him. A woman. Her voice sounded familiar, but he didn't know who she was. All he knew was that she was hurting him, and he wanted her to stop. Every time she moved him, a searing agony twisted in his gut, and waves of violent pain exploded in his head. She was torturing him, and he had to make her leave him alone.

At first she didn't realize it when the signs came that his strength was ebbing. But when she did, she began to seize every opportunity she could to use the motion of his wildly flailing limbs to propel his body toward the pallet. Sweat broke out over her, moistened her skin, and in some places seeped through the cloth of her blouse to dampen it. Her arms hurt. The muscles in her legs trembled and burned.

Then, suddenly, unexpectedly, his strength gave out, and she used the last bit of her energy to roll him over onto the bed. She collapsed beside him, panting, out of breath, with an ache vibrating up and down every bone in her body.

That she'd been able to get him onto the bed was a miracle, and she knew she wouldn't be able to do it again. She had to take measures to make sure nothing like that would happen again, *now*, before he came around again. She pushed upright, then put her feet beneath her and tried to stand. But her legs folded beneath her, and she fell back down. She was simply too exhausted, and her legs wouldn't hold her weight.

Closing her eyes, she lay perfectly still, willing away the tremors that were racking the muscles in her arms and legs. Her body was telling her that she desperately needed to rest. But her mind was telling her that she wouldn't be able to fight Sloan again, either physically or mentally.

With horror she realized what she was going to have to do.

She rolled over and, using her elbows, dragged herself to the saddlebags. She found what she was looking for with no problem—a coil of rope.

Crawling back to Sloan, she fought against the fresh flood of tears that came up out of her, wrenching her heart and her body with their strength. Dear sweet heaven, this was a nightmare. She didn't want to do this to him. At the same time she knew she had no choice.

Kneeling beside him, she managed to get his wrists together and loop a length of rope around them, but her hands were clumsy when she attempted the knot. Silently she cursed herself. The task was taking far longer than it should. She tried again, this time managing to get the rope knotted.

Suddenly Sloan yanked against the rope.

With a gasp she turned to look at him, and what she saw nearly stopped her heart. His face was contorted with anguish. Even in his unconscious state he was trying to pull away from her and the rope. He was like that wolf she had so long ago tried to befriend, with the same deep-seated, primitive fear of being trapped and powerless.

He was lashing out in earnest now. Frantically she fought to hold him down while she secured the rope around his ankles. His foot landed a blow to her body, then another, but she stayed beside him, working with the rope while trying to duck the punishment of his feet. At last she had him tied up.

She collapsed beside him. Exhaustion pulled at her, doing its best to suck her down into a world of oblivion and deep peace, but she was afraid to let go. She had to try to get Sloan's fever down, and she had to be constantly alert for Cummings and his men.

And, dear Lord, what if Sloan died while she slept? As she lay beside him, she could feel the heat of his fever. What if she woke to find him still and cold? Going to sleep would be like deserting him, and she couldn't do that.

She fought with all her might to stay awake, but in the end she lost the battle and sleep claimed her.

*   *   *

"Cally, damn you . . . why did you do it to me?"

Sloan's screams brought her to full wakefulness with fear pounding through her veins. She grabbed for her gun, but a quick scan of the cave showed her no intruders. Confused, she took more careful note of her surroundings. She had no idea how long she'd been asleep, but it was now night. The fire had burnt down, and the air in the cave had turned damp and cold. A light rain was falling out in the box canyon.

She swiveled around to Sloan. It took only a slight caress of his face to tell her that his fever had climbed even higher during the few hours she'd slept.

"Cally . . . why . . . why . . ." His voice trailed off. Emotion had choked his voice.

What was he saying? She knelt beside him, barely able to see his face. "Sloan, it's me, Brianne."

"Cally . . ."

He was calling her by another woman's name. Something that felt like barbed wire twisted in her heart. She knew only too well that he was delirious. But . . . the knowledge didn't make it any easier for her to bear.

She cupped his face and tried to make him look at her. "It's Brianne, Sloan. It's me."

His eyes focused on her, or so it seemed to her in the dark.

"David?" he asked softly.

"No," she sobbed, crying so hard that her lungs were beginning to hurt. Where were all the tears coming from, she wondered. "Sloan, I'm Brianne. Can't you see me?"

"David," he said even more softly.

David's face was so close. With his blond hair and blue eyes he looked so much like their mother. God, but it had been so long since he'd seen him. He felt an incredible happiness come over him. "I've been so lonely without you," he said to David.

She rocked back on her heels and pressed the palms of her hands hard against her eyes. She had to get hold of herself. A weariness that went all the way to her bones slowed her actions, but she crawled over to the fire and built it back up, thinking that in the morning she would have to collect more aspen leaves and wood. Glancing around for the two canteens, she saw them and her rifle out on the ledge. Then she remembered. When she'd walked into the cave and seen Sloan standing up, she had dropped everything.

Levering herself to her feet, she was glad to discover that at least now her legs seemed willing to support her weight. She retrieved her rifle first, checked it, then carefully propped it against the cave's wall, within easy reach.

When she turned her attention to the canteens, she let out a gasp of despair. One was full, the other empty, its cap unscrewed and its contents pooled around it.

She rubbed her forehead with a trembling hand and tried to remain calm as she thought the matter through. She was going to need much more water than the one full canteen. It seemed she had no other alternative. She was going to have to go back down to the creek for more.

She knelt beside Sloan. "I've got to go get some more water, but I'll be as quick as I can. I promise." She knew he couldn't hear her, of course, but somehow talking to him made her feel better. By the fire's light she could make out the awful bruises and cuts on his face and the way his dark hair lay in disorder around his head. She loved him so much, she thought as she pressed her lips to the dry heat of his forehead.

He jerked his head away. "Cally!"

She started down the path. The rain had let up, and the moon had come out, providing some light. She'd been down this ledge path and across the meadow several times now, although never at night and never with the ground as slippery as it was now.

She slipped and fell, rocks biting into her hands. Her leg dangled over the edge. She was close to the same place where earlier in the day her rifle had slid off the ledge, fallen some twenty feet, and bounced off a rock before coming to rest in the grass. Now the same thing had nearly happened to her.

Cold horror held her in its grip. If she'd fallen, Sloan would have been left defenseless. She'd bound his hands and feet for his own protection, but if something happened to her, he would be totally vulnerable to the savagery of the elements and wild animals. And, perhaps even worse, to Dan Cummings.

Sloan's death would be a certainty.

For the first time in her life she realized that she was in a position where she couldn't be careless with herself. She was the only chance Sloan had, and he was completely dependent upon her.

She pulled her leg back up and got slowly to her feet. Brushing her sore, bleeding hands down the sides of her riding skirt, she started out again, this time taking extra precautions to make sure that she had firm footing.

Even so, she had trouble. The darkness, her weariness, and her intense concern about Sloan were combining against her. She'd always taken her physical grace for granted, but now she had to concentrate.

Upon returning, she emptied a portion of one of the canteens into a pan and set it over the fire. She wanted to bathe her hands and the new wound on his head. While she waited for the water to heat, she listened carefully to Sloan's muttered ravings. He kept talking about the woman named Cally. Who was she, Brianne wondered. She'd known that Sloan would have had many women before her. But this woman had obviously been important enough in his life that even held tightly in the grip of a raging fever, he called out to her.

When it came right down to it, what did she know about his life before she'd met him? That during the Civil War he'd been a blockade runner. That he was a successful financier. That he lived in New York City but had been raised in East Texas. And that he'd come to Chango to seek vengeance against Wes McCord for his brother, David's, death fifteen years earlier.

He'd never mentioned a woman to her, and, she

realized with a sinking heart, it wasn't impossible that he was married.

She'd fallen in love with him. Given her virginity to him. Risked her life to save his. But she was just beginning to understand that in many ways he remained a closed book to her. Just after meeting Sloan she had told her brother Patrick that she thought the stranger was a very dark and dangerous man. He'd certainly turned out to be those things and more. *Complex* was now the word that came to mind. She didn't know him at all.

Brianne took the pot from the fire, cut a large piece of material off the other leg of her pantalets, and made her way over to Sloan. Hampered though he was by the ropes, he was still tossing and turning, restless in his fever.

The tenuous control she held over her emotions nearly shattered when she saw that his wrists had been rubbed raw from his efforts to break free. He was panicked and afraid, and as much as she loved him, and as hard as she was trying to help him, she couldn't even reach him to quiet his instinctive fears.

She cleaned the wound on the side of his head, then opened his shirt. The bruises he'd received from the vicious beating had darkened since the last time she'd checked. Large, ugly discolorations covered nearly every square inch of his chest. In a few places the skin was puffy and broken, and she could see the start of what appeared to be infection. In the firelight the bruises looked almost black.

She gently sponged his face, arms, and chest despite his ceaseless attempts to flinch away from her touch. She knew she was hurting him, but it was vital that his fever be brought down. She silently wept as she confronted anew the brutal evidence of how badly his body had been damaged. And she was seeing only what was on the surface. God only knew what was going on inside him. He could be bleeding.

She had no idea how long she worked over him. When one arm would become tired, she'd change to the other. At one point she stripped off his trousers and washed down his legs. Several times she managed to get some moisture into his mouth by squeezing the rag against his lips.

She ignored the ache in her back, and the muscle spasms that threatened her arms. She drove her own pain and weariness from her mind and continued in her efforts to cool his fever.

"Oh, God, I murdered him. I murdered him."

She had her back turned to Sloan and was adding more wood to the fire when she heard him scream. She whirled and ran back to him. "Sloan, what's wrong?"

"I murdered him." His voice was thick and hoarse.

"Wake up, Sloan. Wake up."

He mumbled something, but she couldn't quite make it out. Then he opened his eyes and looked straight at her. "That was a . . . hell of a . . . ride we had."

Gratitude without measure washed over her. "Thank God. You're going to be all right."

"I think that property by the river is a good investment," he said very clearly.

She slumped, crestfallen. For one brief moment he'd been with her. Now he was gone again, and it scared the hell out of her.

"Untie me, dammit."

"Sloan, I can't." The anguish in his voice nearly broke her heart in two. She took him into her arms and held him, rocking him back and forth in an agony of tenderness. "Just be still," she murmured. "Just be still."

"I'm glad you're here."

His words were spoken tenderly, but this time she didn't make the mistake of thinking that he was speaking to her. Somehow she knew he was talking to someone else. She kissed his cheek. His skin was so dry it felt like tissue paper to her lips. But was it any cooler? She couldn't tell. "I'm glad I'm here too."

"I hurt, Mama."

He thought she was his mother, but she was past caring that he didn't recognize her. She'd do anything, be anyone who would bring him comfort. She held him closer and began crooning him an Irish lullaby that Malvina had sung to her many times.

"I wish I could see you," he said. "I'm so lonely."

She understood, she thought. Since Sunday she'd learned all about loneliness. How it could weaken your spirit, how it could gradually gnaw away at your soul, and how it could make you feel as if you'd been forsaken. But feeling sorry for herself would serve no purpose. She continued her lullaby, singing in a soft, broken voice until he drifted off again.

Then, holding his heated body to her breast, she leaned back against the cold, clammy rock wall of the cave and stared out into the darkness. Layers of everything she had thought she was—her strength, her talents, her self-assurance—felt as if they were peeling away, leaving her raw and unprotected.

She had always been sure that she had the ability to do almost anything. Now she was realizing that there was something she couldn't beat. *Death*. And oh, dear God, she could feel it drawing closer and closer.

2

Wes McCord stared grimly at the desolate, blackened ruins of what only two days earlier had been the heart of his scheme for achieving his dream of immeasurable wealth and power. His tent city . . . the place where he'd marshaled men and supplies for the railroad he was going to bring through Chango.

He'd gotten his financing. He'd put men and supplies in place. He'd worked damned hard. And now this.

His gray eyes scanned the devastation around him. More had been destroyed than Dutch had originally reported to him. All the tents were gone, and most of the supplies and building materials too.

The fire had proved costly in terms of both money and time. The people in Washington weren't going to be happy about this delay in starting the railroad

19

line. They might even withdraw the grant money and award the contract to someone else.

Cold fear twisted slowly in his gut. He couldn't allow his project to fail. He was *not* going to lose everything he'd worked for.

Absorbed as he was in his thoughts, the sound of hooves and the squeak of leather behind him came as a surprise. He whirled to see Dutch. He pinned the muscular younger man with a hard stare and barked a question. "Has Cummings found Lassiter and that Delaney woman?"

Deciding not to dismount, Dutch merely shook his head. He didn't need a closer look to tell him that McCord was in a dangerous, black mood. "Seems that girl's pretty good at losing people."

"Dammit, she's got an injured man with her. It can't be that difficult. You go back and tell him to find those two people."

"It's gonna be kinda hard to find Cummings again."

"Don't give me that bullshit."

Tossing up his head, the horse shied at the hard, angry voice and took a couple of dancing steps. Dutch got the horse back under control and leveled a look at McCord. "It's just that Cummings is movin' awful fast. He's not even givin' the men with him a chance to rest."

"No one rests until those two are found and I've got my ledger back. No one. Understand?"

Dutch straightened in the saddle. "Yes, sir, Mr. McCord."

"Round up some men and ride out again. Split up if you need to. But track down Cummings. I want constant reports as to what's happening."

"Yes, sir." He reined his horse around and headed off into the gathering darkness. He was caught between two madmen—Cummings and McCord—and it wasn't a safe place to be. If that ledger wasn't found soon, Dutch reflected, he just might ride out one of these days and not come back.

Wes turned back to view what was left of the tent city. Ruination and disorder were everywhere he looked, and he couldn't shake the terrifying feeling that perhaps it was an omen.

When I find you, Sloan, you're going to pay for what you've done.

Before Sloan had come to town, he'd had everything arranged just as he wanted. Anna. The railroad. All the money and power he'd ever wanted within easy grasp. Now he could feel control slipping away from him.

Dark memories were crowding in on him, and suddenly he wasn't standing in the middle of a burnt-out tent city. He was a little boy in a Nevada mining camp, his stomach empty and cramping with hunger, his thin body shivering with cold.

His hands flew up and clenched his skull with a viselike grip. He *had* to push the specter of that little boy out of his mind. Never again would he allow himself to be so hungry . . . for anything.

Wild with emotion, he spun around. "You," he

barked at a cowhand who was passing, "bring me my horse."

He rode the horse flat out, mercilessly whipping it to ever greater speed. By the time he got to Chango, it was late. His horse was lathered and blowing hard, froth dripping from its mouth.

Wes reined in so hard and fast at the stables that the horse lunged back on its haunches. He leapt off and threw the reins to the stableboy.

Without looking back he headed through the dark streets to Nilsen's Emporium. On an ordinary night quiet would have settled over the town by this time. But this evening Wes saw signs of distinct unrest. Men still milled about, or stood in groups of twos and threes, speaking in hushed tones. And when they saw him, their heads lifted and their gazes followed him. It was obvious that everyone in town had heard about the goings-on out at the tent city, and they were speculating about events, though no one dared approach him with the questions they'd come up with over long hours of gossip.

He turned into a side street that would take him around to the back of the emporium. By now the townspeople would have figured out that the fire was going to cause delays and other problems for the railroad. Everyone would be affected in some way. Suddenly their prospects for the future didn't seem so bright; their pleasant lives, full of promise of even more prosperity, might not be so pleasant for a while.

A thin smile touched Wes's lips. He'd never known a pleasant day in his life. Fear and restlessness constantly pushed him, giving him little rest. Usually he was able to keep a check on the turmoil that churned so violently inside him, concealing the traits that would betray it. But he'd had two days to ponder the consequences of the fire and the possibility that he wouldn't get the ledger back. Two days for frustration and fury to work its corrosive way into his soul.

He stopped beneath the second story window of Anna's bedroom and looked up. Christ. How many times had he stood there when the demons that drove him wouldn't allow him to sleep? At those times he'd done nothing more than stare at the window like a calf-sick boy.

Well, by God, he was going to do more than that tonight. He hurled a spray of pebbles at the window.

When Anna heard the pebbles hit the window, she jerked upright in bed.

What on earth?

She threw back the covers and hurried over to the window. Although she'd retired sometime earlier, she hadn't been able to sleep, and the flame in the lamp beside her bed still burned brightly. But when she looked out and saw Wesley, she wondered if she might be dreaming. He'd *never* done anything like this before.

Taking pains to be quiet, she eased up the window and stuck her head out. "What is it?" she called in a whisper.

"Come down here," he said, making no effort to lower his voice.

"Shhh. Are you mad? Papa's just in the next room. He'll hear—"

"I don't give a damn. If you don't come down, I'm coming in after you."

Anna wasted no more time trying to reason with him. She could see it would do no good. He was in some wild, strange mood that she didn't recognize. She closed the window and left her room on the fly. Alarm beat in her heart as her bare feet skimmed across the floor of her room and down the plank stairs to the storeroom of the emporium. Why had Wesley come here, risking discovery like this? She'd never seen him drunk, but she'd heard what had happened out at the tent city. She supposed it was possible that he might have turned to whiskey. Even so. He should never have come. . . .

Reaching the back door, she quickly grasped the knob, turned, then pulled.

And Wesley was there.

She hardly had a chance to take in his dusty, disheveled appearance before he was shoving her back against the doorjamb and crushing his mouth down on hers. Unprepared for his assault, she knew a thrill of sheer pleasure.

There was no taste of whiskey in his mouth, but rather the familiar hot sweetness she always tasted when he kissed her. Every part of her body that could feel was telling her to cling, but the thought that they were standing in the back doorway of the store where her father or even a passerby might see them made her recover quickly.

Twisting and pushing against him until she gained some space, she gasped out, "What are you doing?"

He laughed softly, but there was something she'd never seen before burning in his pale gray eyes. "I thought it would be obvious. I didn't have you last night. I want you now."

"I went to your house as usual," she whispered fiercely. "You weren't there."

He pressed into her again, and the thin lawn gown she was wearing proved no shield against either the rough wood of the door frame or him.

"You sound upset," he said, his voice a mocking growl. "Did you miss me?"

"No, of course not."

"I missed you. *God*, how I missed you."

Frantically she pushed against him. "Wesley, I don't know if Papa is asleep yet or not. And even if he is, he could wake up at any time."

"Then let's get away from here." He moved suddenly, grabbing her arm and pulling her outside and away from the emporium.

For a moment she was too stunned to resist, her mind slow to follow his actions. He was a different man tonight from the one she'd come to know, and it frightened her. It was as if all civilized restraints had dropped away from him and left his nerves exposed and his emotions raw.

"Wesley, wait a minute. I don't understand. Where are you taking me? This isn't the way to your house."

His long strides never faltered as he dragged her along with him, away from the town, and into the woods that rimmed one side of Chango. "It would take too much time to get to my house," he muttered.

Her blood congealed as she realized that, too impatient to take her to his bed, he planned to have her in the woods like some rutting animal. The idea horrified and disgusted her. "No!" She wrenched away from him and took off, running back toward the town. Darkness enveloped her, the branches of the trees tore at her gown and painfully snagged her long pale hair. Her foot came down on something sharp, and she stumbled. Too quickly, then, she was caught up in his arms.

Moonlight shaded the hard, hungry look on his face, giving him a formidable, virile, and unconquerable air. To her despair, she felt fear and excitement whip through her.

"You're mine, Anna. Don't ever forget that. And when I want you, I'll take you." He turned on his heel and strode off with her toward the heart of the woods.

She beat her fists against his chest, but he was holding her so close her efforts were futile. "This isn't part of our deal. We're not supposed to be together tonight."

His laugh might have scared away wild animals, she thought, for it was cold and menacing.

"New rules, Anna."

"That's not fair," she cried out.

"You expected fairness from me?" he asked as he broke free of the woods and advanced into a glade.

Clouds passed across the moon. Silver light shone, disappeared, then reappeared moments later. There was hardly a break in his movements as he laid her on the ground and came down on top of her.

She didn't have an opportunity to draw a breath before his mouth was claiming hers with a fierceness that shocked her to her toes. It was as if a blind, hungry need held him in its grip, and nothing she could do would stop him from taking her. But she tried. Oh, how she tried.

She clawed at him, scratching his face and drawing blood. She hit out with furious energy and attempted to kick him off her. He dealt with her rebellion, easily capturing her wrists with one hand and pinning them above her head. "Don't fight me, Anna. You could get hurt."

"This *does* hurt."

"Stop fighting me, then. I want you right here, right now, and if you'll admit it, you want me too." His voice was thick and hoarse, and in the shadowed moonlight his eyes seemed to glitter like hot liquid silver. "*Damn*, you've got to many clothes on."

"No," she cried, but he ripped her gown from neck to hem, exposing her pale body to him. She felt the cool night air for only a moment, then he was kissing her again, and the hand that wasn't holding her

wrists was taking possession of her breast. A ball of
heat formed in her stomach and with every touch,
with every kiss, grew bigger and stronger.

How could that be, she wondered wildly. With
complete indifference to either her comfort or pleasure, he was ravishing her. Even as that thought
raced through her mind, his knee jammed itself between her thighs and pressed upward, and his tongue
thrust deep into her mouth. A lightning bolt of pleasure hurtled through her, leaving her shaken. Furious with herself, she bit down hard on his lip.

"Damn." His head lifted, and his fingers touched
the blood welling in his mouth. Incredibly, then, he
smiled down at her. "You like to bite? You never told
me. But that's all right. We can play that game for a
while."

Her respite from his mouth was brief. He lowered
his head to her breast and began nipping around the
already erect nipple. Flames of desire swept through
her, eating away her resistance. Surely she was losing her mind. Every time his teeth made contact
with her skin, he created sharp, hot sensations deep
inside her. It was unbearably exciting.

"Don't fight me, Anna," he said, "I need you too
damned bad."

She failed to stifle the moan that escaped her, but
she knew she had to put a stop to this madness
before she was lost completely to the treacherous
ecstasy. "Wesley, you can't—"

Her cries bounced off him as if he were made of

stone. Her wishes and needs couldn't pierce through the wall of driving passion surrounding him. He lifted his hips, quickly opened his trousers, and positioned himself between her legs.

She wasn't ready, she thought desperately. She was too tense, too dry. He was going to tear her apart.

He bent his head and put his mouth to a particular patch of skin that lay at the juncture of her neck and shoulder. Then he licked. Hot shivers coursed through her.

His mouth moved against her neck, and he muttered something she couldn't understand.

Weakly she pushed against him. "Wait, Wesley. I'm not—"

He wasn't listening.

He drove powerfully into her, and, at the same time, he bit at her throat so that his teeth scraped the wildly sensitive nerves just beneath the skin there.

She screamed in ecstasy and clutched at him. This couldn't be happening, she thought. She wanted him, shamelessly, wantonly, in this way, with no waiting, no gentleness. Inflamed, beyond belief, her responses turned frenzied and demanding. She bucked and twisted beneath him in a fever of compulsive urgency, of primal desire. He slammed into her time after time, and she couldn't get enough. She implored and beseeched and sobbed . . . and she had no idea what words she was using.

Something powerful and violent began to take shape

and move within her. She was sure that she was
going to burn in the fire ... be drowned by the
rapture. She heard cries and dimly wondered what
animals made them. And then sound vanished as did
everything else. Everything, that is, but the fire ...
the rapture ... and Wesley.

His weight was heavy on her, but she was too
exhausted to protest. And stunned. She'd never known
that such emotions existed in her. Where had they
come from?

In the past she'd had such difficulty dealing with
the way Wesley could so easily extract wanton sensual responses from her. But tonight had been different. There'd been something raw and primitive in
the way she had acted. In its own way, her behavior
was as frightening to her as his was.

He rolled to one side and came up on an elbow.
"Anna ..."

She sat up quickly and pulled the pieces of her
nightgown together over her breasts. "I've got to go
home. Papa might have awakened."

He touched her arm. "Are you all right?"

"If he has, I don't know what I can possibly tell
him. I—I guess I'll think of something. I've grown
very good at telling lies."

"Let me carry you back. You'll hurt your feet."

Her laugh was hollow. "It's a little late to be concerned about my feet ... or anything else, don't you
think?"

"Anna . . ."

She stood and felt a fine mist on her face. *How strange.* This was the first time she'd noticed that the air was cool and rain was only minutes from falling. She turned. She had to get away. "Good night, Wesley."

Back in her bedroom, she was relieved to hear only silence from the room where her father slept. She shrugged out of what was left of her nightgown, folded the shredded material, and stuffed it into a bureau drawer. Then, curious, she walked to the mirror.

Shock held her still as she took in her image. Wesley had kissed her so often and so hard that her face and lips appeared to be swollen. Her long golden hair flared outward from her head, tousled and tangled, with bits of leaves and dirt clinging to it. And— most astonishing of all—blood was smeared over her neck and breasts and face.

She took a cloth and dipped it into the porcelain washbowl, then sponged herself off until the water had turned pink and she was clean. Back at the mirror, she peered closer at the evidence of Wesley's brutality. Then she gasped, not sure she wanted to believe what she was seeing.

It was true that just as she suspected her ivory skin was already beginning to discolor in places. In the morning she'd definitely have bruises . . . along with memories . . . to show for the wild hour she'd spent in the glade with Wesley. But the bruises would be only superficial, while the memories would be unsettling. Because her skin wasn't even broken.

The blood on her body had been *his*, not hers. *She* was the one who had bitten hard enough to draw blood. His nips and bites had given only erotic delight.

Troubled, she took a brush to her hair, then pulled a clean nightgown over her head and slipped into her robe. Her room was cold. Her quilt-covered bed beckoned her with its warmth, and, Lord knew, she needed rest.

But the window was drawing her, and she went to it.

Raindrops clung to the glass and combined with the darkness to obscure vision. She leaned closer. Yes. Outside, standing beneath her window, she could make out a dark silhouette.

He stood so still, his head thrown back, his face turned up to the rain . . . and to her. She lifted her fingertips and pressed them against the glass barrier that separated them. But instead of her body's heat warming the glass, the chill of the night seeped into her.

She stayed where she was for a long time, watching him, until finally weariness overcame her and she turned toward her bed.

Anna felt the nausea even before she opened her eyes. She was pregnant. She had been fighting the knowledge for days, but she could fight no longer. She lay very still under the covers and stared at the ceiling of her tiny bedroom, trying to save her strength for fighting the nausea. But fear and a steadily-building rage kept getting in the way.

She'd had to live with the risk of becoming pregnant ever since that day months before when Wesley had stroked her hair and softly said, *I've just bought up your father's notes of debt. Come to me or I'll call them in and he'll lose his store.*

He had always spoken to her like that—softly . . . until last night.

And, just like last night, she'd had very little choice about going to his bed.

But in the glade he'd drawn from her a response that had been unbridled and feral and it had left her shattered. Angrily she pushed the memory away and pressed a hand against her flat stomach. She couldn't feel any life, but there was no doubt about it. Life was in her, growing even now.

Dear God, what was she going to do?

Pregnant. Unmarried. A hopeless, shameful state. With a groan she rolled over, but the motion sent such a strong wave of nausea through her that she barely had time to bend down and grab the chamber pot from under the bed before she was sick.

"Anna, vhat is wrong?" her father called from the next room.

Weak with the efforts of emptying her stomach, she could only lay back against the pillows and close her eyes in despair. *Papa was awake and he had heard.*

Her bedroom door opened slowly, and her father stepped across the threshold. His gray hair was mussed from sleep, and he was squinting at her because he'd forgotten to put on his glasses. His old flannel robe hung open over his nightshirt.

She watched him from beneath heavy lids and thought how very dear he was. No matter what, she had to keep her pregnancy secret. It would kill him if he found out.

"I'm just feeling a little sick, Papa. Nothing to fret about. Something I ate, most likely."

"Vhat could have made you sick, my daughter? The chicken you made for our supper last night was good."

She smiled in an attempt to ease his worry. "I'll be fine. Just let me lie here a little longer, and then I'll get up."

"Mrs. Harcourt asked me to join her at the café this morning for breakfast, but—"

"Good. You go. I'll open up the store." Mrs. Harcourt was a cheerful, pleasant-faced widow. For quite sometime Anna had noted the woman's efforts to catch her father's attention. She supposed that Mrs. Harcourt had finally decided to stop waiting for her father to get the hint.

"Are you sure?" he asked.

She nodded. "It will work out well. If you go to the café for breakfast, I won't have to cook, and I can rest a bit longer."

"Good. I go, then." His expression vague, distressed, he started to leave, but then unexpectedly he turned back to her. "Do you remember your mama?"

"Yes, of course."

"She vas so beautiful . . . like you, my Anna. I vish she vas here. I miss her so."

"I know you do, Papa. I miss her too."

When he'd gone, Anna rolled over and buried her face in the pillow.

Her mother had died in Sweden when Anna was thirteen years old. Her death had devastated both her and her father. God, she wished her mother were with her now, to smooth her hair and tell her everything would be all right.

But it wouldn't be all right.

Nothing had been all right since the day Wesley McCord had seen her and wanted her.

And now nothing might ever be right again.

3

Impatiently Wes took a final draw of his cigarette, ground its smoldering end into the large ashtray that sat on his desk, then reached for the makings of a new cigarette. Why hadn't the emporium opened yet? He'd been watching the store for over an hour, and the doors remained closed. Something was wrong with Anna. He was sure of it.

God. He couldn't remember the way he'd treated her last night without feeling profound remorse. But . . . in spite of that . . . the memories of their passionate encounter in the glade evoked a white-hot flame that went layers deep.

It had been so damned good to go wild, burying himself in her and forgetting for a little while that his world was crumbling around him. Powerful and

37

primitive feelings had moved between Anna and him that he would never forget.

He lit the newly rolled cigarette, and stalked once again to the window to see that the door to the emporium was just opening.

He bolted out of his office, flipping his cigarette into the street as he crossed the dusty main thoroughfare of the town. A buckboard driver had to swerve abruptly to keep his team of horses from plowing into him. Wes didn't even break his stride. A horse and rider drew to a hasty standstill as he walked in front of them. He didn't notice.

As soon as he gained entrance to the emporium, he saw her. She was alone, her head bent with concentration as she tied an apron around her waist. As usual, she was wearing a simple day dress. Only this dress had a high-standing frilly collar that served to conceal the portion of her neck where last night his teeth had scraped, bringing to life the nerve that lay beneath the sensitive skin.

"Anna?"

Her head jerked up and her blue eyes widened as she saw him. Then she pivoted away.

She had looked pale to him, he thought, and he had seen a faint dew of perspiration on her upper lip. "Anna, are you all right?"

"Of course. Why wouldn't I be?"

"Turn around and look at me."

"Why don't you force me to? You're so good at that. If you can't blackmail someone into doing what you want, you use force. And in my case, both."

Frustration and torment were too active in him, making it impossible for him to react calmly to her resistance. Several long strides were all that were needed before he could grasp her arm and turn her to him. "Dammit, stop clawing at me. I only want to know if I hurt you, that's all."

Not expecting him to jerk her around, she lost her balance and fell, and her breasts crushed against him.

As intently as he was watching her, it would have been hard for Wes to miss her grimace of pain. "Oh, hell, I did hurt you."

"Just leave me alone." She yanked away and put the width of a counter between them. He thought he'd hurt her breasts last night, when actually her breasts had been growing more and more tender over the last few days. It was one of the signs she should have heeded. She was carrying Wesley's child, but it would do her no good to tell him.

Her silence and the lack of color in her skin was stretching his nerves to the breaking point. He exploded. "Dammit, Anna, talk to me."

"What do you want me to say? That you didn't hurt me? All right, Wesley. You didn't. I have only minor bruises to show for our . . . copulation. Satisfied now?"

Wes bit back a curse. "Hell no, I'm not satisfied. If I didn't hurt you, then you're ill."

No, she thought angrily. She wasn't ill. Simply pregnant. And unmarried. Disgrace was only weeks away for her, and the thought had her absolutely panicked. "You've never shown any concern for me before."

Then, unbidden, the memory of the night he'd taken her virginity flashed into her mind. After it was all over and he was holding her close against him, he had murmured with exquisite tenderness, *I'm sorry if I hurt you.*

Her mouth tightened. "Last night was no exception. You never for a minute thought of me. You used me, Wesley. You've lost control over your business affairs, so you came to me because you knew I was the one thing in your life you could command."

"Anna . . ."

"Are you trying to deny it, Wesley?"

Mrs. Fitzpatrick sailed into the emporium with a smile on her face and a blissful unawareness of the tension that was hanging thickly in the air. "Good morning, Miss Nilsen. I've come for a pound of coffee beans." Her smile slipped slightly when she saw Wes. "Mr. McCord, how nice to see you." She laughed nervously. "My, my, you must have cut yourself shaving this morning."

Involuntarily his hand went to his face. He'd forgotten Anna wasn't the only one marked by what had happened between them.

Mrs. Fitzpatrick made a sound that combined another laugh with the act of clearing her throat. It turned into a cough. "Such a catastrophe out at the tent city," she finally managed to say. "We're all hoping that the railroad project can be put back on schedule real soon."

Wes's smile of acknowledgment was cynical, though he was sure the good lady gazing so anxiously at him didn't notice. She was the mayor's wife and a thoroughly silly woman. Silly enough to ask the question everyone in Chango had been dying to ask him. He knew that whatever he said to her would have covered the town by the end of the day. "I assure you, I intend to see that any delay is minimal."

"I'm so glad. Everyone has been so worried, you know."

"Of course."

Anna tied a string around the bag of coffee beans and handed it to her, eager to get the lady out of the store before she noticed anything amiss. But Mrs. Fitzpatrick evidently had other things on her mind.

"Anna, do you think you'll get a new shipment of fabric in soon?"

Anna sighed. Mr. Fitzpatrick was a somber gentleman who paid his wife scant attention. As a result, the good lady tended to concentrate a great deal of her energies toward her dress. "We're expecting a new order in next week."

"Do you think there'll be anything in yellow?" she asked anxiously. "I do so want a yellow dress. Something with flowers on it."

Anna forced a smile. "I'm hoping that we'll get in exactly what you have in mind. I did put in a special order for yellow this time."

"And ribbon and thread, I hope?"

"Yes, ma'am."

"Oh, you're such a sweet girl. We had such a dreadful winter, didn't we? And I'm so tired of the same dreary colors. But now spring is here, and spring always brings new life. I think we should celebrate it with bright colors, don't you?"

New life. Wes drew in a sharp breath at the words. *Oh, God, Anna was pregnant.*

He wheeled away from the two women and stared blindly at a rack of ready-made shirts. Behind him, the two women continued to talk, but his mind was too busy to allow the meaning of their words to penetrate through his thoughts.

Anna had missed her monthly flux. She came to him too often for that fact not to have registered at some level of his mind, however deep. But he'd been occupied—with the railroad line, with Sloan Lassiter, with so damned many other things.

He shut his eyes. Could it be true? Of course it was. Even as he stood there, he began remembering subtle changes that had been occurring in her body. But he had not allowed himself to think through to the logical conclusion. Where Anna was concerned, lust drove him, leaving little room for reason.

So what was she feeling, he wondered, knowing that she was carrying his child? Christ, he knew exactly what she was feeling. He'd seen it in her eyes when he'd walked into the emporium. *Hate. Desperation. Anger.* But he'd thought it was because of last night.

Now he realized the reason for those emotions.

And he realized something else too.

Anna wouldn't even come to his bed unless he was blackmailing her, and that meant she sure as hell wouldn't want his baby. He felt as if someone had just knifed him, then walked away, leaving him to bleed to death.

"Good day, Mr. McCord."

He turned to see Mrs. Fitzpatrick eyeing him with determined brightness. She was afraid of him, but then, most of the people in town were afraid of him. He held power over their future. Or at least they thought he did. He nodded his head. "Good day."

When he looked back at Anna, he found her busy with a feather duster, pretending to ignore him. As he watched her, he realized slowly that he didn't want to let her know that he knew she was pregnant. He didn't want to hear her tell him that she didn't want his baby.

"Do you have to work that hard?"

Anna started in surprise. She'd thought because he'd fallen silent he was about to leave. At least she'd been hoping he would. Of all people, she hadn't wanted to have to deal with him today. And she surely didn't want to have to talk to him. "Of course I do."

"You shouldn't have to do things like that. Where's your father?"

"Wesley, *please*, just get out of here. You got your way last night. Now leave me alone."

Yes, he thought grimly. Last night. Damn. He'd

been so rough with her. What if he'd hurt her or the baby?

She jerked the ladder in front of the ceiling-high shelves that lined the back wall. Gathering her skirt in one hand, she began to climb up the rungs, intent on reaching the dusty china that was displayed on one of the high shelves.

Before she could accomplish her mission, strong arms closed around her and carried her against a hard chest. "Dammit, Anna, what are you trying to do? Hurt yourself?"

Even as he said it, fear lanced his heart. Jesus, what if she intended to get rid of the baby? If not by deliberately falling, then by some other means. She could end up mutilating herself. Or killing herself.

"Wesley, put me down," she said. "Someone's going to see us."

He glanced toward the wide window that over-looked the main street and knew she was right. But seeing her on that rickety ladder had badly shaken him. He began walking with her and didn't stop until they were in the back room. There, he slowly set her on her feet. "If those upper shelves need dusting, then your father should do it."

She raised her arm to her hair and pushed a hairpin firmly back into place. "It's hard for him to do things like that. He has rheumatism."

"And you're going to have a broken neck if you keep climbing that ladder. Hire someone to do it for you."

"We don't have the money to hire anyone. I need

to save every cent we make in profit so that I can pay you back, remember?" She knew her voice was trembling with anger, but she couldn't stop it. Every single one of her problems could be traced directly to this man. "Please get out of my way. I need to go back in there. A customer might come in."

"So let them. We need to talk."

"I can't think about what."

He regarded her steadily for a moment, then finally lifted a hand to caress her cheek. "Come to my house tonight."

She gazed at him in astonishment. "You're out of your mind if you think I'm going to do that."

Frustration etched Wes's face as he glanced around the storeroom. Suddenly he grabbed her arm and maneuvered her behind a stack of crates.

Not again, Anna thought. She couldn't stand it if he took her into his arms and kissed her. Her mind was too confused. Her nerves were too exposed. "Wesley, you can't do this."

"No one can see us back here."

Suddenly her despair and anger were replaced by puzzlement. His hands were on her shoulders and he was gazing intently down at her face. It was as if he wanted to say something but didn't know how to begin. Then she became aware of his hands kneading her shoulders. His touch held no passion, but rather it seemed in some strange, inarticulate way that he was trying to comfort her. That couldn't be right.

"Anna?"

Her father's voice. She stiffened as she tried to cope with the fact that her father had returned earlier than she had expected. He couldn't catch the two of them like this. What was she going to do?

Wes threw a quick glance over his shoulder. "I'll be waiting for you tonight," he whispered, then stepped out from behind the crates and walked to the door of the emporium. "Good morning, Mr. Nilsen. I was just helping Anna look for those shirts I ordered last month. She wasn't sure they'd come in, but I'm afraid I insisted she look anyway."

With a frown Lars Nilsen polished his glasses, then set them on his nose and hooked the thin wire over his ears. "They are not here, Mr. McCord. No shirts have come in."

"I see," Wes said smoothly, and smiled at Anna, who had just emerged from behind him. "I guess it's just too soon, Miss Nilsen, but I appreciate your looking."

She rubbed her damp palms down her skirt. "It was no trouble, and I thought it might be possible that they were in."

Lars eyed Wes with barely concealed animosity. "Ve always notify you when your orders come in."

Wes smiled. "Yes, you do. I suppose I'm too impatient."

Anna brushed past the two men and made her way behind the counter. She was feeling ill again. The rich aromas of the spices that lined the shelves of the store were suddenly overwhelming her, and the puzzling, intense exchange with Wesley had left her shaken.

"Then I suggest," Lars said, "that you vait until ve send vord. My Anna is too busy to be checking in the back for every order."

Wes nodded, then looked straight at Anna. "But remember. I'm impatient."

She nodded, getting the message. He wanted to see her tonight. When he had left, she turned to her father. "Why were you being so rude to Mr. McCord, Papa?"

"He is a bad man."

"I realize that's what you think. We've discussed this before, but you know how powerful he is, how important he is to this town."

"Bah. Daughter, haven't you heard? He is after Mr. Lassiter and that nice Miss Delaney. They say Mr. Lassiter is hurt, and Mr. McCord has sent his man, Cummings, after them."

Anna slumped against a counter. She had heard the rumors. And she had also been anxious. But the events of last night and this morning had wiped the thought of Brianne and Mr. Lassiter out of her mind. She lifted a shaky hand to her forehead. "I hope they're safe."

Right now it seemed there was no safety anywhere in the world.

"Don't light the lamp."

Wes stiffened on the bed, his gaze searching the

darkness. He could see the gleam of Anna's fair hair in the shadowy doorway. "Why not?"

Anna moved forward, crossing the room to stand before the window. Moonlight streamed into the room, silhouetting the proud lines of her body.

"I don't want you to." There was a definite edge to her words. "You should understand not wanting to be seen. You don't reveal anything to anyone, do you?"

"I never thought you'd want to know," he said warily.

Her chin lifted. "I don't. I was only curious. Who and what you are mean nothing to me."

It was the child, he thought suddenly. She was wondering what kind of man she'd allowed to plunder her body and give her his child. Christ, she had a right to worry. He'd come from scum and fought his way out of the mud and now he had smeared her with that very mud.

"I'm here only because I was afraid you'd come to my house and make a scene," she said. "But I'm not going to come to bed with you. I'm here, but you can't make me. Not again."

"All right."

She stilled with surprise. "No arguments?"

"No."

She was silent for a moment. "Why not?"

Because you're carrying my child, he thought, and it makes me feel strange, sad, and a little lost. "Maybe I've grown tired of you."

Her gaze searched the darkness. There was some-

thing in his voice tonight. "I wish I would see your face."

"I'll light the lamp."

"No." She turned away. "It doesn't matter. Do you want me to leave?"

"Why?"

"Because we're not going to—" She paused. "There's really no point in my being here, is there?"

"You're here because I want you here." He swung his feet to the floor and stood. "That's the point. The only point."

She watched him move across the room toward her. "You're . . . different tonight."

"How can you say I'm different when you claim you don't even know me?"

"You seem in an odd mood."

"Really?" He lifted her chin on the crook of his finger. "I'm not sure I know myself tonight." His hand fell away, and he sat down onto the window seat. "Talk to me."

"What?"

"Sit down and spin me a tale." He leaned back against the wall of the alcove. "You never talk to me, and we've got to do something to while away the hours that we normally spend . . . doing other things."

She stood uncertainly before him.

"Anna?"

She sank to the floor in front of the window seat and with a heavy sigh settled back against it. "I don't know any stories."

Quite naturally his fingers moved to her hair and

began to pull the pins from it. "No? Then tell me about your childhood."

"I don't remember much." She was silent a long while. "I remember Hilda."

His fingers moved slowly, soothingly, through her silky tresses, and the delicate lilac scent that he always associated with her drifted to him in the darkness. "Hilda?"

"My doll." She closed her eyes. "My father carved it out of teakwood, and my mother made her a beautiful gingham dress. She had jointed arms and legs, and I'd never seen anything like her. I thought she was the most wonderful doll in the world. Then my cousin, Ingmar, broke her. I wanted to kill him."

"So fierce," he murmured. "What did you do to this cousin of yours?"

"Nothing. My mother said that it would be wicked to punish poor Ingmar when he'd already been punished enough by being given a cruel, malicious soul."

"Blessed be the peacemakers." There was a touch of mockery in his tone that was belied by the exquisite gentleness of his touch. "But the mercy you showed your cousin didn't put your Hilda back together again."

"No." There was an unutterable weariness in Anna's voice. "And I loved her so. I pretended she was my baby, and I would rock her and hold her close—" She broke off, and when her words came again, they were very soft and touched by wonder. "My baby . . ."

She was going to tell him now, Wes thought.

But she didn't tell him. For a time, only the sound of silence could be heard in the room.

Then she asked, "Why are you being kind to me tonight?

"I don't ever remember being cruel to you. Perhaps a little rough last night." His mouth straightened into a grim line. "More than a little."

"You didn't . . . hurt me. Not really." Her voice was halting. "You never have."

Christ, how could she say that? He had hurt her in every possible way since the day he had met her. "No one was supposed to get hurt, Anna," he said with sudden urgency. "I never meant you—" His fingers unconsciously tightened in her hair, then relaxed. "Evidently you're one of the peacemakers too. Don't you ever get tired of having your toys broken?"

She threw a quick glance back at him. "Do you?"

"I never had any toys when I was young, but no one takes anything away from me now. Not anymore." His voice was suddenly harsh. "And if you had any sense, you wouldn't let anyone do it to you either. Not me or anyone."

"I've dealt with the circumstances of my life the best way I've known how. I am what I am and I can't let you twist me into something I'm not. Then you would truly be able to destroy me."

He was poignantly conscious of the strength shining beneath her gentleness. "I'm not trying to destroy you."

She didn't look at him; her tone was noncommittal. "I've always known you would destroy me. You can't help it. You have to destroy everything around you. There's such anger in you. . . ."

"No," he said sharply. "There are things I want, but I'm not—"

"I don't want to talk anymore," Anna interrupted. "It's been a difficult day for me. Could we be quiet now?"

He gazed down at her, filled with a wild mixture of emotions. Tenderness, shock, anger, and the beginnings of fear. "Yes, we can be quiet." His fingers resumed their gentle stroking of her hair.

And the moonlight streamed through the window, illuminating the darkness that surrounded them with a naked, relentless clarity.

4

Sloan came awake slowly, greeted by fresh waves of pain.

There wasn't a muscle in his body that was free of the awful, throbbing ache. He tried to sit up, but found ropes around his wrists and ankles. Fear surged through him. Instinctively he struggled even harder until a paralyzing stab of pain in his head forced him to subside.

Brianne was kneeling beneath the lip of the overhang that formed their small cave, gazing out over the meadow. She heard him and turned. "Oh, God, Sloan, what are you doing?" Quickly she hurried back to his side and felt his forehead. He was definitely cooler. The relief she felt was tempered by caution. His fever had been going up and down, and

she didn't for a minute think he was completely out
of danger.

"How are you feeling?" she asked, unsure if she
would get a reply, and, if she did, what kind of reply
it would be.

"Why am I tied up?" he asked.

She stared at him for a moment, noting that his
golden eyes appeared lucid. "I had to do it so that
you wouldn't hurt yourself. You've been delirious."

"I have?"

His voice sounded rough and raspy, as if he'd swallowed gravel. She reached behind her for a canteen
and cup, and poured out some water. "You've been
out of your mind with the high fever you've been
running. I've been spending a lot of time in the last
few days just trying to keep you alive. Here, see if
you can drink some of this."

She put her arm under his head and lifted him. He
could take only a few sips of the water, but his voice
sounded better when he asked, "What day is it?"

She had to think for a minute. "Wednesday. I think.
You've been in and out of consciousness since Sunday night."

"Dammit!" He closed his eyes as if the effort of
speaking had drained him.

Brianne poured more water over a cloth and
sponged down his face and throat. It was an act
she'd done so often over the last few days, she did it
now without thinking.

Hour after hour she'd been living with the lonely
terror that Sloan might die. The burden of his life

had weighed heavy on her. But just a minute ago he had actually looked at her with clear eyes and had asked rational questions. She wanted to let go and sob with happiness, but she couldn't afford the luxury. To fall apart now would be disastrous.

The danger hadn't passed. Sloan was still very ill. For all she knew, he could lapse back into unconsciousness at any moment. And then there was Cummings. He was out there somewhere. She could almost feel his presence.

After a minute Sloan asked, "How safe are we here?"

Another good question. How could she answer it? A gust of wind blew into the cave, making the flames of the campfire bend and sway. Down on the canyon floor the sound of the rustling grasses mingled with soft noises of nature. "I don't know if you remember or not, but there's a butte that rises behind the tent city."

He gave a slight nod, then grimaced at the pain it caused.

"We're in a box canyon inside that butte. I did everything I could think of to make it as difficult as possible for us to be followed, but . . . If Cummings and his men find this place, we'll have problems. We have the high ground, but there're a lot of boulders and rocks that make for good cover. And there's really only one way out of here."

Brianne didn't bother with any more explanation. There was no need. As Sloan grew stronger—*if* Sloan grew stronger—he'd figure it out for himself, and then they'd both know how easily this place she'd brought him to for safety could end up being their death trap.

She sighed heavily. "You should try to drink some broth while you're awake, then I need to go down and check on the horses and get some more water."

"Untie me."

"I can't." Sudden panic twisted his face, and she felt an ache of anguish. "Sloan, listen to me, I can't."

His eyes widened with fear. "But you've *got* to! I can't stand being helpless."

"I know, I know." Soothingly she pressed her hand to his face. "But for now I can't take the chance that you'll slip back into delirium."

"I won't. I know I won't."

"Sloan—" Her voice broke. She cleared her throat and tried again. "There've been times over the past three days when I thought you were finally on your way to being well, but you weren't. These ropes keep you from hurting yourself . . . or me."

He gazed at her incredulously. "I wouldn't hurt you."

"I know you wouldn't on purpose."

"You don't understand . . . Brianne."

His breathing had become labored. She moved her hand over his chest. His heart was pounding like a drum. "It's all right, Sloan. I'll stay here with you. I won't leave you."

"You've got to let me out of these ropes," he said hoarsely. "I can't be helpless. Not again."

His exertion was bringing his fever up. She reached

for the damp cloth and smoothed it over his face. "Shhh. You're going to be all right. I'll cut the ropes soon, I promise. Until then, you've got to trust me to take care of you. Shhh. Be quiet now."

"Brianne, don't do this to me. Don't . . ."

She felt as if she'd always been tired. Her body ached as if she were the one who had been beaten instead of Sloan. And she couldn't remember what being happy and carefree was like. She freshened the cloth with the last of the water and stroked it over him. "When you get better," she told him softly, "I'm going to take you home to Killara. You'll love it. It's rugged and it's hard, but it has a special beauty about it that goes inside you so that you can't ever forget it."

He appeared to be quieting and she continued. "There are mountains around Killara that change colors as the sun moves across the sky. And we have valleys with grass so green, it hurts your eyes. Like Ireland, Malvina says. And in the spring the wild-flowers grow thick enough to make you believe you could walk on top of them. I used to fill vases with them and put them all around the house. And I'd weave garlands out of them and wear them on my head. Everyone would laugh and call me princess. Even Patrick. Especially Patrick.

"And you're going to love my family. Most of them will be here in a few days. Dominic, Falcon, Joshua, Sean, Cort." She looked down and saw that his eyes were closed and his breathing was more even. "They're going to love you as much as I do."

She waited a few more minutes, making sure that he was going to stay asleep, then pressed a tender kiss to his hot cheek, reached for the canteens and her rifle, and once more headed down to the meadow and the creek. But first she had to make a detour.

The hidden entrance into the canyon was little more than a slash in the thick butte wall, perhaps twenty or thirty feet long. At the other end of the passage was the trail that climbed up the back of the butte, the trail that Brianne was praying with all her heart that Cummings and his men wouldn't find.

She approached cautiously, then set down the canteens and rifle. Drawing her handgun, she began weaving her way into the passage, using all the stealth and lightfootedness that her aunt, Rising Star, had taught her. When she reached the high-growing brush that blocked the entrance, she became even more careful. Finally she stopped just short of the entrance and waited a moment, listening carefully. Hearing nothing, she edged out and quickly looked both ways.

As she studied the trail, it didn't take her long to see that there was no sign that anyone had been on it in the past few days—not even she and Sloan. Her efforts at masking their tracks had been successful, but she didn't allow herself a celebration. Dan Cummings was still out there.

She carefully erased any footprints she'd made, then began working her way back through the brush, making sure that not a twig was broken or a leaf was turned the wrong way.

She didn't know Cummings, she reflected, but she'd

had a good look at his eyes as she'd hidden just outside the tent Sunday morning, waiting for them to discover that the tent city was burning. She shivered as she remembered the expression of perverse pleasure that had been on Cummings's face as he had beaten Sloan.

Cummings would be like a wolf on the trail of blood. He wouldn't give up. He'd be coming.

The only question was when.

Dan Cummings squatted on the flattened top of the boulder, his eyes narrowed against the sun as he scanned the country around him. *Where are they?*

He had to hand it to that Delaney bitch. She'd done a hell of a job covering her tracks, and he and his men had been riding in circles for days now. But Lassiter had been hurt bad. That would have slowed her up, and she would've had to stop before the day was out. And whatever hidey-hole she and Lassiter had crawled into Sunday, they'd still be there. He'd given Lassiter too bad a beating for them not to be.

Unless Lassiter had died.

A malevolent smile spread slowly across his face. That thought almost made up for the news that Dutch had brought him this morning. Janice hadn't had the ledger on her when they'd found her, and McCord had set her loose. Damn that interfering son of a bitch.

Ever since Janice had stolen the ledger and gotten away, he'd been looking forward to teaching her a lesson. Why in Hades had McCord let her go?

McCord was a dangerous man when crossed, but if he thought for one minute that he, Dan Cummings, was going to tuck his tail between his legs and slink off just because he'd lost the ledger, then McCord had another thought coming.

He wasn't afraid of McCord. Yes, he was going to find Lassiter and that Delaney bitch, and he was going to get the ledger back. But for *him*, not for McCord.

McCord didn't know it, but he was going to be taking on a new partner. His days of being an inferior to McCord were over, because he knew a secret about him that no one else knew, and he was going to use it when the time was right.

He stood and whirled, all in one motion. "Get your asses back in the saddle," he barked, leaping down from the rock and advancing on the five men with him. "You've laid around long enough."

Wills groaned. "We ain't had a full night's sleep since we lit out after those two."

"And we haven't found them yet, have we? So we keep going."

Red spoke up. "If you don't start lettin' us get more than three hours sleep at night, we're not gonna be in any shape to handle them if we do find them."

"We *are* going to find them. Make no mistake. Just shut up and get on those horses."

"But, boss—"

Cummings had his gun in his hand before the other men had a chance to blink. "Take your choice. You can rest after we find them or you can rest now, permanently."

Wills and Red, along with Thompson, Collins, and Becker mounted their horses without another word.

Satisfied, Cummings holstered his gun, then let his eyes scan the horizon one last time. In the distance the massive form of the butte loomed. *You've got to be out there somewhere, Lassiter.* He swung into his saddle. "Let's go."

Unwilling to fire off a shot and possibly attract unwanted visitors, Brianne had checked her traps and found a rabbit. Together with some biscuits and beans that she had hastily collected from the hotel's kitchen before she'd ridden out of Chango, the roasted rabbit made a fine stew. The only problem was that Sloan was still too ill to eat much of it. But, she told herself, the little bit he did manage to eat would help.

"Will you untie me now?"

She'd been sitting near the fire, heating up the coffee, and looked over at him now. He'd been rational for most of the day, and even though he'd slept, he hadn't lapsed back into anything like delirium. No, he'd seemed to sleep peacefully, deeply. And his fever seemed lower too, thank God. She slid over to him and cut his bonds with her knife.

"I had to do it, Sloan," she said quietly. "I had no choice."

He held up his wrists and looked at them. They were raw and crusted with blood.

She rushed on. "I'll bathe them with hot water. Maybe they won't get infected."

He flexed the muscles in his arms, then shut his eyes and lay his hands across his stomach. He could still remember the panic he'd felt at being so powerless. It had been terrifying to be in that position and able to do nothing about it. Only one other time in his life had he felt that kind of horrifying helplessness, and that was fifteen years earlier when David had died in his arms. Then as now, he'd been too weak to help himself or to help the one person in the world he had loved.

Today he'd fallen asleep, listening to Brianne talk, but when he'd next awakened, she'd been nowhere in sight. Fear had returned tenfold. Never again did he want to be that vulnerable. Never again did he want to be that dependent on another person.

He felt one of his wrists being lifted, and he opened his eyes to see Brianne beside him. She looked pale and drawn, and there were dark smudges imprinted on the delicate flesh beneath her beautiful green eyes.

"I hope this won't hurt," she said, beginning to sponge his wrists with heated water.

"You look tired," he said, grimacing slightly at the sting.

"You've been so sick . . . there was a lot to do. Let me have your other wrist."

"Haven't you gotten any sleep?"

"I've dozed off here and there."

"God, Brianne." It was more a breath than an exclamation.

"I'm all right." She pushed a long strand of red hair out of her face. "It's you we need to worry about."

The lines of his lips firmed. "Tomorrow I'll feel better. Tomorrow I'll take care of you."

"Tomorrow you're still going to be flat on your back. There, I'm finished." She returned his hand to his abdomen. "I wish I had some sort of salve or something to put on these."

"Brianne, I'm serious. I'm going to be up on my feet by morning."

She knew it was an impossible hope, but she didn't argue. His voice was growing weak again. "Do you think you can eat something else?"

"Maybe later." He closed his eyes, tired, frustrated, angry.

Brianne added more wood to the fire, then positioned herself at the mouth of the cave. No sign of Cummings yet. That meant a little more time for Sloan to recuperate, and Lord knew, he needed it. But, thank goodness, the worse seemed to be over. Maybe, just maybe, they had a chance.

She arched her back in an effort to relieve the throbbing ache, and her mind turned to the people she'd left behind in Chango. She hadn't given a thought to Henrietta, Kam, or Phineas since she'd ridden out on Sunday morning. There hadn't been time. She shook her head wearily and tried to convince herself that they'd be all right. Even if something happened to her, her family would take care of them.

Actually, if something happened to her, her family and the riders from Killara would take revenge . . . and they'd find Patrick.

Oh, Patrick, she thought with a sudden wrenching pang. How she missed him.

Strange. She'd always believed that no matter how many miles separated them, if Patrick stopped breathing, she'd feel it in her heart. She'd felt nothing, but he'd been gone so long now, there didn't seem to be any question about it: Patrick must be dead.

Patrick Delaney guided Stormy down the main street of Chango. He sat astride the big palomino with a casual elegance yet unmistakable authority, fully aware of the startled stares directed at him.

Patrick was sure that everyone had given him up for dead. He smiled to himself. Brianne must have caused one hell of a commotion when she'd discovered he'd been kidnapped.

The thought of his three kidnappers—Odis, Hannibal, and Lester Grimes—brought another smile, but this time the smile appeared on his face. He'd never known three scruffier-looking characters in his life. Thank goodness he'd talked them into staying out at their place. They had happily agreed to wait at the hut when he'd assured them that if they did, they wouldn't have to have a face-to-face meeting with Dominic and Falcon Delaney to explain why they'd kidnapped him.

Spotting the three-story facade of the Duke Hotel just ahead, he noticed a maroon-painted wagon with cream-colored trim that proclaimed TOOLEY'S MIRACLE RESTORATIVE, A PATENTED CURATIVE. The wagon stood parallel to the hotel with a horse harnessed to it. Patrick guided Stormy around the wagon, stepped down out of the saddle, and threw his reins over the hitching rail.

Lord, but he couldn't wait to see Brianne, take a hot bath, eat a good meal, and wring Katy's pretty neck—in precisely that order. His eagerness to see his sister made him take the front steps of the hotel three at a time. As he strode into the lobby of the hotel, a funny-looking little man wearing a brown and mustard-yellow plaid suit brushed by him, his arms loaded with gear.

"Brianne," he called. "Where are you?" He had his foot on the bottom stair of the staircase that led to the second and third floors when Mrs. Potter, the wife of the man who owned the Duke Hotel, came hurrying out of the dining room.

"What's all the shouting about? *Mr. Delaney.* Is that you?"

Patrick flashed her a grin. "Sure is, Mrs. Potter. I hope you've kept my room available."

"I did. Your sister insisted." The landlady rubbed her hand across her forehead as if she were developing a headache. "And then she started bringing in all these strange people. Thank goodness you're here. You can help—"

"Strange people?"

"Every time she rode out looking for you, she'd

come back with someone new, each person more bizarre than the last."

"Oh, good, Mrs. Potter, there you are." A woman of perhaps forty-five, wearing a wren-brown traveling suit with a high-collared blouse, rushed down the stairs. A hat perched securely on her tightly bound hair. "I don't know how long we'll be gone. We're just going to keep looking until we find her. At any rate, it is imperative that when the Delaney family rides in, you give them the names of Wes McCord and Dan Cummings as Brianne requested."

Patrick spoke up. "Did you say Brianne?"

Pulling on a pair of gloves, Henrietta gave Patrick her best schoolteacher stare. "That's right. And who might you be, young man?"

Patrick took off his hat and ran his hand through his chestnut hair. "I'm Patrick Delaney."

Her face lit up. "Oh, thank heavens you're safe. And," she added as the next thought occurred to her, "thank heavens you're *here*. Now you can help us."

Patrick felt a twinge of uneasiness. "Help you with what?"

Over Patrick's shoulder she observed Phineas coming through the front door. "I'm Henrietta Jones, and this is Phineas Tooley. Mr. Tooley, this is Brianne's brother, Patrick Delaney."

Phineas's bushy eyebrows rose in astonishment, and a toothy smile of relief bisected his face. "How decidedly fortunate. Now that you're safe, you can go with us. I was just loading up my wagon. Perhaps you noticed it out front."

"Help you with what?" Patrick repeated heavily.

"We were just about to set out to find your sister. She's been gone since Sunday morning."

Patrick went cold. "Do you know where she went?"

"She rode to some sort of tent city north of town. A man named Wes McCord owns it. Dan Cummings is the foreman. But word is she's not there anymore."

"Why not?"

Metal clattering against metal sounded as a brown-skinned young giant came thudding down the stairs. He was dressed only in trousers, with an evil-looking necklace of large, curved teeth around his neck, and what looked to be a blanket filled with iron spears hanging from one shoulder. As soon as he saw Patrick, he froze. A variety of conflicting expressions chased across his face. He took several steps back up the stairs, hesitated, then raised his arm and brandished a bedpost in the air. "*Auwe. Auwe. Auwe.*"

Drawing his gun, Patrick instantly went into a crouch.

"Wait," Henrietta snapped. "Don't shoot. It's just Kam. He thinks you're a missionary. Kam, come down here this instant," she said severely, "and quit waving that bedpost around."

"It is my war club," the young giant said, eyeing Patrick with apprehension. "I will need it when I embattle the evil men who have taken my Brianne."

The full explanation would definitely be worth hearing, Patrick decided, but he didn't have time now. He'd wait until he found Brianne. Holstering his gun, he turned back to Henrietta. "Tell me everything you know."

"Sunday morning Brianne received word that her friend, Mr. Lassiter, was in some sort of trouble out at the tent city. She immediately left to help him. Then we got word that the tent city had burned to the ground."

"She used my Tooley's Miracle Restorative to start the fire," Phineas put in proudly. "You must have heard of my tonic."

Patrick was still looking at Henrietta. "Did you hear anything more about Brianne?"

"It seems she rescued Mr. Lassiter and then disappeared. Everyone is saying that Dan Cummings has gone after her."

He'd heard all he needed to. "Mrs. Potter, can you fix me up a sack of grub for the trail right away?"

"No need for that." Phineas protested. "We have plenty of supplies in my wagon."

"Good, I'll get what I need from there." He strode out of the hotel, untied his saddlebag, and headed over to the wagon. By the time Henrietta, Phineas, and Kamanahua got outside, he was already sorting through their supplies, picking what he wanted and stuffing it into his saddlebag.

Phineas's face crinkled in concern. "My dear fellow, there's no need for that. We'll all be together."

"I ride alone," Patrick said, buckling the flaps of his saddlebag. He was finding it hard to hold on to his patience with them. The trail was already three days old, dammit.

Henrietta was prepared to argue. "Mr. Delaney, we all owe Brianne a great deal. She practically saved each of our lives. And now we want to do the same for her. We've been most concerned. Surely the four of us together will have a better chance than just the one of you."

Patrick managed to bite back the succinct reply that jumped readily to his lips. He threw the saddle-bag over Stormy's rump and tied it into place. "Look, I'm going to be riding fast. The three of you and that"—he jerked a thumb at the wagon—"will only slow me down. If you're really friends of Brianne's, you'll wait here."

He swung up into the saddle, and, ignoring the cries of protest behind him, rode out of town.

5

Brianne awakened to feel the warmth of the sun on one side of her face. Sloan was at her back. Through the night she'd lain beside him, trying to keep him warm. Every few hours she'd gotten up to check the canyon for intruders.

She hadn't meant to sleep. As she lay in the little hollowed-out cave on a bed of pine needles and leaves, she remembered during the night thinking of Patrick, Malvina, and Shamus, and her bed in her room on Killara. The bed had a headboard of rosewood that towered nine feet and a canopy of bottle-green velvet above it.

Now she realized that toward morning she must have fallen into a deep sleep. But it didn't matter how badly she had needed the sleep, she thought, she

shouldn't have allowed her exhaustion to catch up
with her.

From across the meadow she heard her horse nicker.
A bird called out and took flight.

A stone rattled. All her senses became alert.

With great care not to move, Brianne opened her
eyes to a narrow slit. A man with a drawn gun was
creeping up the path that led to the cave. He was
perhaps thirty feet away, and he hadn't yet noticed
that she was awake.

Peering through her lashes, her gaze flew to her
gun belt, lying about four feet away. There was no
way she could reach it. And there was no way she
could wake up Sloan without warning the man who
was advancing toward them with such menace.

In the next moment she reacted. She rolled over,
grabbed up the gun, and fired—all in one smooth
motion. The man cried out and went down.

"What the hell!" Sloan awoke and tried to sit up.

Simultaneously a barrage of rifle- and gunfire
began to rain around them.

They were trapped.

She lunged for her rifle, then motioned to Sloan.
Keeping their bodies as flat as possible, they slithered
on their stomachs toward the pile of boulders that
not only blocked the trail to their right but also part
of the cave.

Sloan's mouth was drawn tight as he strained to
propel his body along the ground. Sweat beaded his
face. Each foot of ground he covered cost him dearly
in pain.

Brianne longed to help him, but she had the responsibility of the guns. She had to be content with staying beside him and sending him anxious glances as they made their torturous way to the boulders. His face was absolutely colorless, and pain had drawn his face into a mask she had come to know well over the last few days.

Finally they gained the cover of the boulders. Sloan's chest lifted and fell as he struggled to drag air into his overexerted lungs. For a split second his eyes met Brianne's. Seeing her fear, he silently cursed himself. She had risked her life to save him, and now, because of him, she was in even greater danger. And he couldn't even offer her reassurance, because they both knew there was no way out.

A bullet knicked the corner of the rock. Another hit the back of the cave.

For the moment, anyway, his strength was depleted, and he couldn't help her. He felt so goddamned *useless*. He stretched his legs out, using the rock to hold up his shoulders and head. As she checked the load in her gun, he asked, "Can you tell how many of them there are?"

She shook her head. "All I saw was the one coming up the path." She glanced across Sloan, toward the ledge where the man was lying motionless in a pool of blood. "He's dead." She felt faintly sick. "I've never killed anyone before."

Briefly he touched her arm. "You did what you had to do. And you saved our lives."

But how long will we be able to stay alive? She saved

her breath and didn't ask the question. Bullets were flying fast and furious, and it was hard for them to hear what the other was saying.

"I've got to go back and get your guns, plus the rest of our ammunition."

"Are you crazy?" he demanded. "Stay put, for heaven's sake." But she was already crawling across the floor of the cave. He was too spent either to make a grab for her or to lay down a covering fire. God, he hated being this weak and helpless, completely powerless to give her any aid.

Brianne hooked the saddlebag with their ammunition supply over one arm, then grabbed Sloan's rifle and pistol. As she crawled back to the cover of the boulders, her gaze searched the meadow intently. By judging where the shots were coming from, she made the calculation that there were five men. With their limited ammunition, she was going to have to make every shot count.

She sat back down beside Sloan and forced a smile. "It's five against two. Hardly seems fair to them, does it? After all, one of us is a Delaney."

Sloan stared at her in angry amazement. They were outnumbered, with their backs to the wall, and she was making a joke. Then he saw the fear in her eyes, and he felt a rush of pity mixed with admiration. Almost like a child caught in a frightening nightmare, she was braving it out.

The cave was being eaten up by bullets. The men below were laying down a hail of them, and for the last ten minutes Brianne had been kept busy return-ing fire. Occasionally Sloan managed to gather his strength, raise up, and get off a shot. It was enough to remind the men who were doing their best to kill them that there were two of them up there.

Brianne paused to wipe a film of sweat from her brow. Was it her imagination, or was the sun hotter today than it had been yesterday? She reached for one of the canteens, unscrewed the lid, and took a sip. A shot kicked up dirt and rock not two feet away from her. She tapped Sloan on the shoulder and offered him the canteen.

"How much do we have left?" he asked, shouting over the gunfire.

"This one and one other that's about half full."

His mouth tightened at her answer, but he took a short swig of the water. It was the hottest part of the day, and it wouldn't do to get dehydrated. He watched Brianne squeeze off a careful shot with her rifle. "For God's sake, don't give them too much of a target."

She nodded and took aim again.

He narrowed his eyes against the blazing sun. Damn Wes McCord's black soul! Because of Wes, for the second time in his life he was broiling under a hot sun in a situation that looked like it would end in his death. The first time David had died. This time it could be him . . . and Brianne. Dear God . . .

The firing was getting heavier now, as heavy as it had been when they'd first been attacked. What was going on, he wondered. Suddenly out of the corner of his eye he caught a movement. A man was crawling

over the boulders that blocked the right-hand path
up to the cave. Brianne's back was to the man as she
knelt and fired down into the meadow.

Sloan swung up his pistol and fired, killing the
man with a bullet between his eyes.

Brianne instantly whirled around and saw what
had happened. She lunged for the man's gun, but the
man slid down the opposite side of the boulders, and
she couldn't reach the rifle without exposing herself
to the gunfire from below.

Brianne sank down beside Sloan, badly shaken.
"That was too close."

He nodded in agreement. "They've been covering
him for the last ten minutes, keeping us occupied
while he crawled up here. We've got to be more
careful."

Fear was so thick in her veins it felt as if her blood
had stopped flowing, but she couldn't stand to see
the same emotion in Sloan. "There's only four of
them left now."

Only four. Brianne closed her eyes for an instant
but then quickly opened them. She couldn't afford to
be this frightened. Yet how could she help it?

All her life she'd thought she was brave, but she
knew now that what she had believed to be courage
had been mere bravado. She'd never really faced a
true test until now.

"Dear God, I don't want to die," she whispered
almost to herself. "I never knew I was such a coward."

Sloan threw her a quick look. "You're no coward,
Brianne."

Her hands tightened on her rifle. "I didn't think I was, but now I'm not sure. There are so many things I want to do. So many places I want to see."

A wrenching pain tore through Sloan. She said she was afraid, but she didn't realize that the mere facing of that fear showed an amazing courage. "Brianne, you're not—"

"No," she interrupted. "I'm sorry ... I'm being stupid." Just for a moment the dreams she had had for her life passed before her eyes. She'd believed that adventure, love, marriage, even children were hers for the asking. It hadn't been a question of *if* these things would come to her, but *when*. Now all that possibility that could have been her life was about to be snuffed out by the men down there in that meadow.

She drew a deep breath and smiled determinedly. "But you can damn well believe when we get out of this, I'm never going to take anything for granted again."

Then, choking on the sickness of her fear, she raised up on her knee and fired off a shot.

"I'm hit," Red yelled, grabbing his right arm, then screaming in pain.

Dan Cummings crawled over to him to look at the wound and saw immediately that the bone had been shattered. The two people up on that ledge were demoralizingly and dangerously accurate. If a man was foolish enough to give them a target, they'd hit

it. "You're out of the action," he told Red with disgust. "Bandage yourself up and stay low."

"The hell you say. I need a doctor."

"We'll get you to a doctor when we get them." Dan
jerked his head toward the cave.

"That could be days, and I'm not waitin'. By then
the lead in that slug could kill me. I've seen what
gangrene can do to a body, and I'm not about to go
that way. I'm headin' back to town." There was a
pile of boulders as big as a Conestoga wagon where
their horses were tied. Red struggled to his feet and
made a quick dash toward them.

Dan waited until he reached the cover of the boulders. A slow smile curved his lips. "Red?" he called
softly.

The man turned toward him.

"No one leaves."

Dan's bullet hit Red squarely in the center of his
heart.

Without a backward look Dan made his way over
to Collins and Becker, knowing that they'd both wit-
nessed what had happened.

Collins wasn't shocked. He'd lived all his thirty
years in the West, and he'd learned early that man
was the most merciless animal of all. But that could
have been him instead of Red. He scratched at the
dark stubble on his chin. "There was no call to do
that."

Dan leveled eyes like flint on him. "We can't afford
to have anyone know what's goin' on out here."

"I don't like the situation," Becker said. "Thompson was kilt this mornin'. Wills took it between the eyes a few hours back. Now, with Red dead, there's only the three of us. Them people up there are too damned good."

Dan's lips thinned. "They may have the high ground, but we've got the advantage. We can't take any more chances, that's all. There's no way they can get off that ledge, and sooner or later they'll run out of ammunition. All we got to do is wait them out."

Becker nodded. "Just shoot enough to keep them pinned down?"

"Right. And force their fire if you can. We'll take turns keepin' watch. They'll get tired before we will."

"Ya think they'll decide to give up?"

"Maybe." Dan smiled with the same pleasure he'd displayed when his bullet had torn into Red. "But it won't matter either way."

Patrick made a wide circle around the tent city for the second time, then headed west. A trail this old was hard to pick up, especially one of Brianne's, but the six men following her hadn't tried to hide their tracks. He wasn't interested in them, though, only his sister.

She was his twin. She was the other half of him. She had always been there for him when he'd needed her, giving him comfort in times of sorrow and laughing with him in times of joy.

He knew her almost as well as he knew himself. They'd been constant companions as children, playing and learning together. And one of their favorite games had been Hide and Track, where she would hide and he would track until he found her, then vice versa.

She was in terrible danger. He sensed it, felt it. Just like the time he'd known she was in trouble and he had found her trying to help a wounded wolf. The wolf would have turned on her at any moment, but Patrick's arrival had undoubtedly brought the attack on sooner.

He'd been able to help her then. He prayed he could help her now. If there was one person in the world who could find her, it was he. He just hoped he would be in time.

For two hours Patrick headed west, choosing the path he thought she'd take rather than relying on what damnably few signs she'd made. Only occasionally would he run across a succession of broken twigs, half-formed hoof marks, or bits of fabric that would tell him he was still moving in the right direction.

Gazing up at the sky, he saw that clouds were fast coming in from the west. Tonight was going to be overcast, and that meant he'd have to stop earlier than he wanted to. He pulled Stormy to a stop. Turning around in his saddle, he scanned the horizon to the east. Something was bothering him. Something wasn't right.

Flame stabbed the night as a shot rang out.

A second shot rang out. The bullet hit the boulder beside Sloan, sending pieces of rock spraying into the air.

Brianne returned the fire, then sank out of the way.

"They're playing it smart now," Sloan said, "shooting only enough to make sure we stay put."

"There's no place we could go anyway."

Tonight there were clouds across the moon, and Brianne was sitting in one of the darker shadows, her back to the rocks. He couldn't see her very clearly, but he heard the fatigue in her voice. It sent him into action. Rolling clear of the boulder, he took aim at the spot where he'd seen the last burst of flame come from, and fired. By the time he regained cover, he was bitterly regretting the precipitous move. It'd taken too much out of him.

"This is so damned futile." Pain added a harsh bite to his words. "There's no way we can know if we hit anything unless they yell."

"On the other hand, they can't know if they hit us either."

He turned his head toward her. "I suppose you're right."

Every muscle in Brianne's body was trembling with weariness and stress. It seemed as though their death was certain—either by a bullet or by starvation and dehydration. But as frightened as she was, the very idea of surrender frightened her even more.

"How's our ammunition supply?" Sloan asked.

"Not good."

She once again went over their options and admitted to herself they had practically none. "There's always our friend down there on the path. The man I shot this morning. It's dark. I could crawl down there and get his gun and ammunition."

"Don't be a damned fool!"

She looked at him in surprise.

"I didn't mean that." He said wearily. "I just feel so . . . You can't go down there. It'd be too risky."

"Sloan, our situation couldn't get any worse than it is right now."

"That ammunition wouldn't do us that much good anyway."

"It would help keep us alive a little longer. If there were just some way we could hold out until my uncles and the riders from Killara reach us."

"What makes you think they'll be able to find us if they even come? Never mind. We won't even have one more day unless we can think of something."

A bullet hit close on their left, kicking up dirt on the ledge. Sloan felt Brianne flinch, and cursed. The men down below were firing at randomly picked spots so that he and Brianne couldn't guess where the next shot might hit. In that way Cummings and his men were effectively keeping them pinned down, telling them without words that to move from behind the boulders would be suicide.

A shot ricocheted off the front of the rocks that were shielding them. Brianne raised up and fired, letting the men down below at least hear the sound of her Model 1873 Winchester .44/40, so that they'd know their quarry was very much alive. Cummings had built a campfire behind an outcropping of rocks, and although Brianne could see only its glow, she used it as a target. "Damn them. They're probably drinking hot coffee and having a plate of beans." Brianne slid to the ground and ran her fingers through her hair. "What are we going to do? Any ideas?"

Sloan tried to shrug and then winced as pain ran through him. "How the hell do I know? I can't—" His words came to an abrupt halt as he suddenly realized what they were going to have to do.

The sun had just eased over the top of the butte when Collins moved over to crouch behind the cover of the rocks and talk to his boss. "They haven't been returning our fire for a while. Think we might've got them in the night?"

Dan Cummings took a swig of coffee from his mug. "I suppose. We've been shootin' up there pretty regular."

"There's no way they could be asleep," Becker put in. "Not with our guns goin' off every few minutes." He grimaced in disgust. "I haven't even been able to catch a catnap."

"We're all beat," Dan snapped, directing his gaze toward the cave. He couldn't see any movement at all. "Pour some fire in there, Becker. Let's see if we can't stir somethin' up."

Becker did as he was told, and for a few minutes it sounded as if the box canyon were exploding.

Silence.

Dan turned his head and spat to the side of him. "Damn . . ." He pondered the matter, then rounded on Becker and Collins. "I want you two to make your way up there and see what's what."

"Are you crazy?"

"Are you forgettin' Wills and Thompson? They died doin' exactly that."

Dan's gun was suddenly leveled at them. "Have you forgotten how Red died?"

Becker and Collins looked at each other. If they climbed up to the cave, they might have a chance to live. Down here there would be no chance. They were going to do it, and they knew it.

Keeping low to the ground, they made use of anything they could for cover—arroyos, boulders, brush—until they reached the ledge that led up to the cave. Cautiously they followed the narrow path upward until they reached the place where the body of Thompson lay, eyes staring sightlessly at the sky. This was not the time for sympathy even if they were so inclined. Stepping over him, they peered into the cave. A bed of sorts had been made near the back wall. Two people were lying in it.

Both men opened fire, emptying their guns into the still figures beneath the blanket.

They'd gotten them!

Down below, Dan grinned in triumph. The ledger was sure to be in one of their saddlebags. Wes McCord was going to feel as if he'd lassoed the moon. Well, let the son of a bitch be happy for the time being, he thought, his grin of triumph turning to one of malice. McCord was going to be in for a little surprise.

The cold metal of a gun barrel pushed against Dan's neck.

The cocking of the hammer sounded like thunder in his ear.

"Throw down your gun real easy," Brianne said.

Fury, not fear, made Dan freeze. Shit. How in the hell could this have happened? He had been so sure that they'd gotten them. A painful prod of the gun barrel forced him to toss aside his weapon. For the moment, at least, he could do nothing else.

"That's good. Now call up to your men and have them come down here, without their guns, their hands in the air."

Dan hesitated and Brianne jabbed the barrel of his gun at him again. *"Do it."*

"Becker, Collins."

The two men turned their heads toward Cummings. The first thing they saw was Brianne Delaney holding a gun on him. The second thing they saw was Lassiter, leaning against the boulder. His face contorted with pain, but the gun he had aimed straight at them was dead steady.

"Toss down your guns," Cummings called to them.

They didn't have to think twice about their decision. Without delay they did as they were told and started back down the ledge.

As soon as Patrick was free of the narrow passage, he touched his heels to Stormy's sides and rode into the box canyon, both guns drawn.

Brianne stared in disbelief. "Patrick. My God, *Patrick.*"

He pulled Stormy to a halt and leapt off. He holstered his left-hand gun but kept the right one poised and leveled at the man Brianne was covering. "I see you've managed to find yourself some trouble," he drawled, scanning the meadow, making a quick assessment of the situation. His relief that Brianne was alive was tempered with wariness. Yet everything appeared to be well in hand. "What was all that shooting I heard?"

She nodded in the direction of Becker and Collins, who were approaching, their hands held high in the air. "They thought we were up in the cave. Lord, Patrick, I can't believe you're actually standing here. What happened to you? How did you find me?"

Relaxing now that he knew she was all right, he laughed at her excited, confused jumble of questions. At the same time, he reached for the lariat on his saddle and began to tie Cummings's hands behind his back. "The sun has never risen on a day I couldn't find you, little sister. I followed your trail west yesterday. Then last night it occurred to me to change direction. I saw the bluff and I knew it would be just like you to hide close to the enemy's home ground."

"Uncle Dom taught us that. Remember?"

"Yeah, I remember. But I was afraid that I might be too late and find you dead."

A cold shiver passed through her. "I was afraid of the same thing."

Patrick shoved Cummings to the ground. "Stay

put." He turned his attention to Sloan, whose rifle still covered Becker and Collins. "You look like a horse kicked you."

"I feel worse," Sloan said dryly. Then his legs gave out, and he began sliding down the rock.

Brianne started toward him.

"No." Sloan straightened abruptly. "I'm all right. Get the rest of them tied up."

Brianne's teeth bit into her lower lip. "Sloan, I only want to help you."

"I'm not a damned invalid."

Patrick's eyebrows rose at the sharp exchange. Something had obviously developed between his sister and Lassiter since he'd been away. Without comment he set about tying up the two remaining men. He threw a brief glance at Brianne, whose worried gaze was still on Sloan. "Where are the rest of them? I picked up the trail of six men following you."

Her face clouded even more. "There were six men originally. Now there're only three. I killed—" She broke off.

A wave of aching sympathy rushed through Patrick. On Killara, Brianne had learned at an early age that death was always a possibility. She'd seen violence firsthand, and she'd lost people she loved. But she'd never killed a man herself. He not only felt her pain, he could see that she was holding herself together only by the greatest of efforts. She'd obviously been through a great deal. He wanted to comfort her, but the armor she'd constructed around herself was very fragile, and he knew he had to be careful not to shatter it.

He made a face and said with deliberate lightness, "Jesus, Bri, you might have left a few for me to take care of."

As he'd hoped, her tension eased and she smiled faintly. "Sorry. I didn't know you were coming, and we had to do something. So in the night we crawled down here—"

"Crawled?"

"We managed to make our way to an arroyo behind them and hid until Cummings sent his two men up to the cave. We'd put our saddlebags and some of our gear under the blanket to make it look as if we were sleeping. They opened fire. Cummings was distracted." She made a gesture. "The rest you can see for yourself."

He gently tweaked a strand of her hair and said lightly, "You're a real mess. Malvina would have a fit."

"How nice of you to point that out. You look like you could use some cleaning up yourself." She sniffed. "And you smell like Stormy."

"Where's your gratitude, little sister? I got into Chango yesterday, intending on a nice long bath. But when I'd heard no one had seen you since Sunday, I made the supreme sacrifice and took off after you. By the way, I've got to admit, you did a great job of hiding your tracks."

"I tried." She shook her head. "But I must have done something wrong or Cummings wouldn't have found us." Suddenly she threw herself at him and gave him a fierce hug. "Oh, Patrick, thank God you're here." For long, sweet, precious moments, she held on to him as if she'd never let him go. Then she eased her grip and whispered in his ear, "Help Sloan. He won't let . . ." Her words trailed off as she took a step back and glanced over her shoulder at Sloan. The care she'd taken to make sure that he wouldn't hear hadn't been necessary. He was paying no attention to them, lost in a haze of pain and exhaustion; he was so white he looked as if he might collapse at any moment. She tried to smile. "Isn't it wonderful to see Patrick, Sloan?"

"Wonderful," he echoed hoarsely.

Patrick ambled over casually. "You did a hell of a job taking care of Brianne." He grinned. "Did she get in your way too much?"

"I'm the one who got in her way," Sloan bit out bitterly.

Brianne took an impulsive step forward. "No, that's not—"

"Bull," Patrick interrupted smoothly. "You don't have to try to save her feelings, Sloan. She's as tough as a mountain goat." He took Sloan's rifle and gently pushed him down to a sitting position so that he was leaning back against the rock. "And a godawful nurse. I'm surprised you survived." He squatted down beside Sloan. "I remember one time when I had the croup. She nearly killed me, fussing over me until she drove me crazy. You too?"

Brianne stood watching the two men with amused exasperation. Patrick had never had the croup.

"She's been very—kind," Sloan said without looking at her.

Patrick nodded gloomily. "That's when she's at her worst. Don't worry, I'll see that you get back to town in one piece," The two men exchanged purely male smiles.

Sloan's smile had a distinct element of relief, Brianne noticed. And her own relief had a strange hurt mixed in with it. She had wanted Patrick to help Sloan but not to shut her out. Sloan had been her love, her ailing child, her responsibility, and now he was being taken away from her. And it was clear he *wanted* to be taken away from her. She turned abruptly. "I'll get the horses."

6

Katy and Alice, two of the girls from Lucky's Saloon, rounded the corner to the back of Nilsen's Emporium just as Anna finished throwing up. "Miss Nilsen, what's wrong? Are you sick?"

Anna leaned weakly against the wall of the building, mortified that anyone had seen her. "No, I'll be fine in a minute." The nausea had lasted longer this morning. It had been stupid of her to come down to the store and try to work. Her father had seen that she wasn't feeling well and had been hovering worriedly around her all morning, making her guilt all the greater.

Without asking, Alice took Anna's handkerchief from her hand and carried it to the water pump to wet it. When she brought it back, she thrust it at Anna with a shy, awkward gesture. "Wash your face. It'll make you feel better."

"Thank you." The wet cloth was cool and refreshing, and by the time she'd finished, Anna did feel better. She straightened and looked at the two girls. Both of them were young and pretty, and, strangely enough, ingenuous.

They came to the back door of the general store so that they wouldn't offend the decent women of the community. Anna had always felt sorry for them. Now she realized that as soon as it was known that she was pregnant, the decent women of the town would look down on her just as they did on these two girls. The despair she felt almost overwhelmed her. Tears rushed to her eyes.

"Miss Nilsen, can we help you?" Alice asked gently.

Hastily Anna attempted to pull herself together, brushing her wet cheeks with the back of her hand. "No, no. I'll be . . ." She swallowed hard. "Did you come for the scents and ribbons you ordered?"

"Yes'm," Alice answered, "but you stay where you are for a piece till you're feelin' more the thing. We'll wait, won't we, Katy?"

Katy nodded. "Miss Nilsen." She hesitated. "It's none of our business, of course, but if you're in any trouble . . ." She trailed off, then began again. "I mean, we might be able to help. You've always been so nice to us and all."

"What do you mean?"

"Well . . ." Katy nervously laced her fingers together. "I hope you won't take no offense, but if you're in the family way, there's things that can be done."

Anna's hand flew to her heart. Oh, God, they *knew*. How long before everyone else did?

Alice nodded energetically. "It's painful takin' care of these things and all. But when you don't have no other choice—well, what else can you do?"

"I heard of some girls usin' a long knittin' needle," Katy said. When she saw all the color drain from Anna's already pale face, she hastened to add, "But there're better ways."

"Gin's the best," Alice put in. "It's called 'mother's ruin,' you know."

"She's right." Katy nodded seriously. "Just put yourself down in a steamin' hot tub of water and drink as much gin as you can as fast as you can. With any luck nature'll take care of the rest. Your stomach'll go into convulsions and you'll be purged."

"Of course, you could always take a harsh laxative, or"—Alice brightened with a new idea—"we've had a wet spring. I bet you could go out and find some black mold off some rye grass and make yourself up a potion."

Anna felt like putting her hands over her ears and screaming. She didn't want to hear any of this. She didn't even want to think about the fact that she was pregnant. But living in the West had taught her that nature was relentless. The baby inside her wasn't going to stop growing just because she didn't want to face the problem. "I—I appreciate your trying to help, but—"

"Don't you worry none, Miss Nilsen, we won't tell anyone." Alice's lips tightened. "We know how this town can be."

Anna turned quickly away. "I'll go get your order."
She walked back into the store, her mind in chaos.
Girls like Katy and Alice learned early that there
were very few choices in life, and Anna had begun
learning the same lesson when she'd met Wesley.

The methods they'd told her about were crude and
cruel, but what were her alternatives? When the
knowledge that she was pregnant became known,
she would be an outcast. She supposed that she could
take being ostracized by the town, but she wouldn't
be able to bear the pain her father would suffer
because of her.

Losing her mother had been a terrible blow to
him, but they'd come to America and he'd managed
to make a new life. He had his business and his
friends. When the town found out that she was pregnant, all of that would change. It was possible that
her shame would be put onto her father. She certainly wouldn't be able to work in the store anymore.
No decent person would want her to wait on them.
And even if she stopped working in the store, there
was still a good chance that the people of the town
would refuse to do their shopping with him. If that
happened, he would lose his business.

But most of all, it would destroy him if he knew
that his daughter was pregnant with Wesley McCord's
baby.

Anna poured the last bucket of hot water into the
copper tub, then straightened. It had taken her a
long time to heat all the water she needed, but at last

she was through. A full bottle of gin sat on the floor within arm's reach. Luckily her papa had choir practice on Thursday nights.

She was alone. Everything was ready.

Except her.

She'd thought about this all day long, and she really had no other choice. With slow, heavy movements, she slipped the robe from her shoulders and let it fall around her feet.

The tendrils of steam curled and twisted in mesmerizing patterns, rising invitingly toward her. Crossing her arms over her slim, naked body, she stared down at the water, savoring her pregnancy for just a moment more. There was a baby growing inside of her, a tiny new life that was a part of her, and the whole idea was miraculous to her.

But this baby was a part of Wesley McCord too. He hadn't cared that the act of going to bed with a man without the sanctity of marriage had been against everything she believed. He hadn't cared that it put scars on her heart every time she had to lie to her father.

And he wouldn't care now that she was carrying his child. To a man like Wesley, who was ruled by power and lust, a child would be nothing more than an inconvenience. He would probably heartily approve of what she was about to do.

He was a destroyer.

She bent and trailed her hand through the water. It was so hot, her skin felt as if it were being scalded. Jerking her hand out, she remembered that Katy and

Alice had said the bath should be steaming hot. It was.

All she had to do was step into the tub and immerse her body in it.

Drink the gin.

And wait.

So simple.

"God, please help me," she whispered, falling to her knees beside the tub. "I'm so scared. And I'm so alone."

Tears began to trickle down her face. She couldn't do it. She couldn't kill her baby. Her sins were great and the consequences of her sins even greater. But how could she inflict the result of her sins onto a helpless, innocent child that hadn't even been born yet?

Slowly a cold rage began to build in her. Lord in heaven, how could she even have considered doing this horrible thing? There was no question in her mind that Wesley would want her to abort her baby. But to do so would make her no better than he. She, too, would be a destroyer.

Her hands slowly clenched into fists at her sides, the nails biting hard into her palm. If she were to turn destroyer, it would not be her baby who would be the victim.

Friday afternoon Wes stood in front of his office window, frozen by the tableau before him. Sloan Lassiter and Brianne Delaney were walking their horses slowly down the street.

Both of Sloan's hands were clenched tightly around the saddle horn. He was slumped in his saddle. Bruises and lines of pain contoured agony into his face. And Brianne was a far cry from the beautiful, spirited girl he'd met in Anna's store the previous week. Now exhaustion was written into every line of her body. She looked as if she'd been through a war. He knew she had.

The problem being she'd obviously won.

Cummings and two of his men came behind Sloan and Brianne. Their hands were tied behind their backs.

A chestnut-haired man on a golden palomino rode behind them. A tethering rein connected three horses to the palomino. Three men lay lifelessly over their saddles, their heads and feet hanging on either side of their horse.

Wes turned away from the window.

Sloan hadn't won yet.

The ledger was the key. Without it Sloan couldn't prove a thing. He was clearly in no condition for a confrontation, which gave Wes time to get the ledger back in his possession. He would send Mahoney after it, telling him to slip into Sloan's room while he was asleep.

There was a chance Brianne had it, of course, but only a slim chance. Sloan wouldn't want that ledger out of his own hands, and Wes knew it.

He knew it all too well.

7

Sloan held up the glass of whiskey and noticed that the reflection from the lamp's flame seemed to be trapped in the golden brown liquid. He gently shook the glass to and fro to watch the flame shimmer, warm and bright. He smiled. *Christ,* it felt good to be back in his room in the Duke Hotel, cleaned up, and lounging in a real bed. He still felt lousy, but by all that was holy, it was great to be alive.

Last night, when he'd decided that they had no choice but to crawl down that ledge, through that rain of randomly placed gunfire, he wouldn't have given two cents for his and Brianne's chance of survival.

He took a sip of the flame-trapping liquid and felt the whiskey burn its way to his stomach, thanking God for doctors who believed whiskey was a cure for most of the ailments of the world. He'd sleep well tonight, and tomorrow he planned to be up and around.

"Sloan."

His hand jerked at the sound of Brianne's voice, and some of the whiskey sloshed onto his hand. Damn, he hadn't wanted to see her again tonight. There were too many feelings he needed to resolve. "I didn't hear you knock."

"That's because I didn't."

There was something different about her, he thought, and it wasn't just because for the first time in days he was seeing her dressed in a beautiful gown with her red hair shining and pinned into a coil. No. It was her eyes—they were of a darker hue of green than usual. And her face appeared pale, her posture rigid.

Then she began to move slowly to the foot of his bed, and as his gaze followed her, he was reminded of the time when his ship had gotten caught in a hurricane off the coast of the Carolinas. When the eye of the storm had passed over, the calm had been eerily chilling.

"How could you have done it?" Her voice was quiet, but her eyes blazed her fury.

So she'd found out. He stared down at the glass in his hands, then raised it to his mouth and took another drink.

"How, Sloan? How could you have allowed me to worry and hurt for Patrick, when all along you knew exactly where he was?"

Lifting his head, he met her stare. "Easy. I wanted you."

"And so using my love for my brother, you made a deal with me that you knew I wouldn't be able to turn down. Then you proceeded to take from me what you wanted, while all the time allowing me to believe he might be dead." Her voice shook with the intensity of her fury. "Do you know how much I suffered?"

"Yes."

"You're despicable."

"You're right."

She moved around the bed and bent over him until they were almost face-to-face. "What else are you?"

He drained the remaining whiskey and placed the glass on the nightstand. "A lot of things you don't want to know."

"Who's Cally?"

"What?" His question was sharp.

"Cally. You called out to her when you were delirious. She's obviously someone important to you, and I want to know who she is."

He turned his head away, his tone flat again. "She's no one."

"You look at me, Sloan Lassiter." She almost whispered the words.

When he turned his head back to her, the gold of his eyes had gone hard and opaque. "Cally's a beautiful young woman whom I almost took one night on the floor of my study. At the time I thought she was my half sister. Understand? I thought she was a blood relative. Only later did I find out she's my stepsister. She means nothing to me. She never did." He paused. "Now, do you want me to tell you some of the other things I've done in the past to convince myself I was alive?"

"I don't really know you at all, do I?" Shaken, she straightened away from him. "When you were sick you also said, 'I murdered him.' Who did you murder?"

He stilled. Then after a moment he slid down into the bed, rolled onto his side so that he was facing away from her, and pulled the covers over his shoulders.

Brianne felt as if he'd slapped her.

Anger made her tremble; hurt made her ache. She started across the room. Her hand closed on the doorknob.

"Brianne?"

She paused but didn't look around.

"Where's the ledger?"

God. Even after all they'd been through, he was still concerned with revenge against Wes McCord. Her lips tightened. "Henrietta has it."

"I want it. Tonight."

Brianne's gaze dropped absently to her hand. She was gripping the doorknob so hard, her knuckles were white. "I'll have someone bring it to you." She pulled the door open and left the room.

A soft night wind blew against the lace curtains at the open window of Brianne's bedroom, causing the panels to billow out. The flame in the lamp beside her bed hardly flickered, though, protected as it was by its glass globe.

Brianne suddenly whirled toward the window. "Did you just hear something?" she asked Patrick, who was sprawled lazily on her bed.

"Nope."

She twisted her hands together and gave him a cheerless smile. "I guess my nerves are on edge."

"You're upset. It's natural."

She shook her head. "I still can't believe Sloan didn't tell me that he'd found you."

"Bri," Patrick said gently, "a Delaney would have done far worse to get someone or something he wanted, and you know it."

"Perhaps, but what would you have done if it had been me who had been missing and someone had withheld information from you?"

"I'd probably kill that person. Slowly."

"Exactly."

"*Except*, if I loved them. And, Bri, there's no two ways about it. You love Sloan."

She crossed her arms and stared at him broodingly.

He shrugged. "Sorry, honey, but there's not enough anger or pain in the whole world to change that fact. However, I'll be glad to face him down in a gunfight if it'll make you feel better."

"Don't be ridiculous," she snapped, then threw her hands up in despair. "I love that man with all my heart and have almost from the first. But he's so damned stubborn. Do you know what he just asked me for?"

"Why don't you tell me," Patrick said obligingly.

"The ledger. It was what he was trying to get that morning out at the tent city when Dan Cummings surprised him and then proceeded to nearly kill him. It's his proof that McCord has been juggling figures and committing downright fraud to divert vastly inflated profits from construction contracts into his own pocket. A girl named Janice sneaked it out of the tent while Cummings was beating Sloan and brought it to me. Henrietta has had it ever since."

Patrick's expression had turned serious as he had listened to her. "Then, I don't think you have a choice, Brianne. You have to give the ledger to Sloan. He nearly died for it."

She came to the foot of the bed and wrapped her arms around one of the high posts. "You don't understand. Sloan came to Chango fully prepared to die, and I'm afraid that if he keeps on with this, that's exactly what's going to happen."

"Have you told him how you feel?"

"Many times."

"Then I think you've got to let him work things out for himself."

"I don't know if I can." Her hands closed on the smooth wood. "Not without trying to make him see . . . Oh, Patrick, there's so much I have to make him understand."

He smiled faintly. "Then what the hell are you doing standing here, talking to me?"

Two hours after Brianne had left Sloan's room the

door was thrown open again. Brianne marched in and hurled the ledger on the bed beside Sloan. "There's your precious ledger. I brought it myself. Are you happy? Now you can go on with this stupid revenge and maybe get yourself killed. That's what you want, isn't it?" She stopped to take a breath, glaring down at him. "Is revenge one of the things that makes you feel alive? Tell me, Sloan, I'm trying to understand."

Sloan raised himself to a sitting position, gazing at her warily. "I thought our discussion was over."

"Not by a long shot." She took a step closer. "I had to get away from you before I was tempted to murder you. You, that Cally, your damned secretiveness—I had to think."

"And what conclusions did you reach?"

"Don't you mock me." Her hands clenched into fists at her sides. "Why are you doing this? You were so different before. Everything's changed." Her eyes were suddenly glittering with tears. "I don't even know why I'm here. I should leave you in your lonely, cold little world and let you rot."

"That's probably an excellent idea. Why don't you?"

"Because I didn't go through the fires of hell out at that canyon to let you ruin everything between us." The softness of her voice was all the more powerful for the intensity it carried. "We're *alive*, dammit. Do you know how wonderful that is? Life is a blessing. How *dare* you not appreciate it."

His lips twisted grimly. "I've never found it particularly uplifting."

"Only because you wouldn't let yourself. You closed yourself in your tight, hate-filled room and refused to open the windows and let in all the beauty and freedom and—" Her voice broke and she was silent for a moment, fighting for control. "But I won't let that go on any longer."

He studied her, absorbing the meaning of her words. "I take it you're going to open those windows."

"I hope I've already opened a few of them." She moistened her lower lip with her tongue. "I hope you feel something for me besides what's between us in bed. Do you?"

It was a moment before he answered. Finally he said, "Yes."

Relief poured through her, but she braced herself for the next question. "Do you love me?"

He looked away from her. "What difference does it make?"

"To me, all the difference in the world. Do you love me?"

Silence.

"Answer me." She knelt with one knee on the bed and cradled his cheeks in her palms, forcing him to look at her. "Do you love me, Sloan?"

A multitude of expressions flew across his face. "I . . . love you," he said hoarsely.

She closed her lids for an instant. "Thank God."

He jerked his head back, out of her hold. "Why?" he said bitterly. "I don't see anything to be thankful about. I'd rather not have been given this love at all. It's going to tear me apart when you leave me."

"I'm not going to leave you."

"The hell you won't. You'll change your mind when your family comes riding in. You'll remember only the lies and the deceit and what I am."

She nodded slowly. "I'll remember all of those things. But I'll also remember that I love you."

"I was the first man to take you, but how the hell do you know that what you feel is love?"

Again she took his face in her hands, needing to touch him. "Do you think I'd go through all this if I didn't love you?" The tears that had been brimming began to roll down her cheeks. "I'd much rather love someone else. Anyone else. You're hard and ruthless and unforgiving, and I don't think you'll ever love me as much as I do you."

"Brianne . . ." He let out a harsh sigh. "God, don't cry. Please don't cry."

"I'm not crying." The tears continued to roll down her cheeks. "Why should I cry?" She managed a cracked laugh. "I probably deserve you. I know that I have to be completely stupid to love someone like you."

"Incredibly stupid," he said softly. "Incredibly generous." He turned his head and his lips caressed her palm. "Incredibly wonderful."

Suddenly she was fighting for breath. "I'm not wonderful, and it's easy to be generous when everything is going well."

"Things weren't going well in the canyon." His words were muffled in her palm. "And you were an angel from heaven."

She made a face. "A very unkempt angel." She paused, and her gaze searched his face. "And an angel I think you resented."

"Because I'm a fool." His voice was low. "I felt so damned helpless. It all seemed somehow so familiar. It reminded me of too many things I'd wanted to forget." He shook his head. "And you were doing everything for me, and I couldn't even protect you from Cummings."

Tenderness moved through Brianne like a shining, gently winding stream. "You did protect me. We protected each other. Don't you see? That's what love is all about. Sharing the bad times as well as the good."

"I'm beginning to see." His eyes were suspiciously bright as his gaze lifted to her face. "I'm sorry, Brianne. About so many things."

She kissed him lightly on the lips and caught the taste and the scent of whiskey. His last words were slightly slurred, and she suddenly recalled the instructions the doctor had given him about having a good night's rest. Perhaps she shouldn't have tried to settle these matters between them tonight, but there was one thing that must be understood between them.

"Sloan,"—she waited until his eyes met hers, then softened her tone but underscored each word with iron—"you will never, ever lie to me again. About anything. There must be nothing but truth between us from now on."

He nodded slowly. "Truth." He added softly, "And love."

She leaned forward and kissed him gently on the forehead. "Go to sleep. We can talk more in the morning." She picked up the ledger from the bed and set it on the bedside table, then crossed to the window and opened it to let fresh air into the stuffy room. "There's so much we have to get straight between us." She started to turn away.

"Brianne."

"Yes?"

"Come to bed, redhead."

Brianne felt a surge of heat tingle through her. It seemed a century since the two of them had come together in that white-hot merging. She drew a deep breath. "Sloan, we can't—"

He sighed, then gave a light laugh. "I'm afraid you're right." A note of regret threaded Sloan's voice. "Between the bruises and the whiskey, I'm still a hell of a mess." He paused. "But I can hold you. I want to be close to you tonight."

Yes, Brianne thought. She wanted to be close to him too. Without disrobing she turned back, extinguished the lamp's flame, and slipped into bed beside him, carefully positioning herself so that the pressure of her body wouldn't hurt him. "Just for a little while."

His arms slid around her and he held her close with a tenderness that filled her with an almost unbearable sweetness. They had known passion, but never this magical togetherness. Passion would come again, but for now this was more than enough.

"I have something to tell you," Sloan said haltingly, his fingers gently stroking her hair.

"Tell me tomorrow. Sleep now."

"I can't sleep until I tell you." He stopped, and when he spoke again, his voice was uneven. "You fill my life, Brianne. You *are* my life. There was nothing before, and, if you leave me, there will be nothing after you."

It was a confession so raw, a statement leaving him so vulnerable to her, it stunned her for a moment. The barriers were tumbling, the steel of his armor shattering. She felt at once humble and fiercely protective. "I'll never leave you." Her arms tightened lovingly around him. "Not as long as I live."

The silence that followed resounded with peace and encircled the two people on the bed with love and dreams.

It was only a short time later that Sloan's breathing evened and Brianne knew he had drifted off to sleep. She lay there for a little longer, enjoying the knowledge that there was now no threat of death hanging over this beautiful intimacy. Finally, reluctantly, she slid away from him and carefully got out of bed. Sloan was on his way to healing, but he needed rest, and she didn't want to risk rolling against him during the night and waking him. There would be a thousand other nights for them.

She tucked the covers around Sloan and then turned and moved toward the door.

There was someone watching her.

She whirled at the door, her gaze flying to the bed

across the room. Had Sloan awakened? She could see nothing in the darkness, but Sloan's breathing was deep and steady and she knew he was still fast asleep.

She stood there uncertainly a moment before shrugging and turning away. She was being foolish. Her nerves were really on edge.

She closed the door softly behind her.

The white batiste curtain at the open window stirred, moved. . . .

"It was easy." Ralph Mahoney laughed. "He was sleeping like a baby. All I had to do was wait out on the first-story roof until the woman left. Once she did, there was no problem."

"Did she see you?" Not that he cared, Wes thought, with the ledger back in his hands.

"No, I was careful."

"Good work." Wes nodded a dismissal. When the other man had gone, he sat at his desk leafing through the ledger. After a moment he unlocked the top drawer and opened it. The notes. He lifted them out and held them in one hand.

His eyes flicked back to the open ledger on his desk, and he placed the notes gently inside before closing the book. Then he rested his hand atop it.

The two most important things in his life. The notes. The ledger. Each were weapons of a different kind. One that he could aim, one that could be turned against him. Triumph was like whiskey in his veins.

Slowly Wes felt his smile die. With movements

that were almost savage, he thrust the ledger into the bottom drawer and locked up his desk. He put out the lamp and made his way up the stairs, a frown on his face.

He had felt triumph before, and he had always enjoyed the emotion. But this time it was a fleeting thing, an elusive thing.

Sometime later Wes lay in his bed, one arm behind his head as he stared at the ceiling. Briefly he raised up and squinted through the moonlit darkness at the clock on the mantel. Two-thirty. Mahoney had said that Sloan was sleeping soundly.

Why couldn't *he* sleep, Wes wondered.

He had the ledger back. Soon his plans for the railroad would be back on schedule. Of course Cummings was in jail, and he knew too much to be allowed to remain in the hands of the law. He'd have to take care of that situation. But everything was going to be all right.

A smile completely devoid of mirth creased his face into hard seams. Why was he lying to himself? He knew damned well why he was worried. Anna was carrying his child, and he hadn't seen her for two days. She hadn't come to him last night—Thursday—one of their regularly scheduled nights.

He conjured her image effortlessly, so vivid it was as if she were there before him. Long golden hair, clear blue eyes, skin like ivory velvet. He felt a strange aching deep within him that had no resemblance to lust.

What in the hell was he going to do about Anna?

His eyes remained open, searching the darkness as if it might hold his answer.

Lord, she was frightened.

She was actually trembling with nervousness, Anna realized. Taking care to be as quiet as possible, she crept down the front hallway of Wesley's house. The house was silent, thank heavens. Aware that he sometimes worked late, she had delayed coming until well after two to make sure he would be asleep.

She walked slowly, feeling her way in the darkness. She knew Wesley's house well, but the possibility that someone had moved something in the last few days still existed. If she were to bump into a table or a chair, the noise might lead to disaster.

The knob to the study door squeaked when she turned it, and she froze. Ice trickled down her spine as she cocked an ear toward the upstairs portion of the house. Nothing moved. She let out her breath, then slowly opened the door and slipped inside. Not wanting to risk having to turn the knob again, she left the door slightly ajar.

Cautiously she made her way across the room until she encountered the desk. She located the lamp, then felt around until she found the matches. Once the lamp was lit, a sense of exhilaration settled over her. *She was so close.*

She glided behind Wesley's desk and carefully tried all the drawers. Locked. But she'd come prepared. She withdrew a sharp kitchen knife from her skirt pocket and inserted it in the top seam of the top middle drawer and began working the knife back and forth.

She had no idea where the blasted notes were, and she'd never forced open a drawer before, but she refused to be discouraged. She'd do it. She had to. Suddenly there was the slight crackling noise of wood splintering, then a click. Eagerly she pulled the drawer open and searched. No notes. Bitter disappointment swept through her.

God, please let me find them.

She turned to the side drawers and repeated the process on the top two drawers without any luck.

But the bottom side drawer yielded bounty—a ledger. There'd been whispers around town about a ledger that Wesley was desperate to find. Could this be it? Perhaps if she couldn't find the notes, she could take the ledger and use it to force Wesley to give her the notes. She pulled the book from its safe resting place and thumbed through it. Numbers, dates, names, none of it meant anything to her, but perhaps— The notes! Miraculously the pages had parted to the center to reveal her father's notes.

Anna closed her eyes and said a prayer of thanks.

She counted the notes to make sure they were all there, then placed them back in the ledger and closed it. She'd take the ledger and look it over later when she had the chance.

She turned the lamp's key until the light was extinguished and tiptoed out of the study.

It was over. At last, it was over.

She stepped out onto the porch, drew in a deep

breath of fresh air, and closed the front door behind her.

Wes sat straight up in bed. *Had he just heard a door shut?* He slid off the bed, reaching for his gun, and moved silently to the door leading to the hall. Downstairs, he searched every room, lighting lamps as he went. Nothing.

He walked into the study and paused in the darkness. A faint smell of lilacs seemed to hang in the air.

God, my imagination needs a rest. First Anna in his bedroom, now in his study.

He put a match to the lamp's wick. Christ. His desk had been broken into. The bottom side drawer stood open. Empty.

Wes sank into the chair, feeling sick.

Damn you, Sloan Lassiter.

Anna had almost reached the emporium when she heard the hoofbeats. Fear washed the warmth from her body. If Wesley caught her, he mustn't find the notes and the ledger.

Quickly she looked around. Just off the path was a broken-down wagon sitting on its axles. The wheels were gone and weeds grew up around it. The wagon had been in that exact spot for as long as she could remember. She lifted up the seat, thrust the ledger into the box beneath, and closed it.

By the time she reached the safety of her back door, all she could hear was the hammering of her heart. She

paused and searched in the darkness for the horse she
had heard. She could see no one.

"I can't believe Lassiter managed to steal that ledger
back," Mahoney said as he walked out the door of
Wes's office. "He seemed dead to the world when I was
in his room last night."

Wes joined him on the boardwalk. As usual on a
Saturday afternoon, Main Street was clogged with buck-
boards and riders, and dust and noise filled the air.
"Maybe it wasn't Sloan. Maybe it was Brianne. But it
doesn't matter who it was. We're going to get that
damned ledger back once and for all and then we're
going to make Sloan sorry he ever thought of tangling
with me."

"What d'ya want me to do?"

"Find the—" He broke off as he caught sight of Anna
coming out of the emporium across the street. She
smiled at two ladies who passed, then began sweeping
down the boardwalk. She exchanged greetings with
various people, but not once did she so much as glance
his way. How could she not be interested in whether
or not he was at his office, he wondered half angrily.
They had shared passion that few people ever knew.
She was carrying his baby as a result of that passion.

Why didn't she look at him, dammit!

Why the hell hadn't she come to him on Thursday
night?

Could it be that she had managed somehow to shut
herself off in a world apart from him? How could she
do that? God. She didn't even have to be close for him

to think of her. Just last night ... He stiffened with shock as his gaze narrowed on Anna's face.

Lilacs.

A hand covered her mouth. Anna awoke instantly to darkness and terror.

A figure was beside her bed, looming over her, his hard hand suffocating her. A scream pushed up from her chest but was trapped in her throat. Her heart slammed against her ribs.

"Stop struggling."

At the sound of the low, harsh voice, she went limp. *Wesley.*

Slowly he eased the pressure of his hand. "I want the notes. Where are the notes?"

"What are you doing?" she whispered, frantic. "Papa will hear—"

"Do you think I care anymore?"

"For God's sake, be quiet." Lord, she had thought it was over. This couldn't be happening. It had to be a dream. "I don't know what you're doing here," she whispered. "But whatever it is, we can talk about it tomorrow."

"The notes, Anna. Where are the notes?"

She couldn't give them up. She *couldn't.* And somehow she had to get him out of there before her father woke up.

"Wesley, go home."

"The notes *and* the ledger."

So the ledger *was* important. Now she had something with which to fight him.

"Anna," he whispered. "Do you want your father to know you're carrying my child?"

Oh, God. She closed her eyes as a wave of pure fear washed over her. Somehow he'd figured out that she was pregnant. What was she going to do?

"Anna?"

"You really wouldn't tell him, would you?"

"Try me." His hand closed around her arm and he pulled her upright. "Get up and put on your robe and slippers."

She had no choice but to do as he said, she thought dully. His knowledge of her pregnancy gave him yet another weapon to hold over her. And soon he would have the notes back too.

While she was slipping into her robe, he asked, "Where did you hide them? In here?"

She shook her head and pointed toward the window. She stepped into her slippers, then turned to him. "Be as quiet as you can. *Please*."

"Why? Your father's going to know sooner or later. Haven't you figured that out yet, Anna?"

"No, he doesn't have to—" She broke off. "This is no time to discuss it." She moved toward the door.

The night was surprisingly warm for this time of the year, but Anna felt cold and miserable. Silently she led the way to the wagon and indicated the box beneath the seat.

Quickly Wes retrieved the ledger and checked to make sure the notes were in it. Then he turned to face her. "Why did you take the ledger?"

"For the same reason you took my father's notes."

With directness she met his gaze. "I wanted to destroy you before you had a chance to destroy me."

A look of shock crossed his face; then a bittersweet smile curved his lips. "You'll have to get more experience in the business of destruction, Anna. You're sure as hell not very good at it." He wheeled abruptly away. "Let's go."

Anna turned to retrace her steps along the path, but about halfway to the emporium, Wes grasped her arm. "No, this way."

"What?" Anna looked around, confused. He was leading her toward the woods. "Wesley—"

"There's no need to worry," he said mockingly. "I'm not going to take you back to the glade. We're going to Moran."

"Moran?" She remembered that Moran was a town several miles west of Chango. Bewildered and frightened, she dug in her heels and jerked her arm out of his grasp. "I'm not going anywhere."

"Yes, you are. I checked around and found out that the traveling preacher is in Moran right now." He paused, and in the moonlight his face appeared fierce and stern. "We're going to be married tonight."

Panic struck at her like a cold blast of wind. "No!"

"Don't fight me on this, Anna."

Her hands tightened into fists. "I'll never stop fighting you."

"Maybe not, but you're pregnant with my baby. You have no choice but to marry me." He paused. "Unless you plan to get rid of it."

"I—" She swallowed hard and felt pain. "Do you think I didn't think about it? I couldn't . . ."

Cold horror washed through Wes as he stared at her for a long moment. For Anna to actually have considered taking the life of a child growing inside her, she must have felt driven, desperate. *He had done this to her.* When he finally spoke, his words were soft but implacable. "Anna, even my name is better than no name at all."

She lowered her head, defeated, then she slowly nodded.

He lifted her into the saddle in front of him so that she was sitting across his thighs, and he kicked the horse into a fast-paced run. She grabbed for the saddle horn with both hands. His arms held her close, and his strong chest was at her back. Against the wind they raced through the dark night.

The town of Moran was asleep, but that didn't bother Wes. At the livery stable he pounded on the door until an old man appeared. "Yeah?"

"I hear there's a preacher in this town. Where is he?"

The old man's sleep-filled eyes widened with outrage. "How the hell should I know? Do you know what time it is?"

Wes fixed him with a steely stare. "I'm going to ask you one more time. *Where* is the preacher?"

The old man shifted uneasily. "He stays at the Fairgates when he's in town," he mumbled, "but I'd try the saloon if I were you."

Wes nodded. "Have a fresh horse ready for me in about thirty minutes and take care of this one."

He walked back and lifted Anna down from the horse. Her bare feet touched the ground, and suddenly her knees gave way. With an exclamation he swept her into his arms. "Where the hell are your slippers?"

"They fell off." Her head dropped to his shoulder. "Wesley, I can't appear before a preacher looking like this. I'm wearing a gown and a robe, for heaven's sake, and my hair—"

"Looks fine," he said in a voice low as a growl, "and don't worry about what the preacher's going to think. If he's at the saloon this time of night, he may not be thinking much at all."

Her first impulse was to try to put some order to the long gold, tangled length of her hair. Then she changed her mind. Why bother, she wondered wearily.

She was about to be married, something every woman dreams of from the time she is very young. But her wedding would not be as other women's. Her wedding would be taking place in the secret of the night. Perhaps even in a saloon. Her bridegroom was a man who did not love her. And she would stand beside him, barefoot, in an old nightgown and robe, with knotted and tangled hair.

Wes used his back to push open the doors of the saloon. Smoke hazed the air, stinging Anna's eyes, and the pungent smell of liquor and cigarettes made her feel queasy. She turned her face into his chest.

Just for a moment his arms tightened around her. Then he set her on her feet.

"Is the preacher here?" Wes asked in a loud voice.

All eyes turned toward the two of them. The laughter and the talk died away.

In the center of the room a poker game was in progress. One man was passed out in the corner. At the bar a bleary-eyed bartender was pouring drinks for a heavily powdered woman dressed in red.

The woman pointed to the tall, gangly man next to her. "This here's the preacher."

The man she had indicated reached for his glass and took a deep swig of whiskey.

Wes crossed the room with long strides, grasped the man by the shoulder, and spun him around so fast, most of the remaining whiskey in the glass he was holding sloshed onto the sawdust of the floor. "Are you?"

The man straightened and looked at Wes with indignation. "I'm Reverend Ezekiel Thomas."

"I'm Wes McCord, and"—he indicated Anna with a nod of his head—"she's Anna Nilsen. I want you to marry us."

"Tomorrow, in the church—"

"Now. Here."

"I'm otherwise engaged." The reverend threw a crooked smile at the bar girl, who responded by suggestively rubbing her full breasts against his arm. Thomas was reaching for her when Wes pulled out a wad of money and peeled off several bills.

Thomas paused and raised a bushy black brow.

"Well, I think I could be persuaded. . . ." He took the money and pushed himself away from the bar. "The bride?"

Wes held up his hand and motioned for Anna to join them.

I can't do this, she thought with sudden panic. Yet she found herself taking a step forward. And another. Then she stopped. A burst of drunken laughter sounded in the background. Smoke curled around her, cutting off her air. Suddenly Wes was there beside her, his gaze concerned. He rubbed her hand between both of his. *I can't feel anything*, she thought. He put his arm around her and led her to the bar.

"Join hands," the preacher said, his breath strong with whiskey, the woman in red hanging on to him as if she were a colorful, obscene growth. He smiled at the woman, then glanced at Anna. "Do you take this man?"

I can't say it.

Wes gently squeezed her hand. "Anna," he murmured.

"Yes," she said.

"Do you take this woman?" the preacher asked Wes.

"Yes."

"Put the ring on her finger."

A startled look crossed Wes's face, but he recovered quickly and pulled a signet ring off his finger. Lifting her left hand, he slipped it on the third finger. The big ring hung loosely on her slender finger.

It's not going to stay on, she thought numbly.

"You're married." Reverend Thomas turned his

attention to the saloon hall woman's voluptuous figure. One hand fastened onto her breast, the other skimmed its way under the red skirt.

I'm going to be sick, Anna thought.

"Not so fast, preacher man," Wes snapped, tapping Thomas on the shoulder. "I want our marriage certificate."

"Dammit, I'd have to get my saddlebag." Irritated, Thomas angled his head around. As soon as he met Wes's gaze, he disentangled himself from the woman. "Be glad to."

The old man at the livery stable had given him a good horse, Wes thought with satisfaction. The bay was covering the distance back to Chango with long, clean strides, and they would easily reach town by dawn.

Christ, the ride had been hard on Anna. She was lying slumped back against him, her lashes shadowing her cheeks like dark bruises. She hadn't uttered a word since she'd murmured "yes" in the saloon. He wondered if she was asleep.

With a naturalness that took him by surprise, he slid his hand down over her stomach.

Mine.

Where had that thought come from? And had he been thinking of the child or of her?

The child. The child was his, with the same blood running in his veins, and now with the same name.

Anna. She'd never been his, and the few terse words they had spoken didn't change that fact. Anna was something he had stolen, taken, and was surely more remote from him now than she'd ever been before.

No, it must be the child who was causing this strong, warm river of emotion flowing through him. His palm moved gently, caressingly, over Anna's abdomen. Soon there would be the stirring of life there, a life they had created together. The thought was wonderfully amazing to him.

Creation . . .

The sky was beginning to lighten with the new dawn when Wes carefully lifted Anna down from the horse.

She blinked sleepily. "Where are we?"

"You're back home."

"Home?" She turned to see that they were behind the emporium. Confused, she looked back at Wes.

He swung into the saddle and rode away, without a word, without a backward glance.

8

When Anna awoke, sunlight was streaming through her window. Disoriented, she rolled over on her back and gazed around her. She had a vague memory of her father shaking her shoulder and asking her if she was all right. That had been sometime earlier, she realized dazedly. She'd fallen back into so deep a sleep that now she felt drugged.

Had last night really happened?

Yes, amazingly it had. Wesley had married her and given her his name. Then he had left her at her father's home, as if she were an unwanted package, and ridden away. Obviously he had felt he had done his duty by her.

What a strange man he was, full of moods she was certain she would never understand and mysteries she would never solve. Time was simply not on her side, as they would soon be going their separate ways. But it was just as well. She wasn't sure she wanted to solve those mysteries anyway. She'd always loved the sunlight, and he was such a dark man.

She raised her left hand and looked at his gold signet ring, her wedding ring. She was vaguely surprised that it hadn't fallen off on the ride back to Chango. Now she slipped it off her finger and cradled it in her palm. The ring was like Wesley, strong, bold.

She suddenly pushed back the covers and got out of bed. Her father would already be back from church by this time and down in the store working on the inventory. She should go help him, but she didn't want to face his questions right now. She walked across the room to gaze out the window. A beautiful spring day with a robin's-egg-blue sky greeted her. Abruptly she turned away from the window and began to dress. For once Papa could take care of the inventory alone. She needed time to gather herself together, a time free of strife and deceptions.

And she knew where there was a meadow . . .

The sun was golden, gentle, and warm, as if it knew Anna wouldn't be able to take any harshness. A soft breeze shimmered through the grass, bending the long blades so that new colors of green were created.

In the center of the meadow she sank down amid a carpet of velvet-petaled buttercups and marigolds, her skirts billowing out around her. She braced her hands behind her and leaned back, letting the tranquility and the beauty of her surroundings soak into her.

"Anna?"

Startled, she looked up. A tall, dark figure stood between her and the sun. She lifted an arm to shield her eyes and stiffened. "What are you doing here?"

Wes dropped down in front of her. "I saw you walking this way and followed you." He tossed his hat to the grass beside him, looked at her, then grimaced. "I'm lying. I was watching for you." His gaze searched her face. "How are you? The baby . . ."

"I'm fine." Feeling unsure and awkward, she plucked a stalk of buttercups and brought it to her nose. All of their meeetings had been in darkness. Now, unexpectedly, they were together in a sunlit meadow. It made Anna feel strangely unprotected.

"Where's the ring?"

She touched the place between her breasts where the ring rested beneath her dress. "I had a long chain. It was my mother's." She hesitated, then lifted her hands to the back of her neck and the clasp of the chain. "You'll be wanting your ring back."

"*No.*" Without thinking about it, he had reached over and pulled her arms down. "No."

She shrugged, puzzled.

Tall flowers surrounded them, the scent of the blossoms perfuming the air. Anna studied Wesley through a veil of thick lashes. Every woman in town agreed that he was very good-looking. Strands of silver

threaded through his brown hair and matched his
light gray eyes. She'd seen those eyes freeze into ice
when directed at other people, but they were never
cold when he looked at her.

He was an enigmatic man, she thought not for the
first time. Then suddenly her confusion vanished and
what had been muddy before now cleared. *She wanted
to understand him.* And she felt strongly that the key
lay in his past. "I suppose you're happy now that you
have the ledger back."

"Why shouldn't I be happy?" He glanced away
from her. "The railroad will come through on schedule, and I'll be the one in charge."

"But what about Mr. Lassiter?"

"I can't think of a thing he can do to me. He'll
most likely leave town soon."

"Just give up? Do you really think so?"

He pulled up a blade of grass and absently ran it
through his fingers, shredding it. "Now that I have
the ledger, I don't think of him at all."

"You can do that, can't you? Simply cut someone
out of your mind and never think of them again."

"I learned a long time ago that you do what you
have to do to survive."

She'd always known he was a hard man, yet suddenly she realized that in the years to come it would
be his gentleness and his passion she would remember. Somehow, in this sunlit moment, it wasn't enough
to know what he was. She wanted to know what he
had been yesterday and what he would become to-

morrow. She said impulsively, "Tell me about yourself. Tell me what your life was like when you were a boy."

He was astonished by her request until he remembered her tentative curiosity of a few nights before . . . and his child growing within her.

Jesus, he didn't like to talk about himself. He hated remembering the ugliness and the pain of those years. But she had asked, and she had a right to know.

He didn't speak for a moment, and when he did, his words came haltingly. "I guess you could say my home was a ragged tent in a mining camp in Nevada. In the wintertime the cold wind used to seep through the holes and under the flaps. In the springtime rain would drive in like ice-cold needles."

"Then your father was a miner?"

"He was a gambler who drifted in and out of the area for the first seven years of my life, then he disappeared altogether. My mother was a prostitute who serviced the miners." He smiled bitterly. "I was a bastard."

Anna felt a pang of compassion as she thought of that desolate little boy. Their hasty marriage the night before had shocked and bewildered her, but now everything was easier to understand. He hadn't wanted his child to be a bastard; he wanted it to have his name.

He was continuing. "I remember going hungry, and falling asleep on cold, hard dirt floors because no one was there to put me into a bed. Some of the dogs in the camp were treated better than I was. Later, I realized that my mother was addicted to opium."

Anna was looking at him in a way that no one ever had, he thought, surprised. In the clear blue depths of her eyes he saw a sadness and a sympathy that was solely for him, and something he couldn't identify moved in his heart. "I learned early how to look out for myself, Anna, and I've lied, cheated, and charmed my way through life ever since." He paused. "You wanted to know, didn't you? You wanted to know what had made me the way I am today, right?"

"Yes."

"So now you do. And there's one more thing you should know. I never saw any sense in the world until I saw you."

Her heart seemed to pick up a beat. "What do you mean?"

"I thought that life in that mining camp where I grew up was the way life was everywhere—raw, mean, dark, ugly. Until you, there had never been anything to convince me differently. But you . . ." His fingers clenched on the blade of grass. "You were like a shining light beaming through my darkness. So I set out to get you."

"By blackmailing me."

"Would you have had anything to do with me if I'd done it any other way?"

She thought about Wesley calling on her at home and meeting her father. She tried to imagine him courting her like a suitor, accompanying her to church picnics, taking her on afternoon buggy rides, perhaps sitting down to dinner with her and her father. She couldn't even envision it and decided he was right. If he'd approached her in any other way, she undoubtedly would have rebuffed him. He'd gotten her in the only way he had known how.

"Well, Anna?"

"I think I wish you'd tried some other way."

He met her gaze. "I wish I had too."

He looked away, feeling oddly vulnerable, and saw a gold and orange butterfly flutter among a grouping of lavender Scotch thistle, then settle onto one featherlike blossom. *So much beauty*, he thought. *So much pain.* He'd never told anyone what he'd just told her. He felt as if a surgeon had taken a knife and laid back several layers of his skin, exposing a misery he'd fought all his life to keep hidden away.

"It's all right, Wesley," Anna said softly.

She knows how I'm feeling. Amazed and moved, he extended his hand, wanting to touch her and maybe in some way get closer to her. Then he realized what he was doing and he jerked his arm back.

The butterfly left its petaled perch to flit around Anna's shoulder. Ever so lightly it landed. She angled her head so that she could see it. The butterfly delicately fanned her face with a flutter of its fragile wings, then flew away from her and landed on the exquisite beauty of a golden buttercup. She smiled as she watched it.

She will be a gentle, loving mother. The baby—his baby—would be so very lucky, he thought.

"When are you going to tell your father about the baby, Anna?"

She glanced at him, startled, and it dawned on her that he hadn't asked about the marriage, only about the child. It was as if the marriage had no further importance for him. "I'm not."

He frowned. "I don't understand."

"I'm not a complete fool," she said, her words coming uncertainly at first. "Last night doesn't change anything, Wesley. We both know that."

A shock of pain went through him. He glanced away, reaching out blindly to grasp a small cluster of dandelions. They came apart in his hands.

Anna didn't want or expect a future with him, and he couldn't really blame her, could he? He'd done nothing but take from her. Now he had to face the difficult realization that there were some things he just couldn't take. And he couldn't force her to spend the rest of her life with him.

He dropped the maimed remains of the dandelions to the ground and took the buttercups from her hands. Instead of pinning up her hair, she'd loosely tied it in a narrow black ribbon at her neck, leaving the rest of it to fall freely down her back like a glistening golden waterfall. He leaned over and placed the flower gently behind her ear.

His hands didn't brush her skin, but Anna felt his warmth as his face came close to hers and his hand passed her cheek.

"I'm going away," she said.

Wes was still. "When did you decide that?"

"I think the decision's been forming from the first moment I realized I was pregnant. It's the only way."

It seemed to Anna that the silence that fell between them pushed a dark tension into the light-filled peace of their surroundings.

With a suddenness that surprised Anna, he reached for his hat and got to his feet. "I need to get back to town." He started away, then stopped and turned back. Bending his head, he ran his hand around the brim of his hat. His gaze holding her own was filled with many emotions—belligerence, sadness, anger, even an odd diffidence. "Will you come to me tonight?"

The gold and orange butterfly had time to flit to four flowers before she whispered, "I don't know."

Wes nodded curtly, spun on his heel, and strode away from her.

As she watched him go, Anna's hand found the ridge of the chain beneath the thin fabric of her dress and traced it down to where the ring lay nestled between her breasts. Her body had warmed the metal, and when she absently pressed the ring into the softness of her breast, she felt the outline of Wesley's initial like a brand on her flesh.

"You haven't learned, have you?" Brianne's quietly spoken question reached across the bedroom to the apple-green medallion-back sofa and the man who sat upon it. "We nearly lost our lives because of your hatred for Wes McCord, and now you're about to put yourself in jeopardy again."

"Someone's got to stop him," Sloan said, the lines of his rugged face grim. "Who better than me?"

"Anyone, for heaven's sake." His set expression told her that she wasn't getting through to him. "Sloan, we nearly lost our lives in that canyon. Didn't that have any effect on you?"

"It gave me one more reason to hate the man."

She went to him and sat down beside him. "How can you place more value on something that happened fifteen years ago than you do on our future together?"

"This doesn't have anything to do with our future together."

"How can it not?"

"There's no danger to us now. Wes thinks I'm not a threat since he has that damned ledger back." He smiled with satisfaction. "And by the time he finds out how wrong he is"—he shrugged—"well, it won't matter. He'll have lost everything, and I doubt if he'll have any fight left in him."

"I wish I could make you understand how wrong you are. Why couldn't you just talk to him about David's death?"

"Talking would be useless." The worry in her eyes made him reach over and gather her hands in his. "Listen to me, Brianne. I know you don't understand, but I want you to ask yourself something. What would you have done if the Grimes brothers had killed Patrick?"

"I would have hunted them down until I drew my last breath."

He smiled crookedly. "See there."

She looked at him for a moment, fighting against agreeing with him before finally sighing resignedly. "I hadn't thought of it in that way before, but now I can understand a little better. But, dammit, Sloan, I still don't approve."

"And I wouldn't approve if you set out to hunt someone down either, but I've got to do this, Brianne. Everything is going to be fine. All it's going to take is two telegrams. And there'll be no violence. At least not from me. I promise."

Brianne found little reassurance in his promise, but she had to be satisfied with it. For the present, at any rate.

Wes's hand tightened around the glass of whiskey he held as he heard the front door open, then the sound of footsteps as they moved down the long entrance hall. They were Anna's footsteps. He'd listened for them too many times not to know her light, graceful step. And, as on those many occasions, his heart was pounding in anticipation of her appearance. However, tonight would be different from all those other nights.

He heard her pause at the entrance to the front room, but he knew she would see that no light had been lit there. The lamp burning on his desk in his study and the flames that were dancing in the fireplace were at present the only lights in the whole house.

"Wesley?"

"I'm back here."

After a moment she appeared in the doorway. "What are you doing in here?"

"I had some work to do." In truth, he had been unable to do any work at all. His mind had been too full of thoughts of her. "I wasn't sure you'd come."

"I wasn't sure I would either." She still wasn't certain why she was there. It was as if she'd been drawn to him by the hint of vulnerability she'd seen in his expression this afternoon in the meadow. And she had a sense that in their final parting there should have been something more, something that seemed to remain just out of reach.

Pushing aside the whiskey, he stood up and walked around the desk. He held out his hand to her. "Come here, Anna."

She hesitated.

"Please."

She crossed the room to him. There seemed to be a new weariness in his voice and manner, she thought. And he looked older, with harsh lines seaming either side of his lips.

"Sit down."

"Sit down?" she asked, puzzled. Something was wrong. Wesley was never in his study on the nights when she came to his house. And once she was with him, they never spent time downstairs talking. Instead, he would hurry her upstairs, undress her, and take her to bed.

He waved his hand toward a small chair by the desk. "Please. I have something I want to give you."

She took the chair he indicated but said, "Wesley, you know I won't accept any gifts from you. We've discussed this many times." A renegade thought entered her mind. Just this once she'd love to keep something he'd given her, something that in years to come she could take out and look at and remember him by. Then again, she knew she'd never forget him.

"This is one gift you'll be glad to accept." From the bottom drawer in his desk he pulled out a locked metal box and set it on his desk before drawing a key from the pocket of his trousers. It took him only moments to unlock the box. He lifted the lid and extracted the documents, then stood, came around to the front of the desk, and handed the papers to Anna.

She gazed at him, bewildered. "These are my father's notes of debt."

He leaned back against the desk and folded his hands. "They're yours now."

"I don't understand. You demanded that I give them back after I'd taken them, now you're simply handing them over to me?"

"I'm setting you free, Anna."

Astonishment, then pain hit her. All she could think to say was "Why?"

Wes looked away from her. He should have known

that she would want an explanation. But voicing his reasons would be impossible for him. There were too many complexities involved, too much agony and torment.

"Wesley . . . I'm not sure I know what to say. This is very unexpected."

He smiled gently at her, his gaze moving over her fair hair with a strangely melancholy yearning. "You don't have to say anything."

He took the notes from her, walked to the fire, and threw them on top of the blazing logs. Fire caught the edges of the notes instantly, and the flames began devouring the paper. Soon all that was left of the notes that had once bound Anna to him were tiny bits of burned paper, blackened with a glow of red, being drawn up the chimney, fragile as the butterfly's wings they had watched together only a few hours earlier.

He stared down at the fire. "I'm going to ask one more thing of you. But, of course, you don't have to do it."

"What is it?"

He raised his head and looked over his shoulder at her. Then he turned and faced her. "Will you go upstairs with me one last time?"

The sudden surge of need she felt for him shook Anna badly. With the specter of blackmail no longer present, she was free to get up and walk out of the house if she liked. But she suddenly realized that she wouldn't leave. This was why she had come. To erase the bitterness that had always existed between them.

And to say good-bye.

She gazed into his eyes. "Yes," she said softly.

For the last time. The words ran through Wes's mind as he plucked the pins from her golden hair and watched the silken strands uncoil and shimmer down her back past her waist.

For the last time. The words echoed hollowly in Anna's mind as she pulled her hair over her shoulder so that he could unbutton her dress.

Their clothes were taken off slowly; kisses were given that lasted long minutes. With dreamlike rhythm they touched and moved and strained against each other. And when at last they lay on the bed, they still found no sense of urgency.

Wes saw the bruises that he had made on her skin that night in the glade.

"They'll eventually fade," she whispered, her fingers threading through his hair.

"But it should never have happened." His lips brushed over the marks as if he could heal them with his touch. "To mar something so perfect is a sacrilege."

She laughed softly. "I'm not perfect."

His mouth skimmed down to her breast. "Don't blame yourself. About anything. Right from the start, everything has been my fault."

Heat was melting through her. "Has it? I wonder."

"Don't wonder. Believe me on this."

"But—"

"Shhh." He took one beautiful rose-colored peak into his mouth.

Silence fell between them.

Always, he thought, *I will remember the taste of her, sweet and feminine.*

Always, she thought, *I will remember the way he smells, elemental and masculine.*

His hand went to her other breast, caressing.

Never again, he thought, *will I know the thrilling feeling of anticipation of being inside her.*

Never again, she thought, *will I know the exquisite longing to have him fill me.*

His lips slid down to her stomach and whispered back and forth across the velvet texture of her skin.

For tonight, he thought, *I will have her, and this possession will have to last me my whole life long.*

For tonight, she thought, *I will not fight him or myself. I will give myself up to the pleasure and forget the guilt and the anger.*

There would be no more nights of having him hold her and feel him move inside her. Sorrow threatened to overwhelm her, but she pushed it back determined that their last lovemaking would not be marred.

His gentleness was more pronounced.

Her surrender was more complete.

His mouth was lower on her now, kissing places of extraordinary sensitivity. Ecstasy bloomed wherever his lips moved. Flames were rising up inside her.

She grasped his shoulders, and with one word broke the silence. "Please."

He'd never known feelings so deep or profound. He held her tightly to him and entered her.

She let the fire take her, joined to him in an alchemy of glittering closeness that bewildered her with its many facets.

His head was beside her, their cheeks pressed together.

He felt the tears on his face and thought they were his.

She felt the tears on her face and thought they were hers.

Each was so absorbed in their own pain of goodbye that neither was aware of the other's tears mingling with their own.

9

Lars Nilsen gave a sigh of satisfaction. "You make apple cake as good as your mama did, my daughter."

"Thank you, Papa."

"And the meat pie—it vas vonderful."

Anna picked up her plate and glass from the kitchen table and took them to the sink. She leaned against the counter and bent her head. Lord, she dreaded the next few minutes. From somewhere she was going to have to find the courage to tell her father that she was leaving town. Telling him might be more painful than actually leaving him, because once she was on the stage and heading out of town, she wouldn't be able to see the distress and bewilderment in his eyes. But this evening she was going to have to look him squarely in the eye.

He was going to be hurt and confused. He wouldn't

understand, because, of course, she wouldn't be able to explain about the baby. That knowledge might kill him. She was comforted in what she was about to do only by the belief that in the long run it would be better for him this way.

Behind her she heard her father push away from the table and stand up. She closed her eyes and took a deep breath. "I'm going away, Papa."

"What?"

Like a knife through her back, she felt his shock. "I—I'll be taking the stage in two days time. And I won't be coming back. I plan to—"

"But vhat about the baby?"

For an instant she froze. Then she whirled and saw the expression on her father's face—as if he couldn't believe that those particular words had slipped out of his mouth. "You know," she whispered.

He averted his eyes and turned toward the door.

"Wait a minute!" She rushed to him and grabbed his arm to stop him. "You *know*." Her brain didn't seem to want to take in that fact.

For a moment he was stiff, then he slumped and without looking at her he nodded.

A thought darted through her brain, a thought so unbearable that she suddenly felt as if something sharp and jagged had sliced through the middle of her heart. "What else do you know?"

"Daughter . . . I . . ."

Nervelessly her hand fell away from his arm. "Oh, my God." Her quietly spoken words were weighted down with horror. "You know everything."

He half raised his hand toward her. "Anna—"

"How long, Papa? How long have you known that Wesley McCord was blackmailing me with your notes of debt?"

"Almost from the beginning," he admitted miserably.

She was cold. So cold. She wrapped her arms around her body, trying to warm herself. "You knew what I was doing to protect you and you didn't put a stop to it?"

"How could I?" he asked, pleading for her to understand. "I vould have lost everything."

She couldn't take her eyes from her father, but his image was blurring. Tears were crowding her eyes and overflowing down her cheeks.

"But didn't you think about what *I* was losing, Papa? My self-respect. Pieces of my soul. For God's sake, Papa, I'm your flesh and blood. I'm your *daughter*. One word from you would have protected me."

"Anna, try to understand," he said pleadingly. "You are young. I am not. I left my home in Sveden and made a new life here. I could not start over again."

Slowly her head shook back and forth. Without being aware of it, she began backing away from him. "It was all for nothing," she said. "For nothing."

"Please . . ."

A sob tore from her throat. "It wasn't Wesley who made me a whore. It was you, Papa. You . . ." Dimly she saw her father make a gesture as if he were reaching out to her. She took another step away from him. She couldn't bear for him to touch her right then. She wheeled and ran from the room.

Down the stairs, out of the emporium, along the path she ran, not knowing where she was going, not caring. She ran. Her hairpins loosened and fell to the ground. She ran. Brambles snagged and tore at her dress. She ran. She stumbled and righted herself. She ran. A pain stitched into her side. She ran and ran and ran.

After stabling his horse, Wes was returning from his barn and heading toward his house when he caught sight of her. "Anna?" he called. She didn't stop. He stood gazing after her worriedly. She was running as if the devil were chasing her. What the hell was wrong?

He started after her, his long, powerful strides rapidly overtaking the flying figure ahead of him. He caught up with Anna just as she reached the bank of the pond and pulled her to a halt.

"Anna, for God's sake—"

Anna felt arms go around her, trying to restrain her, trying to make her stop and remember something too painful to endure. She fought against the memory like someone demented.

"Anna!" She was twisting and pushing against him, hitting out at him with her fists. But one look at her bloodless face and blank eyes told him she wasn't seeing him. She'd obviously had some sort of violent emotional upset, and her anguish slashed at him. "Stop it, Anna. It's Wes. What happened? Who did this to you?"

Deep racking sobs answered him. He swung her up into his arms and headed back the way he'd come.

She kicked and clawed, but he held her tightly. Someone would definitely pay for this, he thought grimly, trying to imagine what could have happened.

By the time they reached the house, she had quieted in his arms and her cries had become whimpers. He carried her upstairs to the bedroom and laid her gently on the bed. He sat down beside her and brushed her hair away from her face. "Can you tell me what happened, Anna?"

She looked up at him. "I'm so cold," she whispered.

He stripped off her dress and wrapped her in a blanket. Then he joined her on the bed and took her into his arms. For a long time he cradled her against his body, trying to warm her. He stroked her hair and kissed her face and willed her to be all right.

He wasn't sure how much time had passed when he heard her murmur in a choked voice. "He knew."

"Who knew, Anna?"

"My father. He knew all along. He knew . . . everything . . . all along."

She was speaking softly, without intonation, and at first he wasn't sure he had heard her right. "What? You mean he knew about you and me?"

"And he knows about the baby."

"But why didn't he say something? To me? Or you? My God, that son of a bitch." How could her father have done such a thing to her, he wondered with a growing anger.

"He was the one person in the world I thought I could trust," she whispered, more to herself than to him. "But in the end he used me just like you did."

Wes's head jerked back as if someone had hit him with a closed fist. He'd just been wondering how Nilsen could have allowed Anna to be put in such an unthinkable position. Yet he was the one who had set the scheme in motion.

She'd been caught in a trap between her father and him, and he could offer her no defense for either of them.

"I'm ... I'm sorry," he said haltingly. "I'm so damned sorry. Try not to think about it for now. Try to get some rest."

"I can't get what he's done out of my mind."

Wes searched for what he could say to her, and what came to him surprised him. "Remember I told you about the mining camp where I grew up? Well, there was this old drunk who used to tell me stories about his days as a trapper in the mountains and his fights with the Indians. The more he had to drink, the better the story would be. So sometimes when the cold, or the hunger, or the loneliness got so bad I couldn't stand it, I'd sneak into the bar and steal a bottle of whiskey for him. He'd drink and talk, and I'd listen and forget ... for a little while." He chuckled. "The deeper he'd get into the story and the bottle, the more Indians there'd be in the battle. Or the more ferocious the animals would be that he trapped. I remember one story ..."

As he talked, Anna curled against him with her head resting in the curve of his shoulder and her hand splayed over his chest. Listening to the softness of his voice, and feeling the gentleness of his fingers as they combed through her hair, she tried to imagine him as a hungry, neglected little boy whose life was so miserable his only escape was the stories of an old drunk.

She knew how hard it must be for him to dredge up memories of his youth and open himself to the pain of the past. But she'd never in her life been in such need of tenderness and caring, and he seemed to know it.

He had wrapped her in a cocoon of security to keep out the ugliness that had touched her. She felt safe with him—in fact, she realized, she had felt safe with him for a long time.

And it was at that moment she understood. He had never lied to her or deceived her. Nor had he offered false promises. He had always been honest with her.

She dozed off and on through the night, and whenever she woke, he was always there for her, protective and concerned.

Sometime in the pale gray light of predawn, she woke and stirred against him. He had fallen asleep at last, she noticed. She shifted the position of her head and gazed on his hard features with a realization that came to her with stark, piercing clarity.

She loved him.

He was not a good man. He was not a safe man. But he was her man.

And she knew her love for him would last her whole life long.

Ribbons of sunlight flowed through the window

and touched Anna's face. She awoke again and had the immediate sensation of being surrounded by warmth. Then she heard a strong, steady heart beating beneath her ear, and knew that for the first time she'd spent an entire night with Wesley.

It had been a night of upheaval and shock for her. First the revelation of her father's betrayal, and then the staggering knowledge that she loved Wesley.

Would it change her decision to leave town? The answer was no, it couldn't.

He'd held her through the night. He held her still.

He'd given her child his name for reasons that she was sure were too complicated for even him to understand.

But one thing was certain: he didn't love her.

She slipped from his arms and sat up on the side of the bed. She was wearing only her shift, and she remembered that Wesley had taken off her dress and wrapped her in a blanket.

"Tell me what you need, and I'll get it for you," he said behind her.

She moved so that she could see him. He'd lain in the same position all night, holding her. Just as she was thinking that he had to be stiff, he raised his arms above his head and stretched. "I don't need anything . . . except my dress. I've got to go home."

He dropped his arms. "You're going back to your father after what he did to you?"

She nodded.

"I don't want you to be hurt, Anna."

How ironic, she thought, when the fact that he

didn't love her hurt her so deeply. "I have to get my things together," she said simply. "I'll be leaving tomorrow."

He slid off the bed and came around to stand in front of her. "Don't go."

Her smooth brow wrinkled with puzzlement. "I told you, I have to get my—"

"I mean, don't leave town. Stay with me."

"I don't understand."

He made an impatient gesture. "Move in with me. Be my wife. Why not? We're married."

"Are we?" she asked softly, her hand going to the chain that still hung around her neck and the ring between her breasts. If it wasn't for his ring, she would almost swear that their marriage ceremony had never happened.

"There's no need for you to leave town, Anna." He drove his fingers through his hair. "You can't hope to support yourself and the baby. And even if you did manage to find some way, how could you take care of the baby? You'd have to leave him . . ." He shrugged and looked away. "I don't like the idea of my child being left alone."

She stood and gently touched his arm. "This baby won't be neglected." She walked around him, picked up her dress that had been thrown over a chair, and stepped into it. "I'm just tired of it all, Wesley. After what I've learned, I can't live with my father anymore. And I don't think I could live with you either. I want to raise my baby with every bit of love I can. Here there's no love."

"Dammit, you don't have any money. How are you—"

"Now that you've burned the notes, I can use a little of the money I've saved to keep me until I can set up a small business as a seamstress. In that way I can sew when the baby's asleep or those times when he doesn't need me." She presented her back for him to fasten the buttons she hadn't been able to reach on her dress.

"Babies always *need*," he rapped out so fast, Anna knew that his mind was on his own childhood.

He tugged and jerked at the buttons until he had finished, then took her by the shoulders and turned her to face him. "You're my wife, Anna. I have the marriage certificate to prove it. That's my baby in your body. I could make you stay here with me."

Her blue eyes showed quiet determination and incredible sadness. "No, Wesley. The days when you could force me to do anything are over. I'm going to make a new life for myself and my baby, and there'll be no shadows or lies in that life." She moved toward the door. "Good-bye."

"Wait," he called, but she was already halfway down the stairs.

Her father was sitting at the kitchen table when she walked in. He was hunched over a cup of coffee, looking as if he hadn't slept, and he had on the same clothes as he had been wearing the night before.

"It will soon be time to open the store," she commented, going to the stove to pour herself a cup of coffee. "Hadn't you better get dressed? By the way, I won't be working today. I have to pack. You'll be wanting to hire a helper as soon as you can."

He didn't look at her. "Vill you ever be able to forgive me?"

"I don't know, Papa. Certainly not anytime soon." She took a sip of coffee and immediately felt the bracing effect of it.

He got to his feet with jerky motions and held out his hands beseechingly. "I did not vant you to be hurt, my daughter. I was hoping—"

"You were hoping that somehow things would work out for the better, just like in those fairy tales Mama used to tell me when I was a little girl. You chose not to face what was happening to me. You chose to live in some sort of hazy dream world. Well, it's time to wake up, Papa."

"Mr. McCord is a powerful, important man to this town. If you had married him, you could have been like a first lady. Everyone in town would have looked up to you."

"And maybe the business in the emporium would have benefited. How could you be such a hypocrite, Papa? Remember all the times you told me what a 'bad man' you thought Wesley was?"

Tears gathered in his eyes. "Anna, I do love you. I do. Since your mama died, you've been so strong. I thought . . ."

Anna slumped back against the stove. Over the years all of her instincts had been right. He did need someone to look after him and protect him. First her mother had taken care of him, and then she had stepped into the breach created by her mother's death. When she left town, he would find someone else to take care of him, perhaps Mrs. Harcourt.

Bittersweet feelings flooded through her. He couldn't help what he was, and some part of her was even aware that she couldn't stop loving him. He was her father. But she knew nothing would ever be the same between them again.

She went to him and kissed him on the cheek. "It's time to open the store, Papa. I'm going to pack."

He was crying openly now. "Anna, don't—"

She forestalled him. "I can't stay here, Papa. I can't."

In the sheriff's office, Cummings angrily pulled against the ropes that were binding his wrists and glared at Wes. The sheriff had left the two men alone, giving Wes permission to deal with the situation as he saw fit. Even the sheriff was afraid of him, Wes thought, but without satisfaction now.

"I didn't expect to have to spend all this time in jail," Cummings growled. "Didn't you get the note I sent you by way of that stupid deputy?"

"I got it." Wes propped his hip against a corner of the sheriff's desk.

Cummings bit back the nasty retort on the tip of his tongue. Not yet, he thought. "But you're gonna get me out today, right?"

"You didn't do your job."

"I'll get your damned ledger for you, McCord. Just get me the hell out of here."

Wes regarded the tip of his boot. "I notice you don't mention your two men."

"Them too." The way things were going, he had a feeling he was going to need them.

"Don't worry. I'm going to get you out of here. There's your gun belt." He waved his hand toward the desk. "But you've got to do something for me."

Dan grinned cockily. "The ledger, sure, I—"

"I have the ledger."

"Then what?"

"Leave town. As of now, you're off my payroll. And I don't want to ever see you around these parts again."

Stunned, Dan tried to think. "I know too much, is that it? Is that why you want me out of town?"

"I want you out of town because I don't like you." Wes's lips twisted. "And because you're a fool. I have no use for fools."

"Listen to me. With me helping you, there'll be no stopping you. I've got plans."

Wes gave the man a hard smile. "It's damned difficult to have any plans when you're rotting in jail, Cummings. And that's what will happen to you if you don't agree to leave town today."

Hell. Things were falling apart fast, and there wasn't much he could do about it with his hands tied like this. "I'll go for a price. Say, twenty-five thousand dollars."

"You'll get what I owe you in salary up to today and not a penny more."

Cummings's hold on his temper was slipping fast. "Come on, McCord. What I'm asking is a drop in the bucket compared to what your profits are gonna be once the railroad comes through here. And I've been a part of making it all happen."

"A very small, insignificant part."

Cummings drew in a deep breath. "Okay, McCord, I was hopin' I wouldn't have to use this, but you should know, I know something that could ruin you and . . . someone very close to you."

Wes tensed. "What's that?"

"I know that you and the shopkeeper's pretty daughter are *real* close, if you catch my drift." He saw McCord tense and smiled with satisfaction. "I came over to your house late one night to deliver some papers and looked through the window. Guess what I saw?"

Wes leveled gray eyes like cold stone on him and spoke very quietly. "I'm married to the woman in question, and I have the certificate of marriage to prove it. If I hear so much as a hint of a rumor that casts aspersions on her good name, I'll come after you and kill you."

Shock widened Dan's eyes. Then, immediately, he was furious. The son of a bitch had stolen his weapon from his hands. For a moment the red veil of his rage made him unable to speak. He gritted his teeth, forcing himself to appear calm. McCord thought he was so high and mighty, but if he thought everything was going to go his way, he was wrong. Dead wrong.

Dan leaned back in his chair and looked up at Wes.

"Okay, I'll leave town, just like you say." He lifted his bound wrists. "Only cut me loose, will ya?"

Cummings tied on his gun belt and started out the door after McCord. He'd done everything McCord had ever told him to do. He'd ramrodded the tent city. He'd lit out on the trail after Lassiter and that girl. And it hadn't been a picnic in that canyon.

After all he'd done he sure as hell deserved better treatment. He'd be damned if he was just going to ride out of town and let McCord stay on as king of Chango. McCord would be sorry he ever tried to get rid of him.

He stared straight ahead at McCord's broad back. Savage joy jolted through him. He had a clear, close, absolutely deadly shot. His hand grasped the handle of his gun, drew it out of his holster, and he carefully took aim.

Pain!

Cummings was spun around by the impact of the hot burning pain that seared through his chest. What was happening? He gazed around wildly only dimly aware he had heard an explosion. Sloan Lassiter stood across the street, his gun drawn, smoke curling out of its barrel.

The gun in Cummings's hand was now too heavy to lift, and slipped from his hand. The pain was no longer burning, but cold. Very cold.

He crumpled to the boardwalk.

At the sound of the shot Wes had whirled around with his gun drawn. He saw Cummings, lying lifeless on the ground, and his gaze tracked to the source of the shot. Sloan was holstering his gun.

Sloan slowly crossed the street and stepped up on the boardwalk, coolly meeting his enemy's gaze. "I wouldn't even let a murderer be shot in the back."

Wes raised his eyebrows. "I wasn't going to thank you."

"I don't want your thanks." Sloan glanced away for a moment, then brought his gaze back to Wes. "I just saved your life. That means you owe me one truthful answer."

Wes's hard face showed no emotion. The silence between the two men was thick and tense. It was a strong and tall wall that had taken fifteen years to build.

Suddenly Wes shrugged, and a faint smile touched his lips. "What do you want to know?"

Sloan had memories of Wes's smile. Wes had smiled as he'd said, *Turtle Rock Water Hole is two days walk, due east. Use the sun for direction and you'll make it. Stay there. Sooner or later someone will be by.* Then with a jaunty salute he'd ridden off with their hard-earned money and left Sloan and his brother without food, water, horses, or weapons.

Sloan swallowed to ease the painful tightness of his throat. "I have to have one question answered. Did you know that water hole was dry?"

Long moments passed and Sloan wondered if Wes was going to answer. Then Wes looked him squarely in the eyes. "No." He turned and walked away.

Sloan watched intently as Wes walked down the

broadwalk and entered his office. The short exchange with Wes had left him shaken. There was a fight going on inside him, one that dealt with fifteen years of his life. Dark terrors and violent torments were colliding in his brain, creating a tremendous tumult. Could it be that after all this time, that was it? Just a simple one-word answer.

Brianne rushed up to him, her green eyes wide with worry. "Sloan? I was in the lobby of the hotel when I heard the shot. What happened?"

"Let's go back to your room."

"Sloan, you're frightening me."

He took her arm. "Come on, I'll tell you everything."

The afternoon sunlight filled the bedroom with warm light and illuminated the tiny dust particles that had settled onto the polished rosewood surfaces of the dressing bureau and armoire.

"I don't know why I saved his life," Sloan said. "I sure as hell didn't plan to."

"Maybe at last you've learned that life is a blessing."

"I came here to kill him. And then I turned right around and saved his life." He shook his head, bewildered. "He said he didn't know that water hole was dry."

"Do you believe him?"

Sloan hesitated, then grimaced. "I don't want to, but . . . well, the hell of it is, I do. Deep down, dammit, I do." He rose and walked to the window to stare broodingly at the corral below. "He had no reason to lie to me. Not now."

"Sloan, what's wrong? This ought to be a time of great relief for you. Finally after all these years you can put the past behind you and get on with your life . . . our life."

"I wish it were that easy." Sloan's gaze took on a distant look. "When Wes came into my life, I was as green a kid as you can imagine. All I'd ever known was farm life. Wes spun yarns about a great big beautiful country to the west that I hadn't even known existed. He fired my imagination. He talked about horses that ran free and wild over the frontier and how it would be relatively simple to round up a herd, head into the New Mexico Territory, and sell them. The profits were bound to be enormous, he had said.

"To me it all sounded like a great adventure, and I . . . I talked David into coming along. For God's sake, he was only fourteen years old!"

The disgust and pain in his voice made Brianne jump up and go to him. "Sloan, you can't possibly be blaming *yourself* for David's death?"

"That is what I'm doing, *have been* doing ever since he died. But I was able to bury my own guilt beneath my hatred of Wes. Now I don't have that anymore. Now I have to face what I did."

She put her arms protectively around him and pressed her cheek against his chest. "I won't let you do this to yourself. You were no more to blame for David's death than Wes was. Things just happened. The water hole *happened* to be dry. There *happened* to be a snake there. Things could just as easily have gone the other way."

He looked down at the top of her head and smiled tenderly. "One of the first things I came to admire about you was your loyalty to those you love. I think I'm very lucky to be one of those people."

She pulled away and gazed up at him. "You're not alone anymore, Sloan. Your pain is my pain. From now on we'll face everything together."

"You make it sound so easy."

"Hasn't exposing this guilt that you've hidden so long made you feel better?"

"No. I'm afraid it's something I'm going to have to live with for a long, long time."

"Then we'll live with it together. Any burden that's shared is lessened."

He stared at her, his expression grave. "I think I have a lot to learn from you, Brianne."

"And I have a lot to learn from you." She pressed her lips to his. "But now we have a lot of time for lessons."

10

Wesley had almost died!

Anna had no idea how long she had stood at the upstairs window of the emporium, staring down in horror at the street. Cummings's body had been dragged away. Even the shocked, curious townspeople had dispersed. Yet still her heart was slamming against her ribs, her stomach twisting with the terror she had felt when she had seen Cummings pointing the gun at Wesley's back.

She had tried to scream, but no sound had come. She had tried to run down to him, to warn him, but her limbs had been frozen.

It had all happened so fast. Mere seconds. And Wesley could have been the one lying on the street instead of Cummings.

The knowledge released her from the vise of horror

that had held her immobile, and she whirled and ran downstairs and out the door. Her trips to Wesley had always been in the secret of darkness, down the path at the back of town. Now, for the first time, she went to him in daylight, crossing Main Street to his office without caring who saw her.

She walked into his office and found him at his desk, pen in hand, his brow furrowed with concentration as he studied several documents in front of him. She closed the door behind her, then leaned back against it.

Wesley was *alive*. Her relief almost overpowered her.

But she was also very determined.

His head came up and his expression changed to puzzlement. "Anna?"

"Make love to me."

The pen slipped nervelessly from his hand. "What's wrong?" He saw her smile uncertainly. She had rarely smiled at him.

"I want you to make love with me."

Thoroughly baffled, he pushed away from his desk and came to his feet. "Anna, I don't understand."

"Is it so difficult?" she asked, then repeated, "I want you to make love to me."

He studied her for a moment, trying to fathom what was going on. This had to be a dream, yet she looked very real, and he certainly was reacting as if this were really happening. His heart was pumping like a locomotive and he could feel himself readying. God knew he wanted her, wanted her so much it frightened him. He hesitated, then, caught up in the urgency he could sense in her, he started toward her. "We'll leave separately and—"

"No. We'll leave together."

His eyes darkened, but somehow he managed to keep himself in check. "Anna? What is it?"

She held out her hand to him. "What I'm asking is such a simple thing, Wesley. Are you going to come with me or not?"

Without another word he took her hand and walked out the door. But when he turned in the direction of his house, she shook her head and stopped him. "The meadow."

Wes asked no more questions. Curious glances followed them, and his hand instinctively tightened on hers. He was worried about her reputation, not his. But the speculation didn't seem to be bothering her. Out of the corner of his eye he watched her. She remained silent, serene, giving no indication of what she was thinking. He didn't know why she had come to his office and asked him to make love to her. He knew only that he didn't have the strength or the desire to refuse her. Once they left the town behind them, they made their way to the middle of the meadow.

Together they sank to the ground. The meadow was awash with sunlight, and the air was saturated with the heady scent of the perfume of flowers.

"Undress me," she said.

"Anna—"

"Please."

He wished he could interpret the mysterious new
glints that he saw in the depths of her eyes. He
wished his body weren't already hardening with need
for her. And most of all he wished the heat that was
taking over his body weren't making thought impossible. But she had taken things beyond his control
with just the simple words *make love to me.*

He lifted his hand to the front of her dress. One by
one he freed the buttons. Slowly her dress fell away
until it was around her waist. Uncharacteristically
Wes stopped, uncertain of what to do next.

With languid movements Anna lifted the chemise
over her head.

Wes sat back and stared at her, his breath caught
in his throat. How could any woman be that beautiful, he thought. Her ivory breasts were high and
round and tipped by tight pink buds. Between them
lay his ring.

She lifted her arms to her hair and began pulling
out pins. She dropped them heedlessly among the
flowers, then shook her head, and her golden hair
spilled down past her waist to around her hips.

She lay back amid the yellow buttercups and held
out her arms. He drew a ragged, painful breath and
went down to her.

His kiss was filled with a need he had never known
before. Vibrant and hot, Anna responded to him. It
was she who unbuttoned his shirt and pushed it off
his shoulders. It was she who smoothed her hands
over his chest and back as if the feel of his skin were
a necessity for her next breath.

The sun warmed his back. Drawing a deep breath, he pulled in perfumed air and the feminine, lilac scent of her. Her breast in his hand felt like bliss. He fastened his mouth to the pink tip, sucked, and tasted ambrosia.

Together they finished undressing each other.

Against the lush green grass, Anna's body appeared like lustrous ivory. Her hair spread around her head, its golden strands weaving among the yellow flowers. Lying beside her, Wes picked more flowers and sprinkled them around her breasts, down her stomach and the length of her legs. Then he rubbed the flowers over her, burnishing her with the scent of the flowers and the golden pollen.

"Ah, Wesley . . ." The feelings he was creating were almost too intensely erotic for Anna to bear. She arched her back off the ground, and he saw the sun catch the shimmering glow of her skin.

Unaware of what she was doing, she reached out and her hand closed around a cluster of the flowers, crushing them. Then, still holding the flowers, she brought her hand to his chest, then went lower, through the coarse hair to close around the rigid, pulsing length of him.

As she smoothed her hand up and down him, the petals created an exotic friction, bringing to life nerves he hadn't known he possessed and setting them on fire.

"Would you taste like flowers?" she whispered.

He made a sound like something had torn apart in his chest. He pulled her into his arms and rolled with her through the grass and the blossoms. Her hair flowed around them, and long, gleaming strands of it stuck to her hot, damp flesh and entrapped yellow and gold flowers within its mass.

When he stopped, he was on top of her and her legs were parted, but he couldn't bring an end to their golden ecstasy. Not yet.

"Will *you* taste like flowers?" he whispered, and lowered his mouth to her skin. Her fragrance dizzied him. Her sweetness intoxicated him. And when he reached the soft, intimate core of her, he thought he might lose his mind. He kissed and licked and sucked, ravenous for her.

Inflamed, Anna bit her bottom lip to stop herself from crying out, then she forgot her resolve and screamed. Her need for him was no longer gentle. A heavy pressure was building within her, yet she felt weightless, like a flower petal on the wind. If he didn't take her soon . . . "Wesley . . ." She gasped, then shuddered as he entered her.

Gripping her hips tightly, he began guiding and controlling the rhythm and movement of their bodies. Sweet golden pleasure shuddered through her. She felt him, hard, deep, perfect inside her, almost as if he were a natural part of her. She resented even his partial withdrawals. When he thrust into her again, she wrapped her legs around his back and surged up to him.

They were one. They were golden. They were their own source of light.

*   *   *

They lay on their sides, facing each other, Anna's flower-textured hair spreading over their cooling bodies like a gold silk coverlet.

He hadn't been able to bring himself to pull away from her, and he was still inside her. Her eyes were closed, her dark lashes lying over her cheekbones in thick, fringed half circles. Her skin had lost its flush and had returned to its ivory perfection. Her leg was thrown over his thigh, and while he studied her, she unconsciously nestled closer to him.

Deep within her he felt the movement as a caress. "Anna?"

She opened her eyes, and her eyes were so clear, it seemed he should be able to see all the way to her soul. But he couldn't. In truth he had no idea what she was thinking or feeling.

"Stay with me," he whispered. "Be my wife."

Slowly she smiled. "Yes."

Wes walked Anna back to town, unobtrusively guiding her to the path that would bring them to the back of the emporium, and deliberately avoiding Main Street. Giving her a glance out of the corner of his eye, he saw that there was hardly any sign left of the woman who, just a short time ago, had rolled through the flowers with him, sharing a passion that went beyond common and usual bounds. She'd retreated behind a lovely serene expression. But she'd left her hair loose, allowing it to tumble freely down her back, and the long golden strands were still entwined with yellow and gold flowers.

His heart swelled with emotions he couldn't name. Things seemed to be going his way now. Anna was staying with him. Together they would have a child. The railroad would go through without a hitch. Finally he was going to have everything he'd ever wanted.

He planned to provide Anna and his child with a life he'd never known, one without worry for anything. But he felt a shadow. . . .

And because their life together was going to start today, because of their child, because of the years that were to come, he felt he owed her an explanation.

"Anna?" With a hand on her arm he stopped her beneath a tall aspen tree. "I know that you've heard the talk around town about Sloan Lassiter and me. You may have even heard the fact that he thinks I was responsible for his brother's death."

She nodded, her blue eyes clouding. "I've heard."

"And you've wondered what the truth was, right?"

She leaned back against the tree trunk, gazing up at him. "Yes."

"You deserve to know what really happened. Sloan thinks I directed him and his brother to a water hole that I knew was dry." He paused. "I've done a lot of unscrupulous things in my life, Anna, but being responsible for that boy's death is one sin I'm not guilty of. I didn't know, and that's the truth."

The relief Anna felt at his confession surprised her. These past few days she'd been confronted by major revelations that had ripped her life from its very roots. But while she had been learning to deal with the hurt and confusion that had assaulted her at every turn, somewhere at the back of her mind there had lurked the fear that Wesley was guilty of murder. A cool wind rustled the leaves in the branches above their heads, and she raised her face to the soothing caress of the breeze and to Wesley. "I'm glad you told me."

Her obvious relief eased his mind. He'd never tried to hide the type of man he was from anyone; he'd never cared what people thought of him. But now, if there was one person in the world whom he wanted to believe that he was not capable of murder, it was Anna. "I wish I could give myself a complete whitewash. But I can't. Although I didn't deliberately cause David's death, indirectly I did, and there's nothing I can do to change that."

"I guess our lives would be a lot different if we had the ability to change things," she said softly, as if her mind were suddenly far away.

He reached out and lay his hand flat on her stomach. "There are a lot of things I would change if I could, Anna, but this baby is not one of those things."

"I know."

She spoke so softly that Wes had to bend his head to her so that he could hear. He wasn't certain, but her words seemed to have held a faint trace of sadness. "How long will it take you to pack?"

"Not long. I'd already started."

A somber expression came over his face as he thought of how close he'd come to losing her. He didn't know what had changed her mind about leaving town. He could only be grateful. "I'll be back in about an hour with a buggy. Be sure you get everything you want."

Anna folded the last dress and put it into the carpetbag, then turned to the dresser and the silver brush and comb that had been her mother's. Taking them, she laid them on top of the dress in the bag.

"You are leaving now?"

She threw a glance over her shoulder at her father, who was framed in the doorway. "Yes."

"Anna—" He paused, seeming to search for words. "You must not go off on your own like this. A voman alone does not have an easy time." He shook his head. "But a voman pregnant and not wed—"

"I appreciate your concern," she said, not entirely successful in keeping the sarcasm from her voice, "but it comes too late."

He dropped his gaze from hers. "It vas not my intention for matters to end like this."

"No, of course not," she said, keeping her tone mild with great effort. It still hurt her to think of her father's betrayal. She glanced around the room to see what she'd missed. "It was your intention that you keep your store. Which reminds me, Wesley will be here in a few minutes."

His head lifted. "McCord? Here? Vhy vould he come here?"

"I—I think I'll let him tell you." She wasn't deliberately trying to be cruel to her father. It was just that she was finding it very difficult to talk to him.

She wasn't sure she'd ever again be able to carry on a normal, easy conversation with him.

She heard the sound of footsteps in the next room, then Wesley appeared in the doorway behind her father. She felt an immediate sense of comfort.

"Are you ready, Anna?" Wes asked.

"I think I've got everything. I just have to close this bag," she said, bending over it.

"Wait." Wes stepped around her father as if the man weren't there and crossed the room to her. "Let me do that for you." Quickly he fixed the fastener, then stood and motioned to the two other carpetbags by the bed. "Just these three?"

"Yes."

Lars Nilsen nervously cleared his throat. "Mr. McCord?"

Wes turned a hard gaze on him but didn't say anything.

"My daughter ... Anna, that is ... has said that you have something to tell me. Perhaps about the store?"

Wes looked at Anna. She gazed back at him, her face totally without expression. But in her eyes he saw her hurt. Then she turned her back on the two men and walked to the window. Wes returned his attention to Lars Nilsen. The sooner he got Anna out of there the better.

"The store is yours free and clear. I've burnt the notes."

Her father's face cleared. "That is *vonderful.*"

Wes hid his disgust for the older man under words

that were terse, calm, and free of any emotion. "Anna
and I were married a few days ago. She'll be living
with me now. You'll be able to see her, but only if
that's what she wants. And if you come to the house,
I'll make damn sure I'll never be there."

At the window Anna listened and realized that
what Wesley wasn't saying was more interesting than
what he was saying. It was obvious to her that Wesley condemned her father, and still more obvious he
didn't feel he had the right to cast stones.

"Anna?"

She turned toward Wesley. "I'm ready to leave."

He nodded and picked up her carpetbags. "The
buggy's downstairs."

"In the front of the store or the back?"

He met her gaze. "The front," he said firmly.

Anna looked at her father. "You have what you
want now, Papa. You'll be fine."

"But Anna—"

"Good-bye."

Wes stowed Anna's bags in the back of the buggy,
then helped her up onto the seat. "Be careful," he
cautioned.

She smiled down at him. "I'm not made of glass,
Wesley."

He grinned. "No?"

The sight of the cozy familiarity between Wes
McCord and Anna Nilsen was enough to make Mrs.
Fitzpatrick stop in her tracks on the boardwalk a few
yards away and frown with disapproval. "Why, Anna,

my dear, I didn't know you were planning on going away."

Instinctively Anna started with guilt. One impulsive act of walking hand in hand down Main Street earlier this afternoon hadn't entirely wiped out the habit of months of clandestine meetings.

Mrs. Fitzpatrick went on. "And your *hair*. Really, my dear, whatever has happened that you haven't had time to comb it and put it up?"

Anna's hand flew to her hair in horror. *It still had flowers in it.*

Wes turned on the woman. "I think Anna's hair is beautiful just the way it is, and since Anna has done me the honor of becoming my wife, how she wears her hair is now my concern, and only *my* concern."

Now it was Mrs. Fitzpatrick's turn to show shock. "Your *wife!*"

My wife. It was the first time Wesley had used those words and it both startled Anna and filled her with a buoyant warmth.

From the buggy Anna had an excellent view of Mrs. Fitzpatrick's face turning the color of ash as she suddenly realized she had seriously offended Wes McCord. Silly woman, Anna thought. She waves a red flag in front of a bull and realizes the danger only after she's been gored.

Mrs. Fitzpatrick moistened her lips nervously. "Oh, well, how simply wonderful. But, really, how was I to know? I'm sure that no one else in town knows. Or I would have found out. I mean—"

"We wanted our wedding to be private," Wes said smoothly. "I'm sure you can understand."

"*Absolutely.* But, of course, the news *will* get out." A sudden thought occurred to her. "The mayor and I insist on giving you and your lovely wife"—she bestowed a beaming smile on Anna—"a reception."

Wes swung up into the buggy and took the reins in his hands. "That's very kind of you, but my wife and I are planning a small reception at our home. Just a few of our closest friends will be invited." With an abrupt flick of the reins he set the horse into a trot. "Good day, Mrs. Fitzpatrick."

"Good day, Mr. McCord," she called after them, then hastily added, "and Mrs. McCord."

"Stupid woman," Wes muttered.

Suddenly Anna felt a bubble of happiness form inside her, and she started to giggle.

Wes cast her a look of surprise. He smiled. Then he, too, started to laugh.

Anna stepped through the front door of Wesley's house and gazed around her with wonder. Everything looked somehow different, which was strange, because she was as familiar with most of the rooms of this house as she was with the rooms above the emporium.

Maybe it was she who was different.

She was Wesley's wife now. That meant this house was her home. Would she ever get used to it all, she wondered.

"I'll take your bags upstairs," Wesley said, coming in the door behind her.

She nodded. He brushed past her, but she didn't look at him. She felt awkward and uncertain. How would they get along together? Here in this house that had been the scene of so many illicit meetings. Man and wife now, instead of lovers.

Wesley's wife.

What did he expect from her as his wife?

What did she expect from him?

The last question, she decided, was the easiest of all to answer. *Nothing.* She expected nothing.

He'd given her his name. Protected her from gossip. Now he was sharing his house with her. That was all she could expect.

An incredible sadness engulfed her. She turned, then went still as she saw the clumsily arranged vase of buttercups and marigolds on the hall table. Her cheeks flushed as the implication of the flowers hit her. When Wesley had left her at the emporium, he must have gone back to the meadow and picked this bouquet.

She reached for the vase and brought the flowers to her face. Their brilliant colors and velvet beauty brought back the enchantment of her and Wesley's time in the meadow.

She heard him coming down the stairs and quickly replaced the vase on the table but kept her gaze on the flowers.

When he reached her, he looked down at her and

smiled. "You must have been smelling the flowers. You have the faintest touch of gold on your nose."

A sudden shyness made her voice soft. "I'm sure that I have the color of the flowers all over me."

"Me too," he said huskily.

For a moment she thought he was going to kiss her, but he simply brushed a gentle fingertip down her cheek. "Come to the kitchen with me. You need to eat something."

He took her hand and led the way down the hall.

And deep within her, fledgling hope was born.

"Usually I eat at the café or the hotel," Wes was saying, "except for the days when Mrs. Elliot comes in to clean. On those days she also shops and cooks for me." He grinned. "We're lucky. She came today and there's a pot of stew on the stove."

"I'll heat it up," Anna said, glancing around. "Do you have an apron?"

"No."

The humor she heard in his voice made her look at him. She smiled. "No, I guess you don't. It doesn't matter." She poked through drawers and shelves until she found a dish towel and wrapped it around her waist.

"I'll do it. You just sit down and rest."

She looked at him, astonished. "Wesley, I'm used to putting in a full day's work at the store, then cooking dinner. Heating up a pot of stew is not going to hurt me."

He shrugged and took a seat at the kitchen table.

"All right, you can do a little around the house if you want. But no heavy work, understand?"

She nodded, turning to the stove. He was concerned for the baby. After all, she reminded herself, that was why he had married her. "Mrs. Elliot bought some nice apples. I can make a pie for dessert."

"That would be nice," he said. He watched her as she moved around the kitchen, feeling a deep, almost primitive sense of satisfaction. Dreams were so ephemeral, sometimes a person couldn't catch hold of them long enough to see what they were made of. Maybe in the deep, secret darkness of his mind, he'd envisioned having Anna in his kitchen, in his home, in his life. He didn't know if he had or not.

But she was here now. This was no dream. He had a wife. He was going to be a father.

His attention was drawn to the towel at her slender waist. "I'll buy you some aprons," he said.

She looked at him in surprise. "Why?"

"Well, you obviously won't be able to get that dish towel around your waist much longer."

Her head snapped back as if he'd slapped her and he cursed himself for being a clumsy fool. "Come here, Anna."

Slowly, reluctantly, she did as he asked. As soon as she was close enough he put his arm around her waist and drew her between his legs. "I'm looking forward to the months ahead when your waist thickens and your stomach grows larger and larger." He pressed the side of his face into her belly. "My child," he said softly. "I can't wait until I can hear his heartbeat."

Touched, Anna threaded her fingers through his hair. "*His* heartbeat, Wesley?"

"Or hers." Gently he rubbed his face back and forth over the softness of her stomach. "It doesn't matter. I think I'd like a little girl who was as beautiful as her mother."

Tears rushed forward, clouding Anna's vision as her fingers tangled in Wesley's hair. Would she ever be able to deal with this man's many complexities and moods, she wondered. Heaven knew, she wanted to learn everything about him. And now she was beginning to hope that perhaps she would have the time to do that.

11

"**B**rianne!"

The door of the bedroom burst open.

Brianne's head jerked up in surprise as she saw Henrietta hurtle into the room. While she watched in puzzlement, the older woman pushed the door closed and turned the key in the lock, her face white and tense. Brianne flung aside her sketchbook she'd been studying and immediately went to her friend. "What on earth's wrong?"

"He's *here*. That—that man is here!"

It took Brianne no more than a second to figure out about whom Henrietta was speaking. "Your husband, Mr. Bartholomew?"

"That's right. He walked into the hotel, big as you please." Suddenly her voice dropped and she pressed three fingers into the center of her forehead. "He's come to take me back with him, but I'm not going. And if he forces me to go with him, I—I'll just run away again."

Brianne took hold of Henrietta's hand and led her to the green velvet sofa. "No one's going to force you to do anything you don't want to do, Henrietta, but you must calm down."

Once seated, Henrietta paused to take several deep breaths. "You're right, I know. It's just that I was hoping he wouldn't find me. I guess what I was *really* hoping was that he wouldn't come looking for me at all." She made a sound of disgust. "You should have seen him, Brianne. He was holding this awful bouquet of flowers in his—"

"Flowers? Really?" Her brow wrinkled. "Tell me exactly what he said."

Henrietta looked at her in surprise. "Said? I didn't give him a chance to *say* anything. I took one look at him and ran up here."

It was definitely time for some frank speaking, Brianne thought. She rose, walked to the rosewood dressing bureau, where a pitcher of water sat, and poured a glass for the distraught woman. Returning to Henrietta's side, she handed it to her. When she indicated she'd had enough, Brianne took the glass and set it on a side table. "Henrietta, I want you to hear me out. I've learned a lot in the last couple of weeks, and one of the most important things is that you have to accept the bad qualities of the man you love along with the good."

Henrietta shifted restlessly as if she wanted to interrupt, but Brianne continued before she had a chance. "I know you're not in love with your husband, but have you considered that you might have fallen in love with him had you stayed and gotten to know him? After all, you traveled all that distance from Philadelphia to California in answer to a mail order bride advertisement. That in itself shows you have an adventuresome and romantic soul."

Pink stained Henrietta's cheeks, and despite the fact that the older woman was twisting her hands together, Brianne was encouraged. "I'm sure that Mr. Bartholomew frightened you in his haste to consummate the marriage. But perhaps hitting him over the head with a pitcher and taking the first stagecoach out of town might have been a bit precipitous of you."

Henrietta could no longer control her agitation and jerked to her feet to begin pacing the room. "My dear, I know you mean well, but a young girl such as yourself can have no idea about the carnal nature of men."

Remembering the night that she and Sloan had just spent, wrapped in each other's arms, she took a moment to decide how best to answer. "Henrietta, what my grandmother failed to tell me, I learned by growing up on a ranch. I learned that lovemaking doesn't have to be bad or distasteful between a man and a woman. As long as there's kindness and caring and respect from both people, then the—uh—carnal side of marriage can be quite pleasant." Henrietta stopped her pacing to look quizzically at her, prompting Brianne to add, "Or so I'm told."

Her face clouded. "I guess that was the problem. By his actions Horace made it obvious that he truly didn't respect me."

"That's because you didn't give him a chance to get to know you. Did you try to talk to him? Before you hit him over the head with a pitcher, I mean."

"No." She threw her hands up in the air and her voice broke. "Oh, what does it matter anyway?"

Henrietta's stern facade cracked, giving Brianne a sudden glimpse of a vulnerable, lonely, frightened woman. "I think it matters very much," she said softly.

Brusquely Henrietta dashed away a tear that had begun to slide down her cheek. "At any rate, I've decided to stay here in the West and teach."

Brianne's mouth dropped open in astonishment. "I thought you hated the West."

"I do. That is, I did. But . . . well, I've come to the conclusion that the West badly needs civilizing. If this part of the country is going to be shaped into the cultural and enlightened society it should become, then someone's obviously going to have to stay here and do it. In my view, no one is as well qualified as I—" A timid knock on the door halted her speech and shattered her newly gained composure. "Oh, my Lord, it's he!"

With resolve Brianne stood. "Good. I think it's about time I met your husband for myself.

"You're not going to let him in, are you?" Henrietta asked in horror.

Another knock sounded. "Just a minute," she called, and put a soothing hand on the older woman's shoulder. "He *is* your husband, and he's obviously gone to an awful lot of trouble to find you. Now, if you don't want to go back with him, you won't have to, but I think it's only right that you should at least talk to him, don't you?"

Henrietta hesitated, then reluctantly nodded.

Brianne made her way to the door and rotated the key in the lock. Before she turned the knob, however, she looked over her shoulder. "Are you ready?"

The effort was visible as Henrietta attempted to hide all signs of vulnerability behind her usual front of schoolmarm poise.

Brianne opened the door to a big, oxlike man whose large body looked as if it had been shoehorned into the black wool suit he wore. And although his hair had been heavily pomaded, two clumps of hair at the back of his head seemed determined to stand straight up. "Horace Bartholomew?"

He swallowed hard. "Yes, ma'am. I'm sorry to bother you, here in your bedroom and all, but, well . . ." Remarkably to Brianne his ruddy face turned bright red. He sneaked a quick peak at Henrietta, who was standing behind her, then hastily looked again at Brianne.

"You'd like to talk to Henrietta?" she prompted.

"Yes, ma'am."

"Well, I think that's a fine idea. By the way, I'm Brianne Delaney."

Evidently relieved to have someone talking to him, he smiled. "Pleased to meet you. I've come from California for my wife."

"That's a very romantic thing to do, don't you think, Henrietta?" She took a step to the side so that she no longer stood between husband and wife. "I believe it shows admirable sensibility."

Happy to find an ally, Horace went on. "I left the workings of my mines to my men. It's taken me a while, but I'm real glad I finally found Henrietta."

"Mines? You're a miner, then?"

"Yes, ma'am. I own about six of them."

"Own? Henrietta, you never told me that."

Henrietta shrugged.

"I think that any man who comes the distance Horace has come and has left his business in the hands of others is obviously sincere and deserves a chance to be listened to. Horace, you do have some things to say to Henrietta, don't you?"

"Yes, I do." He dug into another pocket and came out with several crumpled pieces of paper. "I've made notes."

"That's very nice, Horace." She whispered in Henrietta's ear, "Remember when you told me how you wanted to help civilize the West? Well, that civilizing can start with one person. Horace would be the perfect person."

Henrietta frowned uncertainly. "I don't know."

"Oh, Henrietta, he came all this way for you. And

legally he is your husband, no matter how much you try to deny it. At the very least you have to give him a chance to say his piece."

Henrietta cast a dubious glance at her anxious husband, then squared her shoulders. "Horace, we will go down to the parlor, and you may court me."

"We could kiss here for a while," Sloan said. He and Brianne were alone in the dining room. "Then we could go someplace else."

She stood, walked around the table and settled herself on his lap. "Where, for instance?" Bending her head, she gave him the kiss he'd requested.

"The parlor," he said, returning her kiss and deepening it.

She curved her body against him, softening. "That's where Henrietta and Horace are."

"The front porch."

"I believe that's where Kam is."

"Then,"—he kissed her again and his hand found her breast—"we may just have to go back up to your room."

"The maid may be there."

"Then my room." Her nipples was tightening beneath his hand and his caresses turned urgent. "Suddenly I want to do a lot more than kiss you."

"Alarm! Alarm!" Kamanahua came running into the room.

Both Brianne and Sloan came to their feet. Brianne straightened her dress selfconsciously. "Kam, what's wrong?"

"The missionaries have landed!"

With desire still strong in his body, Sloan couldn't

tear his gaze from Brianne. Her face was flushed from his kisses and caresses. "Chango isn't a port town, Kam," he said absently. "Boats can't dock and people can't land."

"It has come to pass! They are here!" His chest was heaving with exertion.

"Now, Kam, you must calm down. You've suspected everyone you've met of being a missionary, including me, and you've always been wrong."

"No, no, they have landed!" He took her hand, dragged her to the window, and pointed. "Listen!"

Brianne could hardly believe her eyes . . . or her ears. Kamanahua was right. A buckboard containing six black-frocked men and women was being driven down Main Street. A man was driving the buckboard with a woman sitting beside him. The remaining four people were in the back, sitting in chairs that had been roped down. With hymnals open in their laps, they were loudly singing, "Bringing in the Sheaves."

By this time huge tears were streaming from Kam's eyes. "Make them stop the joyful noise unto the Lord!"

"Kam, they're just worshiping in their own way. And it's only a song, after all. Nothing to be afraid of."

"I will hide," he announced.

"No, Kam," she said firmly. "You've been hiding from these people long enough. We're going out to meet them."

The driver of the buckboard, a tall, skinny man with a hollowed-out face and tufts of whiskers attached to his chin, was just climbing down from the buckboard when they came out on the porch. At the sight of Kamanahua his somber visage brightened somewhat.

"Kamanahua, my son, at last we have found you."

Brianne moved forward to the edge of the porch and Kamanahua followed her. "I'm Brianne Delaney, and I'm a friend of Kam's."

The man tugged at the celluloid collar he wore, the only relief for his otherwise entirely black attire. "Oh, how do you do. I'm Brother Jedidiah, and this is my wife, Sister Ruth."

Sister Ruth was a tiny woman with stooped shoulders. With her husband's help she climbed down from the buckboard. When she was on the ground, she clasped her hands at her waist, as if in prayer, and peeked at Brianne from under her bonnet. She reminded Brianne of a banty hen without any of the fiestiness.

Brother Jedidiah continued. "And our fellow travelers are Brother Albert, Sister Sarah, Brother Markum, and Sister Gertrude." His piercing eyes fixed on Kamanahua. "We've come to save a heathen from the depths of hell."

"Your mission is very admirable, I'm sure, Brother Jedidiah, but if the heathen you're referring to is Kam, he would rather not talk to you."

Brother Jedidiah drew his skeletal frame up to its full height. "Who are you, my good woman, to stand in the way of his salvation?"

"Don't you mean stand in the way of your taking the land that belongs to him and his ancestors?"

He put one foot on the bottom step of the porch and gestured broadly. "Giving up their land is the only way that the heathen Hawaiians will be able to free themselves from their idols and superstitions."

"I'm certain it's also the easiest way to line your pockets."

Brother Jedidiah looked down his bony nose at Brianne, which was a real feat, since she was standing above him. "A Christian is above argument, but for your enlightenment, our mission to get Kamanahua to the Boston missionary school is of a high order of importance."

"But he doesn't want to go."

"The Hawaiians are as children. They must be led."

"Their way may not be your way, Brother Jedidiah, but it has served them well for centuries. They've been a happy people, without illness or disease."

He pointed a finger heavenward. "And quite without shame. Miss Delaney, you do not know of what you speak, I assure you."

"And I assure you that you will not take this boy anywhere he does not wish to go."

Brother Jedidiah blinked, not used to encountering resistance from a woman. His gaze turned on Sloan, who was standing behind Brianne. "Sir, surely you can see the reason of what I say. I implore you to take this headstrong young woman in hand and show her a woman's place."

Sloan leaned toward her and murmured, "Miss Delaney, I believe I suggested earlier what and where your place might be. My bedroom. Surely Brother Jedidiah would agree."

Brianne threw a brief scowl at Sloan.

Brother Jedidiah motioned for his group to gather around them. After a quick conference he turned back to Brianne. "Out of Christian charity I have decided that if Kamanahua will simply sign this document"—he paused to pull a folded piece of paper from the inside of his jacket—"we will be on our way."

Brianne's trust of the black-frocked people was nonexistent. "Let me see it."

He climbed the stairs and put it into her outstretched hand. After a quick scan of the document, Brianne looked up at Brother Jedidiah in puzzlement. "But this calls for the king of Lakahani's signature."

Brother Jedidiah's somber expression turned even more grave and he began intoning in a deep, droning voice. "It is my most unfortunate duty to inform Kamanahua that his father, the king, has gone to that dark place where the fires burn. It is to my great sorrow that I have to admit this, but, lamentably, we were never able to convert him."

Behind the post Kamanahua let out a great wail of grief.

Brianne put her arm around him. "Kam, I'm so sorry."

Brother Jedidiah tried in his own way to comfort. "It was inevitable, my son. The king embodied so many of the deadly sins—sloth and gluttony to name but two. He finally succumbed to advanced years and impure living."

Kamanahua began uttering words of Hawaiian and keening loudly. His anguish and grief were monumental.

"Brother Jedidiah, if you say one more word," Brianne snapped to the missionary, "you're going to be a step closer to your maker! Come on, Kam, Sloan and I will take you upstairs to your room."

Kamanahua's mourning continued all afternoon. He stayed in his room, sobbing and wailing, refusing any food or water, dealing with his grief in the way of his ancestors. The sounds carried to all parts of the hotel. But no one could do anything for him.

"We'll have to take turns watching him to make sure he doesn't hurt himself," Brianne told Sloan, Phineas, and Henrietta.

"I will take the first vigil," Henrietta announced. "Poor boy, his father's death was such a shock. Horace, you may come up and sit with me."

The big man who had been lurking at the edge of the porch smiled broadly. "Thank you, Henrietta."

The many creases on Phineas's face were folded into a design of genuine worry. "I feel so bad for the boy."

Silently Sloan picked up Brianne's hand. She smiled up at him, grateful for his comforting presence. To Phineas she said, "For now, at least, I think the best thing to do is to make sure he knows that he has our support and love."

"The second watch will be mine," Phineas said. "In fact, if necessary, I'll stay the night in his room."

"Thank you, Phineas. That's very nice of you."

"Not at all. I've become very fond of the boy."

It wasn't until just before sunset that Kamanahua's wailing stopped. Those assembled on the front porch exchanged uneasy glances.

"What do you think it means?" Henrietta asked.

"I'm not sure," Brianne murmured. She looked around. She could feel a change in the air. Unless she missed her guess there was a storm heading their way.

Suddenly Kamanahua walked out the door. Brianne noted that his eyes were dry. He looked the same, yet there seemed to be something different. With his arms folded across his bare chest, his bearing was majestically erect in a way she had never seen before. He strode out to the street where the six missionaries were waiting.

Brianne hitched up her skirts and went down the steps to him. "Kam, are you all right?"

He nodded. "My father is dead, Brianne. I am now the King of Lakahani."

"Yes, that's right."

Brother Jedidiah spoke up. "Since you are now king, the—"

Brianne rounded on the irritating man. "Leave him alone. You're not concerned for his soul. Only his land. You took him from his home when he didn't want to leave, and had him so frightened of you and that school in Boston where you were taking him that he ran away."

He held up his hand. "Brianne, you are a goddess, but you no longer need to protect me. I am a king now, and a king cannot be afraid."

"Yes, you are a king, Kamanahua," Brother Jedidiah eagerly agreed. "Your actions must be above reproach. You must be an example for the people of Lakahani. You can no longer worship idols or you will go to that dark place where fires burn eternally as your father did."

"You lie, Brother Jedidiah!" Kam bellowed, causing Sister Ruth to gasp. "My father has gone to the world of cool waters, gentle winds, and brights suns."

Brother Jedidiah made a vexed sound. "A heathen does not go to heaven, King Kamanahua."

Kamanahua thumped his chest. "I am not a heathen. I am a Hawaiian!"

Brother Jedidiah opened his mouth to speak, but Sloan, having come off the porch to stand beside Brianne spoke first. "You can't argue with him on that one."

"No, you can't," Brianne agreed. "And I think it would be an excellent idea if you and your brothers and sisters left town."

The missionary nodded solemnly, but there was a light in his eyes. "Perhaps you are right, Miss Delaney. We will take King Kamanahua with us. He must return to Lakahani, and we will go with him. He will need much guidance and direction."

Brianne looked uncertainly at Kam. Unfortunately

Brother Jedidiah was right. Now that Kam was king, he did need to return to his island and his people. "What do you want to do, Kam?"

Brother Jedidiah pulled from his pocket the document he so desperately wanted Kamanahua to sign and clutched it to his breast.

Kamanahua ignored him. "I have missed the rolling surf, the crying of the sea birds, the swaying palms. And my people desire my body to be on my island. I must go. I will be a great king and have many wives and great numbers of children."

Showing a high degree of agitation, Brother Jedidiah waved the document in the air. "You and your people cannot survive if you obstinately cling to the old ways. God's wrath will be expressed!"

Kamanahua looked wildly around, spotted a box of matches on the ledge beside the front door lantern, bounded up the stairs, grabbed the box and yanked it open. Matches flew everywhere, but when he turned around, he had one match in his hand. Three long strides took him back down to the street. He flicked the tip of the match with his thumb nail. Snatching the document away from a stunned Brother Jedidiah, he held the burning match beneath the paper. "Now Pele has expressed her wrath!"

After the document had gone up in flames, he planted his feet apart and spoke in a booming voice. "Later, when I feel the hour has come, I will call upon the missionaries to come and teach us. But I will never surrender my land. Nor will my sons. And when the missionaries come, they will not be you, Brother Jedidiah."

Up on the porch, Henrietta called out, "Bravo!"

Phineas yelled, "Well done!"

Brother Jedidiah turned to his wife and fellow missionaries. "We have failed. Obviously this is a heathen town, and Satan has a strong hold on these misguided sinners. Let us leave them to their woeful ways and find more fertile waters upon which to cast our nets."

They marched around the hotel to where their camp was set up, and for a few more minutes, they could be heard muttering prayers that were occasionally punctuated with loud "amens" and "hosannas."

Brianne turned to Kamanahua. "I am so proud of you, and I want you to know that Sloan and I will help you in every way we can. As soon as possible, we will make sure you get on a ship heading for Lakahani. We can't go with you this time, but we will come and visit."

He beamed. "That will be happy. And I will not misplace the ocean again!"

Brianne turned to Sloan. "It worries me that he's going to have to travel all that distance alone."

Phineas bounded off the porch and came down beside them. "I'm a traveling man by nature. Perhaps I could accompany Kam."

Brianne grinned. "How much of this urge to go with Kam is because of the irate gentleman who's after you for selling him some of that snake oil you call medicine?"

"It's quite true that Mr. Fairfield's unfortunate and quite *erroneous* idea that my medicine is the cause of several embarrassing adverse effects makes my departure most desirable. But at the same time, Kam and I have grown rather found of one another, and I can see a real future for a partnership between us."

She shook her head, amused. "All things considered, it sounds like a wonderful idea. You'll be out of danger, and you can keep Kam out of trouble."

Sloan bent down to whisper in her ear. "You're joking, right?"

"We'll all have a nice long talk before the two of you leave," she added hastily.

Phineas nodded. "Fine, fine. Who knows? I may find the tropics most agreeable. Kam, let us retire to the dining room for a small repast, and you can tell me more about your homeland."

The small man and the tall boy climbed the steps and entered the hotel, both talking and gesturing at once. Brianne saw that Horace and Henrietta had settled on the porch in chairs set close beside each other.

Sloan took Brianne's hand and kissed it. With her heart full of happiness, she gazed up into his eyes. "And just what are you looking so smug about?"

"It's simple. Kam, Phineas, and Henrietta's problems have finally been solved. You've even made arrangements to get George away from that drunken father of his so that he can be raised and schooled on Killara. Now that all your 'little chicks' have been taken care of, you'll have more time for me. I'm looking forward to the calm."

They both heard it at once—a rumble, almost like thunder, and it was getting louder and louder. Sloan tensed, but Brianne laughed. "I think we're going to have to wait a little while longer for the calm."

A cloud of dust appeared at the south end of town and grew larger. The pounding hooves could be heard more clearly now.

Sloan took Brianne's arm and headed her toward the steps. "I don't know what's happening, but we'd better be ready. Go upstairs and get your gun."

"A Delaney never raises a gun to another Delaney."

"You mean—"

"I think you're about to meet my family, or at least part of it."

A dozen men rode their lathered horses down Main Street at a break-neck pace and reined them in hard in front of the hotel.

A tall, lean man with diamond-hard, blue-gray eyes was the first off his horse. Brianne ran to him and threw her arms around him. "Dom, I'm so glad to see you! I wasn't sure if you'd ride in with the others or not, since you had to come from St. Louis."

"I met up with them not too far out of town." His eyes had softened as he looked at Brianne. "Is there any news on Patrick?"

"Yes, we found him. Or rather Sloan did."

"Thank God," he murmured, then switched a questioning gaze to Sloan who was standing behind Brianne.

Brianne reached for Sloan's hand and drew him forward, her face full of love as she looked at him. "Sloan, this is Dominic Delaney, my uncle. Dom, this is Sloan Lassiter." The two men nodded. Her smile widened as she embraced in turn four more men who had just dismounted and had come to stand by them. "This is Falcon, Cort, Sean, and Joshua Delaney."

"Gentlemen." Sloan nodded, warily studying the five Delaney men. Any one of them alone would have been impressive, but together they were daunting, though not to him.

As a group, the Delaneys eyed him suspiciously, and Sloan found himself amused. Obviously they hadn't missed the expression of love on the face of their niece. Just as obviously their Delaney princess was very precious to them. He braced himself for scrutiny.

"Where was Patrick?" Falcon asked.

Sloan spoke up. "Three brothers had him in a small adobe hut. They had used ether on him to knock him out, but by the time I found him, he'd recovered from its effects."

"When was the hanging?" Dominic asked.

Brianne cleared her throat. "There was no hanging."

"All right, so when *is* the hanging?"

"Dom, Patrick wasn't hurt, and well . . ." She swiveled toward Joshua. "The brothers who kidnapped Patrick are named Odis, Hannibal, and Lester Grimes. They say you once fired them from a cattle drive." At Joshua's puzzled look, she added, "Hannibal shot a jackrabbit and stampeded the herd."

Recognition dawned on Joshua. "Good Lord,Bri, none of those three have the brains of a chicken."

"Exactly, and Patrick felt sorry for them—"

There were varying degrees of disgust on the faces of the five Delaney men. Dom's lips tightened. "I can't say that I feel any sympathy. We've come a hell of a long way for a wild-goose chase."

Brianne shrugged. "Patrick is sleeping off the effects of an all-night poker game, but he should be up soon. You can talk to him about it."

"I doubt if it will do any good. He appears to be as softhearted as his sister," Sloan drawled. "He's agreed to pay them their ransom so that they'll have a grubstake."

As one the Delaneys turned their gazes back to Sloan and fixed particularly on his hand, which was now resting on Brianne's shoulder.

"What did you say your name was?" Falcon asked.

Brianne planted her hands on her lips. "You remember very well what his name is. And just to save you the trouble of asking, he's from New York City and he's a financier. And one more thing you should know." She took a deep breath. "I love him."

Her statement was met with silence.

Brianne smiled sunnily. "You're going to like Sloan. He reminds me of a Delaney."

Faced with Brianne's happiness, some of the tension began to ease out of the group.

Sean actually grinned. "I'm not sure that's a recommendation, Bri. We were hopin' you'd find someone . . . tamer."

12

Dominic Delaney was waiting in the lobby when Sloan descended the oak stairway for dinner. He inclined his head in a polite nod as Sloan reached the bottom step. "Mr. Lassiter."

Sloan had been expecting this. He had not known which of Brianne's relations would be designated to confront him, but he was not surprised that it was Dominic. He had judged Dominic to be a dangerous man from the moment he had caught sight of him, and Brianne's menfolk would want to make sure he was conscious of an underlying threat. He nodded with equal coolness. "Mr. Delaney."

"I believe we have a few things to talk about." Dominic Delaney gestured to the parlor. "Before dinner."

"And, if our discussion doesn't please you, I take it

you have no intention of letting me join you at the festive family table?" Sloan asked, amused.

Dominic's icy blue eyes met Sloan's. "Exactly."

"Then perhaps I'd better accede to your request." Sloan headed leisurely toward the parlor. "I have an excellent appetite tonight and wouldn't want to have to satisfy it at a table for one."

The parlor was deserted, and Sloan moved toward the window and stood looking into the darkness. Outside, the storm had broken, and at irregular intervals thunder rolled overhead. He waited for Dominic's opening barrage; it came immediately.

"Are you marrying my niece for her money?"

"I've heard the Delaneys are rich as Croesus," Sloan said, not turning around, "and no I have no need of marrying Brianne for the Delaney fortune. As a matter of fact, I've not asked her to marry me at all as yet."

There was a weighted silence behind him.

"Am I to assume you have no intention of asking Brianne to be your wife?" Dominic asked with dangerous softness.

"You may assume what you please." Sloan whirled to face him. "I have no intention of answering your questions as if I were some bumbling, bashful boy going courting for the first time."

Dominic's gaze narrowed on Sloan's face. "No?"

"Hell no." Sloan's lips tightened. "At first I thought this was funny. But now I'm tempted to tell you all to go to the devil, and if I didn't think it would make Brianne unhappy, I'd do precisely that." He punched his index finger at Dominic. "But she does happen to love you all, so I'm hamstrung to do anything but be polite to you so she won't get upset."

Dominic studied him, his face expressionless. "Does it bother you that she might be upset?"

"You're damned right it does," Sloan said quietly, "and that's why I'm going to tell you and the rest of your family what you're so eager to know about me." He folded his arms across his chest and leveled a direct gaze at Dominic. "One. I have enough money to support Brianne in at least the luxury with which you've surrounded her, perhaps even more. Two. I love her so damned much that's it's beyond your imagination. Three. I'll ask her to marry me when and in what fashion I choose and that will not be dictated by you or her family, understood?"

Delaney's gaze searched Sloan's face, then, slowly, the faintest smile tugged at his lips. "I believe you've made yourself reasonably clear."

Sloan had the sensation that a gun pointed at his heart had suddenly been holstered. "I tried," he said wearily. "God knows why Brianne loves me. Everything's gone wrong since the moment we've met and there's been nothing normal or . . ." He trailed off. "But I have a chance now to make all that up to her. So, dammit, stay out of my way."

Some undefinable emotion flickered across Dominic's face. "We'll see," he answered. He started for the door, but then stopped and turned back. "I think you've told me the truth, and I appreciate your honesty, so let me return the favor. One. We'll be checking up on your credentials in New York to make sure you came by that money honestly. Two. We'll give you time to make your declaration to Brianne, but it had better be damned soon. Three. If your relationship with Brianne hasn't been a normal one, don't you think she'd appreciate knowing you want her for a lifetime? You may not be courting your first woman, but you're Brianne's first man. She deserves to know your intentions now, not when *you* decide it might be best to do so."

Sloan felt an instant of shock as Dominic's words sank in. "I'll think about what you said."

"Do that." Suddenly Dominic smiled with genuine warmth. "Oh, and one more thing."

"Yes?"

Dominic bowed slightly. "Will you give the Delaney family the pleasure of your company at dinner, Mr. Lassiter?"

The two men exchanged a glance that contained mutual respect and the beginnings of understanding.

Sloan's arms dropped to his side and he returned the bow. "It will be my pleasure, Mr. Delaney."

The blue tafetta material of the elegant dress Brianne had chosen for the evening glistened in the lamplight of the bedroom as she stood in front of the bureau and brushed her hair. Delicate lace edged the rounded neckline of the frock, and a line of tiny pearl buttons decorated the back, along with deep tiers of flounces that cascaded into a train.

When Sloan came in the door, she smiled at him in

the mirror. "Did you forget something? Or is everyone getting impatient with me? I'm nearly ready. All I have left to do is put up my hair."

He returned her smile. "Yes, I forgot something. And no, no one is getting impatient with you."

She took the long length of her hair, twisted it up on her head, and reached toward a pile of hairpins. "What did you forget?"

He crossed the room to her, pulled her hands from her hair, and turned her to face him. The mass of red curls and waves came tumbling down over the sapphire-blue taffeta. "Leave your hair alone. It's beautiful just the way it is."

"But dinner—"

"Never mind that now. Come sit with me."

Despite his smile, his strange behavior bothered her. "Sloan, what's wrong?"

He waited until they were seated side by side on the couch before he answered her. "I have to beg your forgiveness."

At first she thought he was joking and she almost laughed. But before she could, she caught a glimpse of something deep within his golden eyes that told her he was very serious. "Why?"

Rain drove against the window, but the fireplace that was so beautifully inset with blue and green cloisonné held a fire that heated the room and cast a warm light over the furnishings and the two people sitting on the couch.

He reached for her hands. "It was raining that night just over two weeks ago when I rode into

Chango," he said. "So many things have happened
since then, we've been through so much, but it doesn't
excuse the fact that I've been stupid and neglected
something very important."

"What?"

"I haven't asked you to marry me."

Breath caught in her throat as she realized that
Sloan was proposing to her.

He touched her hair tenderly. "It just seemed so
evident to me that there couldn't be any other end to
our love. The problem was, I didn't put my thoughts
into words. I'm sorry."

She pressed a finger to his lips. "Don't. I've been so
incredibly happy the last few days. In my heart I
knew that we were going to spend the rest of our
lives together."

He smiled slowly at her. "Marry me, Brianne. Be
my wife, my love, forever and ever."

"Yes," she whispered. "Yes." And she went into his
arms.

He held her tightly against him, his eyes closed,
his voice husky with intense emotion. "I had come
here prepared to die. Now, instead of facing death, or
perhaps even worse, facing endless, bleak years alone,
you and I are going to have a glorious life together.
There's only one question remaining. How am I ever
going to be able to love you the way you deserve to
be loved?"

She pulled away and smiled up at him, her eyes
moist with tears of happiness. "It's going to be so
easy, you won't even be aware of making an effort."

He laughed, a genuine laugh completely devoid of bitterness or cynicism. "You are so beautiful," he said, "in body, in spirit. . . ."

She lay her head against his chest and pressed against him.

Contentment filled him to overflowing, warming him, giving him true peace. "We have so much ahead of us. We won't need to spend a lot of time in New York City if you don't want to, but it would be senseless to liquidate all of my business holdings. I plan to deed over my present house to my stepmother. But we'll build a new home that's entirely our own, perhaps on Fifth Avenue."

"Fifth Avenue?"

"We'll buy up some land adjacent to Killara, or at least somewhere in the vicinity and start our own ranch. Would you like that?"

"I'd love it."

"So would I. And traveling back and forth won't be too hard. Thanks to the telegrams I sent, by now I'm a major stockholder in a railroad company. I'll buy a private car, and we'll be able to travel in comfort."

"I've grown very fond of traveling." She shifted so that she could brush her lips against his throat.

He stopped making plans long enough to glance down at her. "In spite of everything?"

She lightly pressed a finger into the fullness of his bottom lip. "*Because* of everything."

He bent his head and kissed her. "Brianne?"

"Ummm?"

"Where would you like to be married? When? You

realize if it were up to me, I'd just spirit you off to the nearest town and marry you there."

She chuckled. "Let me tell you something. If you deprive Shamus and Malvina Delaney of a wedding on Killara for their granddaughter, you'll learn the true meaning of fear." He laughed and she went on. "George will be there, of course, and I want Kam and Phineas, and Henrietta and Horace to detour by Killara on their way west so they can attend our wedding."

Sloan groaned, but it was a half-hearted groan.

In response she turned her head and took a little nip of his jaw, then daintily licked at the spot. Sloan almost forgot what they were talking about.

Brianne didn't. "They're already traveling to San Francisco. Killara won't be that much out of the way."

"I'd like to see the map you've been looking at."

She shifted away and regarded him earnestly. "It's going to be wonderful. Killara has a beautiful chapel. All our friends and relatives will be there. Patrick's ward, Silver Dove, will come in from St. Louis, along with Elspeth, Dom's wife, and Victoria, Falcon's wife. And you'll get to meet my grandparents."

He gave a mock grimace. "Oh, good, more Delaneys." But in the next moment he smiled tenderly. "It sounds very agreeable. As long as I marry you and *soon*, I'll steel my courage and ride quietly and meekly into the land of the Delaneys." He gathered her to him. "And in the meantime I plan to court you."

Intrigued, she asked, "And what does being courted by Sloan Lassiter mean?"

"You'll be the first woman I've ever courted, and I'm going to make it unique, with lots of laughter and an equal amount of quiet times."

"And long, long hours in bed?"

He looked down at her. "Not until we're married. I want to do it right, redhead. The time will pass fast. The next time I make love to you, I want to know that you're Mrs. Sloan Lassiter, and that nothing will ever separate us again."

She felt something like awe. "Paradise couldn't be better than this," she told him.

"I agree," he said softly. "By the way, where would you like to go on our honeymoon?"

"How about Ireland? I've heard so many stories about the place where my family came from, I'd love to see it for myself."

"All right, but perhaps after a short stay there we could travel on to Paris. I don't want to stay in Ireland too long."

"Why?"

He flicked his finger under her chin. "We're bound to run into Delaneys over there, and on our honeymoon I want to concentrate on *one* Delaney. You, my love."

A low laugh escaped from her, unknowingly seducing him with its sound. "I can't argue with that. And perhaps they'll have strawberries in Paris."

He gathered her to him. "Brianne Delaney, when I found you, I found my life."

13

The crash of thunder invaded the soft cloud of Anna's untroubled sleep. She stirred and felt Wesley at her back, curved around her, his hand tracing the lines of her waist and hips. Was it the violence of the storm that had awakened her, she wondered, or the warm gentleness of his touch?

His hand slipped over her side to cup her breast, and she rolled onto her back.

"I'm sorry," he whispered. "I couldn't sleep."

"Don't be sorry." She reached up to him and brought his mouth down to hers.

Hunger grew slowly, and Wesley didn't rush her. It was as if he felt as she did—the storm raging outside could not touch them. Not tonight. Strangely it was as if their protection was being in each other's arms rather than the walls and the roof of the house. Outside it was cold and dangerous; inside it was warm, secure, and pleasurable.

He raised up on his elbow, and in the brief illumination of a lightning bolt she saw his face. His features were, as always, hard, but the flash of brightness also showed tenderness. The impression vanished with the light.

In the darkness he found her breast, and his lips closed carefully around the tip. With easy pulling movements of his mouth, he sucked and teased. His gentleness was the most sensuous thing she'd ever known and caused muscles deep within her to clench with rapture.

Just as a crack of thunder sounded overhead and a white light momentarily shafted through the window and across the bed, he raised his head. She saw his mouth, firm, well-shaped, with the bottom lip slightly fuller and—unexpectedly—vulnerable.

Then faster than her eye could blink, the room was plunged into darkness once more, leaving her feeling as if she had imagined both the white light and the vulnerable shape of his lips.

She slid her hands down the smooth skin of his back and felt the muscles ripple beneath his flesh.

Heat riveted through her and seemed to follow the path of his hands, around her breasts and down her stomach. When his fingers burrowed through the golden curls to delve into the softness between her legs, there was fire flaming with a rhythm that kept time with the rapid beating of her heart.

Wes could feel his body tremble with the urgency

of his need for Anna. Yet, without hurry he rose over her and positioned himself between her legs. Then with a slowness that rivaled the pace of a flower unfolding its petals to the heat of the sun, he sank into her and began to move.

He was lost to the beat of the rain against the window. Lost to the lightning and thunder. There were only passion and need. Beneath him Anna was all silk and heat. A powerful sweetness flooded through him, and he was left drenched with wonder.

Anna felt languid, sated, and yet she was wide awake, vividly aware of the storm outside and the peace within. She felt Wesley stir beside her, and heard the scrape of a match. Lamplight cast a golden glow over the bed, muting the storm.

"I still can't sleep." He sounded almost apologetic. "The storm, I suppose."

She listened to thunder rolling away to the mountains and turned her head to look at him. He was on his stomach beside her, raised on his elbows, looking down at her. She didn't know what he was thinking, couldn't guess from his expression. He seemed calm, but she wondered if he could ever really, truly, be at peace. "The storm," she said finally, agreeing. "I can't sleep either."

He moved one hand far enough to touch a strand of her hair on the pillow, winding it around his fingers absently. His gaze shifted, focusing on what he was doing. "I'll build another house for us," he said suddenly.

She watched his face. "What's wrong with this one?"

He half shrugged, bronze shoulders hunching for an instant, muscles rippling. "Nothing. But it wasn't built for a—a family." The last word emerged almost tentatively, and he shot a quick look at her face before returning his gaze to what he was doing.

"I see." She didn't, really, but she was curious to see and to understand. She had committed herself to this man; understanding him had never been so important.

Wesley seemed to feel the need to explain. "A bigger house," he said. "Farther out of town."

"With a porch swing?" She heard the wistfulness of her own voice.

His face seemed to soften a little, but he didn't look at her. "With a porch swing."

Anna was aware of thunder rumbling distantly as the storm faded, but all her senses and thoughts were trapped in the glow of the lamplight. It was a fit place for dreams, and she allowed herself that luxury. What could be the harm in it?

She kept her voice soft. "A little garden for spices? One for roses?"

"If you like." He was almost smiling.

"And big windows to let in the sunlight?"

He nodded. "Big windows. Even a white picket fence."

For an instant she suspected sarcasm, because there had been something in his voice. His expression was the same—calm and almost smiling. Still, it had been enough to remind her that she was dreaming.

She didn't doubt Wesley would build a house. There would be a porch swing, and gardens, and big windows. There would even be a white picket fence. She felt her throat close up, felt the hot sting of tears.

"Anna?"

She realized that she was no longer gazing at him, that her eyes were fixed on the ceiling. And her voice sounded flat to her ears, flat and numb. "It will be a nice house." But not a home.

"I'll be good to you, Anna." His voice had changed as well, had become slightly rough. "You know that, don't you?"

"Yes, Wesley, I know that." He would be good to her. He wouldn't beat her or bully her. She would always have the best of everything money could provide. But she would never have the heart of her husband.

Nothing had changed, really. He hadn't changed. He had married her to give his child a name because he knew the pain of being a bastard. He had asked her to remain with him, to live with him as his wife, because the child was his. She was the mother of his child, and so her place was assured. If she hadn't loved him, it might have been enough.

"Anna?" His voice was a little tight.

"Yes, Wesley."

There was a moment of silence, and then she felt his hand move on her neck, felt the chain she wore tighten. She half turned her head, and watched as he unfastened the chain and drew it away, then freed the ring.

"Give me your hand."

She hesitated, but something in his taut voice pulled at her. Slowly she held out her left hand. He slid the big signet ring on her third finger and frowned slightly.

"I'll get a proper ring for you tomorrow," he said.

Anna felt a sudden urge to laugh, even though she felt no humor. *Proper*. As if anything between them had ever been proper. She felt his gaze on her and tried to smooth away the bittersweet smile. But he must have seen it, because his fingers tightened on hers.

"What are you thinking?" he asked, his voice on edge.

She was wondering if he had placed his ring on her finger to remind them both she belonged to him now. It was likely, she thought. But it wasn't a question she wanted to hear him answer. So she said, "Nothing. I'm thinking of nothing."

"I can't get inside your head."

She looked at him, surprised by the frustration she heard in his tone of voice. "I didn't know you wanted to," she said slowly.

He didn't respond for a long moment, just stared at her with narrowed eyes she couldn't read. She heard a rolling boom of thunder, realizing vaguely that the storm was returning, building again. It fit the mood she could feel growing in him, fit the tension of anger and something else . . . something she didn't understand.

Still holding her left hand, he slid his free hand suddenly over her stomach, resting it there possessively. "I put this baby inside you," he said softly with a strange intensity. "I forced you to be my lover, made you my wife without giving you a choice. I've changed your life, Anna, changed your future. And I don't know what you're thinking."

Anna didn't know how to respond to that. Her heart was thudding unevenly, and she felt as though she were teetering on the edge of a precipice. *I'm thinking how sad it is that I love you.* No. No, she couldn't tell him that. He hadn't changed. She thought she could bear that, but she couldn't risk telling him that she loved him because he could turn the knowledge into a weapon, and that was something she would never be able to bear.

"I don't know what you're thinking either," she countered, holding her voice steady with an effort. "I never have."

Wes looked down at his hand on her as a sudden flash of lightning replaced golden light with stark whiteness for an instant. His flesh lay over hers like a shadow. Bronze against ivory fairness, hardness over softness. Ruthless male strength possessive over female flesh nurturing a new life.

What was he thinking, he asked himself. What was he feeling?

Mine. Anna was his wife; her child was his. He had tied her to him with bonds that were primitive and ancient. He hadn't stopped to think when he had carried her off that night. He had been conscious only of the implacable determination to make her his wife.

He wondered now, for the first time, how long it had been in his mind. What would have happened if Anna had not been backed into a corner by her pregnancy, with little choice but to marry him? Had he married her for that reason alone? Because he had known she had no choice? He had known . . . and yet he had swept her off in haste, giving her no time to think, no chance to reject him.

Wes heard a ragged sigh escape him. How long had he wanted her to be his wife? Long enough to have hidden the desire even from himself. He had wanted something from her that he couldn't take, couldn't steal, couldn't force her to give him, and he hadn't been willing to risk her refusal. He hadn't even known how to ask her.

Mine. But not by her choice, not really.

"Wesley?"

He tore his gaze from his possessive hand and looked at her lovely face for a moment. Then he reached over to put out the lamp, and in the darkness lit only by flickering lightning, he pulled her into his arms and held her close to him.

"Nothing, Anna," he said thickly. "I'm thinking of nothing."

Wes took in the sight of Anna in his black silk robe. "It never looked that good on me."

Her dimples appeared as she smiled at him. "Would you please come roll up the sleeves for me?"

"I'd just as soon you wore nothing at all."

Silently she held out the arm that was lost within folds of black silk.

"Oh, all right." Grinning good-naturedly, he crossed the room to the bed where she was propped up against the pillows. A breakfast tray rested on her lap.

"I hope you like what I fixed," he commented as he concentrated on the sleeve. "I didn't know if you'd be sick this morning or what you'd be able to eat, so I made a little of everything."

He finished rolling back both sleeves and sat down on the end of the bed.

"I feel wonderful, and I'm amazed you've prepared all this." Her hand waved across the tray. A large plate held crisp strips of bacon and a mound of light, fluffy eggs. Another plate displayed a stack of perfectly shaped pancakes, topped by a pat of butter and a river of maple syrup. On a smaller plate a stack of golden brown toast resided, and, beside it, a little bowl of plum jelly.

He shrugged. "One way or the other, I've been responsible for my own food for as long as I can remember."

She laughed softly. "I know, but do you really expect me to eat all of this?"

"I'll eat whatever you don't."

She picked up a strip of bacon and bit off the end. "Ummm, just the way I like it." She took another bite. "Tell me," she said teasingly, "am I going to get this treatment every morning?"

"Why not? As long as you're pregnant, there's no

reason for you to drag yourself out of bed. You need to rest."

Last night, when he had said he was going to take care of her, he had meant more than providing a good home for her. She was intrigued. "And after I have the baby?"

"It would still be better that you not cook, at least in the mornings." His eyes darkened with emotion. "The baby will want to be fed."

Suddenly he took the tray off her lap, set it aside, then shifted closer to her. Pushing the black silk robe off one shoulder, he took the tip of her breast into his mouth and gently pulled at it. The unexpected action had Anna gasping for breath.

When he finally raised his head, he said, "I can hardly wait to watch. My baby suckling on your nipple."

"Wesley . . ."

They both heard it at the same time. Someone was knocking at the front door. He made a face. "Be back in a minute."

He left the room, and she smiled to herself. They'd better finish eating breakfast in the kitchen, she decided, or they probably wouldn't eat anything at all. She got off the bed, picked up the tray, and followed him out of the room. She'd only reached the top of the stairs when he looked up and saw her.

"Put that tray down," he ordered as he opened the front door. "It's too damned heavy for you."

She shook her head with amusement but did as he said, placing the tray on a nearby table. "I don't know how I've managed to take care of myself all this time."

He didn't answer. He was on his way back up the stairs, reading the telegram that had just been delivered to him. As she watched, his face hardened savagely, and within seconds all traces had vanished of the man who had indulged and pampered her this morning.

"Wesley, what's wrong?"

"That son of a bitch, Sloan Lassiter! This is from the president of the railroad, informing me that Sloan Lassiter is now the major shareholder, and has requested 'that all future dealings with me be halted.'" He looked at her, and his eyes were like slivers of ice. "That means Sloan now has the power to cut me out of the railroad altogether. By God, he's gone too far!"

He brushed past her and hurried into the bedroom. She started after him but stumbled and had to pause to gather up the long hem of the robe. "Wait, what are you going to do?"

"I'm going to make him goddamned sorry he didn't die with his brother at Turtle Rock." He was back on the landing with her, buckling on his gun belt. "Stay in the house. Don't go out for any reason."

"No, Wesley, *wait*. Don't do this. You'll get yourself killed!" She grabbed at his arm to stop him, but he jerked out of her grasp and ran down the stairs, taking them two at a time.

At the front door he turned and looked up at her. "Stay out of this, Anna. You don't understand. By doing this he's taken everything I've worked so hard for from me."

He threw open the door.

"Wesley!"

He looked over his shoulder, then froze. Obviously intending to come after him, Anna put her foot out, then brought it down on the first step. But the long sash of the robe trailed to the floor, and her foot came down on the end. Watching in horror, he saw her lose her balance and pitch forward.

Speed, his brain told him. But his muscles wouldn't respond. As he tried to move, his legs felt like lead. Outstretched toward her, his arms felt as if they were carrying two hundred pounds.

She was tumbling down the stairs, and the sound as her body struck each step made the hair on the back of his neck stand up and his blood turn to ice.

Terror for Anna had chased everything from his mind but the picture of her falling like a lifeless doll someone had hurled down the stairs.

Why couldn't he get to her?

Why couldn't he stop her?

Why were there so goddamned many steps and posts to batter and beat her?

He made a diving lunge and caught her just as she hit the bottom step.

Dear God, she was so still. Tenderly he brushed the hair away from her face and and saw that her eyes were closed and her skin was white.

He held her. Tears streamed down his face.

"Anna," he whispered. "Anna."

*   *   *

He couldn't get drunk.

Wes had tried though. All through a hellishly long day and a worse night, he had tried. Alone in his study, drinking whiskey that hadn't blunted the pain and fear, he had paced. There had been no sounds from upstairs, but he knew what was happening. It hadn't taken the grave expression on the doctor's face to tell him.

Oh, Christ, she'd been so pale and still!

He had killed their child.

He recalled the agony that had twisted inside him when, hours after Anna's fall down the stairs, the doctor had told him she had lost the baby.

He had gone upstairs despite the doctor's orders for him to stay out of the way, knocking on the door of his own bedroom, terrified to open it and go in because it was so *quiet* in there.

"Wait downstairs, McCord," the doctor had said brusquely after cracking the door.

"My wife . . ." He hadn't recognized the sound of his own voice, and he hadn't been able to see the bed because the angle was wrong. "The baby . . ."

The doctor had given him a sharp look, and his voice had slowed briefly to compassion. "I'm sorry, but I couldn't save the baby."

Wes had seen his hand come out and grasp the doorjamb. He had felt a painful constriction in his chest and a sick, icy fear. "Anna?"

"I don't know." The doctor's voice was brusque

again. "Wait downstairs. I'll tell you when I know anything." The door had closed firmly.

Shutting him out.

He had returned to his study and swallowed drink after drink. Smoked cigarette after cigarette. It hadn't helped.

Their child was gone, and he had killed it. Anna never would have fallen if she hadn't been trying to stop him, hadn't been trying to make him see reason in the blind fury of his obsession. It was his fault, all his.

His obsessions was so unimportant now. He didn't care that Sloan had triumphed, destroying everything Wes had worked and schemed for. None of that mattered, not any longer. Only Anna mattered now. If she died, he wouldn't be able to survive.

He watched the sunrise from his study window, not so much conscious of weariness as of defeat. *My punishment is more than I can bear.* It took him a moment to remember where he had heard it—a shout from a maniacal preacher far back in his boyhood. A line from the Bible, he realized.

He should have paid attention to the warning.

Concerned only with his ambition, he had never before counted the cost to others. He had plotted and schemed, stealing what he couldn't win, breaking what he couldn't steal. It had never occurred to him before that every goal he had reached had cost someone else; and if he had considered the matter, he wouldn't have cared.

Now . . . he had lost everything. His obsession had

ultimately cost the baby's life. Everything he had worked for. And Anna. Most of all, Anna. She would hate him now, hate him for everything he had done to her, for everything he had cost her.

The price was more than he could bear.

"McCord?"

He turned away from the window, so cold he thought he might shatter, like ice. "Doctor? How is she?" His voice was hoarse, afraid.

"She's weak, but she'll be fine. I've left her sleeping. She'll need someone to look after her for a day or two, at least." The doctor's sweeping glance clearly indicated what he thought of Wes's probable abilities along those lines. "Mrs. Hunter has done some nursing, and I'm sure she'll be happy to oblige."

"Yes." Wes cleared his throat. "I'll pay her well."

"She'd do it for nothing. She likes Miss—your wife." The doctor turned on his heel and left.

Wes stood there for a moment, feeling no resentment at the doctor's setdown; it was deserved, he knew. He left his study finally and went up the stairs, moving slowly in order to give himself time to control his expression and to bury what he was feeling deep inside himself. He opened his bedroom door and went in quietly, crossing to the bed and gazing down at Anna.

She was still sleeping. Her lovely face was pale and seemed, to his anxious eyes, more delicate than ever. There was a chair by the bed, and he sank into it without taking his eyes off her face.

He knew now why he had wanted her to be his

wife. He had known in the flashing instant he had turned to see her fall down the stairs. But it was too late. Even if he had known how, it was too late now to mend what he had broken this time.

She moved slightly, her lashes lifting, and he yanked his gaze away to stare fixedly down at the bed. He had to do this. No matter what it cost him, he had to do it. It was the only thing he could do for her.

"Wesley?"

She was shocked by his appearance. A dark stubble of beard covered the lower half of his gaunt face, and his eyes were red-rimmed and sunken. His clothing was wrinkled, his thick hair tumbled, and the odor of whiskey and smoke clung to him. He was sitting stiffly, not looking at her, his jaw tight and his lips pressed into a thin, hard line.

Anna was about to repeat his name when he suddenly jerked to his feet and strode across the room. The door slammed behind him.

"Do you feel like having company?"

Anna turned her head to see Brianne Delaney in the doorway of her bedroom. She smiled warmly. "Of course. How nice of you to come."

Brianne entered the room. Anna was sitting next to the window, a blanket over her lap. Brianne chose a chair next to Anna's. "It's wonderful to see you up. I thought perhaps you might still be in bed."

Anna's dimples deepened. "I'm doing very well, and despite Mrs. Hunter's protestations, I refused to spend one more minute in that bed."

"Good for you." Brianne studied Anna for a moment. There were shadows under her eyes, and lines of strain on her face—signs of the trauma she'd been through. "Anna," she said softly. "I was so sorry to hear about the baby."

"Thank you."

"I wanted to come see you sooner, but I felt you probably needed to rest more than you needed a visitor."

Anna's smile faded. "You would have been most welcome. I've discovered in the past few days that being left alone with one's thoughts is often not good medicine." *Neither was wondering why Wesley hadn't been to see her since he'd bolted from the room several days before.*

Brianne nodded. "By the way, I brought you some strengthening soup from the hotel's kitchen. I left it downstairs with Mrs. Hunter."

"That was very thoughtful. Thank you."

Brianne leaned forward. "Anna, I want you to know that I'm sorry we couldn't have become closer friends while I was here, especially since it turned out we had something in common."

Anna looked at her, puzzled. "Something in common?"

"That stupid conflict between Sloan and Wes." Brianne paused. "Your marriage came as a surprise to a lot of people."

Anna lowered her eyes. "We preferred that no one know. And as for the feud, I'm not sure that would have been a good basis for our friendship."

Brianne shrugged. "Perhaps not, but I think it would

have been nice to talk about it with someone who could look at the matter rationally. Sloan and I had to go through a lot before he got to that point."

"I know," Anna said quietly. "Wesley has hurt a great many people in his life."

"And you can accept that?"

"I have no choice. I can't change the kind of person he is."

Brianne frowned. "Why not? I don't see—" She suddenly stopped and made a wry face. "I'm sorry. I didn't mean to say that. You've been blessed with a serene temperament. I, on the other hand, tend to leap into the middle of frays and try to make things come out the way I want them to. Sloan would much prefer that I leave things alone."

Anna gazed at Brianne and felt a pang of wistfulness. She was positively luminous with happiness and eagerness for the future. How wonderful to be so confident about yourself and the man you loved, she thought. "I'm sure you and Mr. Lassiter will be very happy."

"I'm sure too." Brianne stood up and held out her hand. "I have to go. We're planning on heading home this afternoon. We're all riding out about three. I'm sure you'll be able to hear the sigh of relief Mrs. Potter makes at the sight of our backs."

Anna smiled and took Brianne's hand. "You, your friends, and your family will be missed."

A burst of laughter escaped Brianne. "You mean the good people of Chango will have to find something else to talk about, don't you?" She paused. "Good-bye, Anna, and good luck."

"Thank you for coming. Perhaps we'll meet again."

Brianne's smile lit her face. "You never know." She turned and moved toward the door. "Life is filled with possibilities."

And all of them bright happy ones for Brianne Delaney, Anna thought. "Good-bye, Brianne."

Brianne opened the door. "By the way. I've asked Mrs. Potter to bring you some more soup tomorrow. I hope—" She broke off. "Oh, hello, Mr. Nilsen. Come in. I was just leaving." With a final wave of her hand to Anna, she was gone.

Anna gazed at her father. He stood at the threshold, nervously clutching the rim of his hat. "What are you doing here?" she asked, then inwardly cringed at the sharpness she heard in her voice. He was still her father, she reminded herself, no matter what he'd done. She lifted her hand and pointed to the chair Brianne had just vacated. "I mean, I would have expected you to be at the emporium this time of day."

He perched on the edge of the chair, obviously ill at ease. "I hired a helper. Mrs. Harcourt recommended her nephew for the job. He seems a nice boy."

"I'm glad."

He looked down at the hat he held in his hands. "Are you feeling better?"

"Yes, Papa, I am."

He nodded with relief. "It vas . . . unfortunate that you lost the child."

Unfortunate? she thought with incredulity. The loss of her baby was the single most traumatic event of her life, and her father called it unfortunate. She looked at him impatiently. "Was there a special reason that you came this afternoon, Papa?"

"Yes. Mr. Foster, the bank president, came to see me today at the store. He did not vish to bother you by coming to the house, but he vanted you to be aware of certain things." He paused, frowned at the brim of his hat, then continued. "It seems Mr. McCord has made complete restitution to all those who vere injured by his business dealings. And"—he cleared his throat—"this is the part that concerns you, my daughter, vith the money that vas left, he has provided for you. He has also transferred the deed of this house to your name."

Anna stared at her father in astonishment and growing uneasiness. "But why would he do that?"

Lars Nilsen shrugged. "To make things right before he left."

"Left? Papa, look at me. What do you mean, before he left?"

He raised his head. "I thought you knew. Mr. McCord left town today."

Anna felt as if she had just taken another fall down the stairs. Wesley had left town. Without telling her of his plans. Without saying good-bye.

Her father was saying, "So now I vas vondering if you vould come back home. Things vill be different from now on. I vill take care of you. I—"

Anna dropped her head in her hands. "No, Papa."

"But I told you, things vill be different."

"You can't turn back the clock. No one can. The past *always* influences the future, no matter how hard you try to change things. Please go now. I'd like to rest."

He nodded. "Perhaps I vill come again when you are feeling better."

"Good-bye, Papa."

She waited until she heard him close the door behind him before she raised her head. Saying that she needed to rest had just been an excuse so that her father would leave. She had wanted to be alone so that she could try to sort things through.

Her heart felt as if it were breaking in two. *Wesley had left her.*

She knew he'd never loved her, but she had thought that they had a chance for a life together. At least she'd hoped.

She turned her head to gaze out the window. She supposed she'd been living in a dream world, but for a while, before she had lost the baby, she'd believed that the future held a potential for a good life. She should have known that it wouldn't, couldn't, work out between the two of them. After all, theirs had been such a troubled past. And hadn't she just told her father that no one can turn back the clock?

But that was exactly what Wesley was trying to do. He was starting over, stripping himself of all his possessions and setting out for a new life, alone. So alone.

Anna blinked back the tears that were stinging her

eyelids. It was all such a waste. Loneliness and sadness for both of them and nothing they could do to—

Suddenly she went still as she realized what she was thinking. Why was she just sitting there, wringing her hands and moaning over the injustice of it all? How did she know there was nothing she could do? All through her relationship with Wesley, she had accepted, only rarely initiating, and she was still doing it, dammit. She threw the blanket off her lap, stood, marched across the room to the armoire, and threw open its paneled doors.

14

Wes had to fight himself not to look back as his horse plodded steadily out of town, knowing that if he did look back, he might not be able to leave. Just as he hadn't dared to see Anna again these last few days. Only the thought of the hate he would see in her eyes had kept him away from her, and only that made it possible for him to leave her.

What little he was taking with him was packed into a couple of carpetbags and slung across the horse behind his saddle. He had ended up with a small stake. With luck, it would be barely enough to start again somewhere else.

Life was going to be hard for a long time, he knew. A hard life didn't frighten him . . . and he had been alone all his life. But for the first time he felt the bleak awareness of being lonely.

He was so caught up in his own pain, he didn't realize at first that he was being followed. He wouldn't have heard anything if his horse had been moving faster, but the plodding pace made it possible for Wes to hear hoofbeats behind him.

He stopped his horse, holding the gelding still as he braced himself and looked back over his shoulder. He couldn't believe what he saw, in fact, almost refused to believe it. But . . . He swung off his horse with the stiffness of tense muscles and stood waiting until the horse and rider reached him.

As she approached, he saw that Anna was dressed for travel in serviceable dark clothing, and that two carpetbags were tied behind her sidesaddle.

"What are you doing here?" he asked in a rough, strained voice. "You should still be in bed."

Anna sat on her horse for a moment looking down at him. *What if he doesn't want me?* she thought, and wondered how in the world she was going to manage to keep her expression free of the fear and nervousness she was feeling. "The doctor agreed I was recovered. He did warn me that I shouldn't ride from dawn until dusk, so if that's your habit, I may have to ask that we rest from time to time."

"Anna—"

She interrupted in a calm tone. "I've talked to Mr. Javits at the bank twice today. He'll expect instructions whenever we reach our destination. The house and furnishings can be sold, and the proceeds transferred to us without delay."

"You aren't coming with me," he said tautly.

"Yes, Wesley, I am. My place is with you."

"Anna ..." He held his voice steady with a tremendous effort, still unable to believe that she didn't hate him. "I've lost everything, do you understand? Everything. It will take years to rebuild—if I can even do it."

"You'll do it; you'll build another empire."

"I'm a destroyer, remember? You said that, and even though I didn't want to believe it then, you were right. I've destroyed everything I've ever touched. That won't change."

"You've changed."

He couldn't deny that, because he knew it was true. He just didn't know what the change in him really meant. "Anna, go back to town. I wouldn't ask any woman to live the way I'll have to until I can rebuild."

She heard the hesitation in his voice, the need, and she smiled at him, her face filled with sudden radiance. "I'm not any woman. I'm your wife."

Wesley struggled against the urge to give in, even though he had never wanted anything so much in his life. "My God, you don't know what's good for you, do you? Dammit, Anna, I'm doing the right thing."

After a moment Anna lifted her knee from the curved horn of the sidesaddle and slid to the ground before he could move to help her. She stood holding one rein, gazing at him searchingly. "Is that why you're trying to make me go back to town, Wesley? Because you believe it's the right thing? Or—" Her voice broke for the first time, then steadied. "Or is it that you don't want me?"

"I just . . . I don't want to hurt you anymore."

"It will hurt me if you leave me behind." Anna gave a little sigh and her arms slipped around his waist. "Don't you see," she said softly, "you won't hurt me again unless you leave me."

"The only life I can offer won't be easy," he said in a husky voice, his hands touching her shoulders tentatively as if she were a wondrous gift that might be taken away from him at any moment. "You deserve so much more." He hesitated, then went on with obvious reluctance. "You should stay here. I can send for you when things are—"

"No. I told my father that no one could turn back the clock, and I believe that's true. But I also believe that most worthwhile things are built by people who have learned from their mistakes. Our beginning was flawed, Wesley, but our future doesn't have to be. Not if we work at it. It can be beautiful." Her arms tightened around him. She had to make him take her with him. "I'm going with you."

His smile was crooked. "To keep me on the straight and narrow?"

"I won't have to do that. The next empire you'll build will have a solid and *honest* foundation."

For the first time, he felt a surge of optimism. He could have laughed out loud. Nothing was impossible, not with Anna beside him. But he had to ask, "Why? Tell me why, Anna."

She pulled away, gazed up at him, and took a deep breath. "I love you."

He closed his eyes for an instant. "God." When his eyes opened, they were glittering moistly. "Anna, I don't—" He stopped.

She waited, barely able to breathe. When he said nothing more, she thought, *He doesn't want me.* She gave a small laugh made shaky by threatening tears. "Wesley, say something."

"What can I say? I don't deserve you, but, my God, how I love you."

She felt the shock, then the joy. "Me?" she whispered. "It wasn't just the baby? You love *me?*"

"I loved the baby because it was part of you." He tried to break away from her. "I shouldn't let you come with me."

She saw the suffering on his face. She heard the torment in his voice. And she knew he really did love her. "You don't have any choice. Do you think I'll let you go now when I know you love me? If you leave me here, I'll follow you from town to town until you're too old and weary to get away from me."

Suddenly it was as if a great weight had fallen from him, and he chuckled. "Then I guess I'd better give in gracefully. And gratefully." He lowered his mouth to hers and kissed her with exquisite gentleness. "I'll try to make sure you're never sorry."

"Neither one of us will be sorry."

"I love you," he said, making it sound like a prayer.

"I love you," she whispered back, "and while you're building an empire, I'll be making a home for us."

"I've never had a home," he said wistfully. "Not really."

"Then there's no time to waste," she said firmly. "Where are we going, by the way?"

He realized it hardly mattered to her, and he did laugh out loud. "How about California?"

"I've always wanted to see California. I heard someone say once that the end of the rainbow is there."

"If it isn't there," Wes said, lifting her onto her horse, "we'll keep looking until we find it." He mounted his own horse.

And side by side, hands clasped, they rode away together and never looked back.

My Dear Maureen,

Isn't it awful? It's been *six* long months since I've had the time to write, but being a part of the Delaneys means there's always something happening. And believe you me, I've got a lot to tell you.

First off—oh, goodness, I'm just about to pop with the news—Mr. York and Miss Sierra had the most beautiful baby boy you could ever imagine. And healthy! All that time I spent on my knees praying really paid off. Well, first things first. The darling child's name is Dominic, after old Shamus's son, Dominic. Did you know that the original Dominic was a gunfighter. My bones just chill whenever I think about it. But the man was a Delaney after all, and that makes whatever he did just fine by my way of thinking. At any rate, this little angel of Mr. York's is going to be a president of the United States. Or even something *more* important. Of course, since I'm having a large hand in raising this next generation of Delaneys, I feel they're all going to do great things. In fact I feel it so strongly, I'm wondering if the good Lord hasn't blessed me with second sight.

Maureen, you'd better sit down for my next piece of news, because its fair wondrous. Are you ready? Mr. Burke and Miss Cara are expecting! Don't you see? Now all three of my Delaney boys will be fathers. A year ago, we thought Mr. Burke, Mr. York, and Mr. Rafe were the only remaining Delaneys on earth. And now we have the three Delaney girls in Australia and a new generation of Delaneys started here. It's all so exciting.

My, I do go on, don't I? But I haven't finished!

Cougar and Bridget have moved back to Killara. At least for the time being. Just between you and me, that Cougar has always struck me as half wild, but I must admit that it's a wonderful thing how happy Bridget has been with him, and she's made a lovely home on his ranch in the upper part of the state. It makes me go fairly teary-eyed to see how soft she is around him.

Wait a minute.

I got off the subject.

The *reason* Bridget and Cougar are back at Killara is because Miss Cara is expecting twins. Can you believe it? And everyone, from Bridget and Cougar right on down to the other two boys and their wives, is fussing over her, trying to take care of her. But

Miss Cara just laughs and then goes right on and does what she wants. And Mr. Burke always seems to have this look on his face like he's captured a leprechaun and found the end of the rainbow and the pot of gold.

Needless to say, Maureen, I'm a happy person. All these babies to take care of! It's like a dream come true.

A month later

Maureen, you just won't believe what's happened! Three weeks ago those movie people out in California had their Academy Awards ceremony, and guess what? Roman Gallagher won. I watched the whole thing on television and shed more than a few tears of happiness and pride, let me tell you. After all, he is part of the Delaney family now.

Well, after it was all over, Miss Manda and Mr. Roman came to Killara for a visit. They wanted to see the family, *and* they needed to escape from all the news people that was fair hounding them like a foaming-mouthed pack of dogs. Of course, as I've often told you, if a body wants to be protected, there's no better place to be than on Killara. And with Cougar here and all, well, I'll tell you, no one got on or off the ranch without him knowing about it. Oh, and on the first day of their visit, I baked up the biggest batch of gingerbread you've ever seen and while I was serving it, I told Mr. Roman that I'd known all along he would win. He was amazed, and now I really am beginning to believe I have been blessed with second sight.

At any rate, Miss Manda and Mr. Roman were really excited about all the news they had to tell us. The reason I know they were excited was because they were so busy talking that they barely ate a bite of my gingerbread.

The told us that Deuce Moran has finally won the heart of the lady, Mandarin. It's all so terribly romantic, don't you think? Two lost souls finally finding each other. I predict they'll have a very happy life, and my predictions are nothing to sniff at. Even though, I must say, Bridget does. But never mind.

The next piece of news they told us set my head to spinning. Miss Sydney and Mr. Nicholas are expecting a wee one! They live on the Isle of Charron, on what they call the "wild side" of the island in a house that's built on a headland that juts out over the untamed sea. And there's a lagoon by the house that black swans fly to every evening so they'll be safe. It's a truly wondrous place. The only thing is, now I'm in a quandry. Miss Manda swears to me that Miss Sydney's life is as blissful and peaceful as a body could want. But I'm worried. Somehow I just don't think it's fair for that branch of the Delaney family to have to go without my services. I mean, imagine! There's going to be a spanking, brand new Delaney baby halfway across the world, and I'm thinking that perhaps I should offer to go over there and take care of the little bairn.

I don't know what I'm going to do. My mind is busy turning the matter over and over. I'll have to let you know what I decide.

But even if my Delaney boys won't let me go that far, they might let me go to Kentucky to see Miss Addie and Mr. Shane and their wee one, a blessedly fair little girl who they say can already charm anyone.

Well, I'd better get this letter in the mail to you. There's so much going on around here that I'm afraid I might miss something if I don't end right now. You take care of yourself and, remember, it's your turn to write me.

Love,
Kathleen

THE DELANEY DYNASTY

Men and women whose loves and passions are so glorious it takes many great romance novels by three bestselling authors to tell their tempestuous stories.

THE SHAMROCK TRINITY

- [ ] 21786 **RAFE, THE MAVERICK**
  by Kay Hooper $2.75
- [ ] 21787 **YORK, THE RENEGADE**
  by Iris Johansen $2.75
- [ ] 21788 **BURKE, THE KINGPIN**
  by Fayrene Preston $2.75

THE DELANEYS OF KILLAROO

- [ ] 21872 **ADELAIDE, THE ENCHANTRESS**
  by Kay Hooper $2.75
- [ ] 21873 **MATILDA, THE ADVENTURESS**
  by Iris Johansen $2.75
- [ ] 21874 **SYDNEY, THE TEMPTRESS**
  by Fayrene Preston $2.75

- [ ] 26991 **THIS FIERCE SPLENDOR**
  by Iris Johansen $3.95

Now Available!

THE DELANEYS: *The Untamed Years*

- [ ] 21897 **GOLDEN FLAMES** *by Kay Hooper* $3.50
- [ ] 21898 **WILD SILVER** *by Iris Johansen* $3.50
- [ ] 21999 **COPPER FIRE** *by Fayrene Preston* $3.50

Buy these books at your local bookstore or use this page to order:

- -

Bantam Books, Dept. SW7, 414 East Golf Road, Des Plaines, IL 60016

Please send me the books I have checked above. I am enclosing $_____ (please add $2.00 to cover postage and handling). Send check or money order—no cash or C.O.D.s please.

Mr/Ms _____

Address _____

City/State _____ Zip _____

SW7—10/88

Please allow four to six weeks for delivery. This offer expires 4/89. Prices and availability subject to change without notice.

THE LATEST BOOKS
IN THE BANTAM
BESTSELLING TRADITION

☐ 27032	**FIRST BORN** Doris Mortman	$4.95
☐ 26513	**PRIVILEGE** Leona Blair	$4.95
☐ 27018	**DESTINY** Sally Beaman	$4.95
☐ 26991	**THIS FIERCE SPLENDOR** Iris Johansen	$3.95
☐ 27235	**SOMETIMES PARADISE** Judith Green	$3.95
☐ 26990	**LABELS** Harold Carlton	$4.50
☐ 27283	**BRAZEN VIRTUE** Nora Roberts	$3.95
☐ 27284	**THE FORTUNE TELLER** Marsha Norman	$4.50
☐ 25891	**THE TWO MRS. GRENVILLES** Dominick Dunne	$4.50
☐ 25800	**THE CIDER HOUSE RULES** John Irving	$4.95
☐ 27746	**BEACHES** Iris Rainer Dart	$4.50
☐ 27196	**THE PROUD BREED** Celeste De Blasis	$4.95
☐ 24937	**WILD SWAN** Celeste De Blasis	$3.95
☐ 25692	**SWAN'S CHANCE** Celeste De Blasis	$4.50
☐ 26543	**ACT OF WILL** Barbara Taylor Bradford	$4.95
☐ 26534	**A WOMAN OF SUBSTANCE** Barbara Taylor Bradford	$4.50

Prices and availability subject to change without notice.

- -

Bantam Books, Dept. FBS, 414 East Golf Road, Des Plaines, IL 60016

Please send me the books I have checked above. I am enclosing $_____
(please add $2.00 to cover postage and handling). Send check or money order
—no cash or C.O.D.s please.

Mr/Ms _____

Address _____

City/State _____ Zip _____

FBS—9/88

Please allow four to six weeks for delivery. This offer expires 3/89.

Special Offer
Buy a Bantam Book
for only 50¢.

Now you can have Bantam's catalog filled with hundreds of titles plus take advantage of our unique and exciting bonus book offer. A special offer which gives you the opportunity to purchase a Bantam book for only 50¢. Here's how!

By ordering any five books at the regular price per order, you can also choose any other single book listed (up to a $5.95 value) for just 50¢. Some restrictions do apply, but for further details why not send for Bantam's catalog of titles today!

Just send us your name and address and we will send you a catalog!

BANTAM BOOKS, INC.
P.O. Box 1006, South Holland, Ill. 60473

Mr./Mrs./Ms. _____
(please print)

Address _____

City _____ State _____ Zip _____
FC(A)—10/87

Please allow four to six weeks for delivery.